AIR TRANSPORTATION 1975 AND BEYOND:
A SYSTEMS APPROACH

AIR TRANSPORTATION 1975 AND BEYOND: A SYSTEMS APPROACH

Report of the Transportation Workshop, 1967

Cochairmen
Bernard A. Schriever
William W. Seifert

The M.I.T. Press

Massachusetts Institute of Technology
Cambridge, Massachusetts, and London, England

FOREWORD

In June of 1967 a group of air transportation experts from industry, government, and the academic community were asked to join the Transportation Workshop, an *ad hoc* group whose general purpose was to make a systems-oriented study of the national air transportation system and its interfacing modes, with special emphasis on the future. Cognizance of the impending crisis in air transportation motivated the participants and kept them working against tight deadlines.

It was recognized that many people representing many organizations had already devoted great effort to examination of the air transportation system and that such efforts were continuing. Nonetheless, the Workshop's organizers felt that a unique approach was needed.

The air transportation system cuts across many facets of our life, affecting individuals, local areas, and the federal government in ways which make it almost useless to study it piecemeal. Elements of the solution are not divided into discrete related tasks. Attempts to improve one aspect of the system frequently tend to pull others out of balance. The trade-offs are not visible and the range of alternatives is not made clear for decision-makers. The problem cannot even be defined by an approach which attacks only one part at a time.

Consequently, this Workshop was organized to look at the entire air transportation system. The organizing group identified six major subdivisions under which the work would be carried on, enlisted individuals to serve as chairmen of panels representing these six areas, and then, with the aid of the panel chairmen, recruited approximately 80 members, including a coordination staff. The members represented a spectrum of interests and backgrounds and were drawn from industry, government, and the universities. The panel chairmen and members are listed on the pages following the Foreword.

The panels formed from this group included a *socioeconomics panel,* which addressed itself to outlining the socioeconomic environment in which the air transport industry would be operating in the late 1970's; a *government panel* to spell out the government policy climate which might be anticipated; an *air vehicle panel* to outline anticipated advances in the technology of air vehicles; an *airports and terminals panel* to examine the functions and characteristics of existing and proposed forms of airports; an *air traffic control panel* to examine present requirements, the ability of existing equipment and operating procedures to meet these requirements, and the directions future advances may take; and, finally, a *"mixed-mode" panel* to examine the problems of getting people and goods to and from airports.

The entire membership of the Workshop was convened for four days in June 1967, and again for two days in September. In the interim the members worked independently, and the panels held several individual meetings.

The Workshop concentrated on anatomizing the system and dividing it into subsystems. In this manner it was possible to study the various elements in some depth, despite the limitation of time, and to identify key problems within each subsystem. Concepts were developed, alternatives were recognized, and some systems-oriented options for the planner were developed. The Workshop made some specific evaluations of what must be done to solve the air transportation problem; these are presented as recommendations at the end of each chapter. In a word, the Workshop made a first attempt at a systems analysis of air transportation.

The number of participants in the Workshop was kept small so that coordination of individual and panel timetables could remain manageable. This limitation was accepted with the knowledge that many persons who could make significant contributions to the end product were not included. This loss was traded off against the stimulation that comes from crossfeed within a group of manageable size.

The Transportation Workshop has been an impressive experiment in cooperation. A number of industrial firms donated funds to meet the Workshop's out-of-pocket expenses. They and a large number of other firms donated the time of participants and covered their expenses. Each recognized that the interests of objectivity demanded a blend of talents. Each accepted that the payoff, if there were to be one, would take the form of broadly useful results and an enhancement of our general knowledge of air transport. Other organizations and individuals not represented in the Workshop population also contributed material on request. The cochairmen are deeply indebted to those whose cooperation made the Workshop possible.

It is this kind of cooperation that is going to solve the air transportation problem. A solution will not come from the private or public sector alone. It is symptomatic of the mood of the Congress, industry, government, and the academic community today that leaders from these areas have supported the Workshop. It is a sign of new times.

No one really wants government to grow bigger and more powerful; we all lose when that happens. But it is healthy to recognize that private solutions, without conscious public leadership, will not solve our major social and economic problems. On the other hand, the size and complexity of problems like transportation and urban decay are such that government alone is not big enough to solve them. It must call on the enormous potential of the private sector to help.

BERNARD A. SCHRIEVER
President, Bernard A. Schriever Associates
formerly Commander of the Air Force Research and Development
Command, later of the Air Force Systems Command

WILLIAM W. SEIFERT
Assistant Dean of the School of Engineering
Massachusetts Institute of Technology
Director, M.I.T. Project TRANSPORT

TRANSPORTATION WORKSHOP PANELS

CHAIRMEN

SOCIOECONOMICS

Stanley Berge
Professor, School of Business
Northwestern University
Evanston, Illinois

AIR VEHICLE

Rene H. Miller
Slater Professor of Flight Transportation
Massachusetts Institute of Technology
Cambridge, Massachusetts

William L. Hamilton
Director, Systems Analysis
Commercial Airplane Division
The Boeing Company
Renton, Washington

AIR TRAFFIC CONTROL

Winfield H. Arata, Jr.
Deputy Director
Northrop Nortronics
Hawthorne, California

AIRPORTS AND TERMINALS

W. E. Leonhard
Senior Vice President
The Ralph M. Parsons Company
Los Angeles, California

MIXED-MODE COLLECTION
AND DISTRIBUTION

James O. Murcklen
Study Director, Air Transportation
TRW Systems
Washington, D.C.

GOVERNMENT POLICIES

James T. Pyle
Director, Aviation Development Council
Flushing, New York

Secor D. Browne
Professor, Aeronautics and Astronautics
Massachusetts Institute of Technology
Cambridge, Massachusetts

STAFF COORDINATOR

Stephen G. Saltzman
Colonel USAF (retired)
Deerfield, New Hampshire

SOCIOECONOMICS PANEL

Chairman
Stanley Berge
Professor, School of Business
Northwestern University
Evanston, Ill.

Edmund F. Barnes
Manager, Market Research
Douglas Aircraft Company
Long Beach, Calif.

G. A. Busch
Director of Planning,
Washington, D.C. Area
Lockheed Aircraft Corporation
Washington, D.C.

Harry A. Carter
Commercial Airplane Division
The Boeing Company
Renton, Wash.

Joseph Famme
Vice President, Engineering
Rohr Corporation
Chula Vista, Calif.

Aaron Fleisher
Professor, Department of City Planning
Massachusetts Institute of Technology
Cambridge, Mass.

James E. Gorham
Southern California Laboratory
Stanford Research Institute
South Pasadena, Calif.

William E. Larned, Jr.
President, DMS, Inc.
Greenwich, Conn.

E. Daniel Morton
Director, Development Planning
Eastern Airlines, Inc.
New York, N.Y.

Leon Moses
Professor, Department of Economics
Northwestern University
Evanston, Ill.

Richard A. Roche
Assistant Director,
General Transportation
Marketing and Advanced Planning
North American Rockwell Corporation
Los Angeles, Calif.

AIR VEHICLE TECHNOLOGY AND TRENDS PANEL

Chairman
Rene H. Miller
Slater Professor of Flight Transportation
Massachusetts Institute of Technology
Cambridge, Mass.

Cochairman
William L. Hamilton
Director, Systems Analysis
Commercial Airplane Division
The Boeing Company
Renton, Wash.

L. L. Douglas
Assistant General Manager
Boeing/Vertol Division
Morton, Penna.

Hubert M. Drake
Mission Analysis Division (OART)
NASA Ames Research Center
Moffett Field, Calif.

John E. Gallagher
Executive Vice President and Director
New York Airways, Inc.
Flushing, N.Y.

Walter J. Hesse
Vice President
LTV Vought Aeronautics Division
Dallas, Texas

George B. Litchford
Aviation Systems Consultant
Northport, N.Y.

E. J. Nesbitt
Chief, Technical Support
Sikorsky Aircraft Division
United Aircraft Corporation
Stratford, Conn.

Stanley K. Oleson
Office of Noise Abatement
Federal Aviation Administration
Washington, D.C.

T. R. Parsons
Chief Engineer
(Frontiers of Technology Study)
North American Rockwell Corporation
Los Angeles, Calif.

Kearney G. Robinson
Commercial Airplane Division
The Boeing Company
Renton, Wash.

Robert W. Simpson
Professor, Aeronautics
and Astronautics
Massachusetts Institute of Technology
Cambridge, Mass.

AIR TRAFFIC CONTROL PANEL

Chairman
Winfield H. Arata, Jr.
Deputy Director
Northrop Nortronics
Hawthorne, Calif.

Russell L. Biermann
Systems Research & Development Service
Federal Aviation Administration
Washington, D.C.

Joseph D. Blatt
Associate Administrator for Development
Federal Aviation Administration
Washington, D.C.

Clifford P. Burton
Executive Director
Air Traffic Control Association, Inc.
Washington, D.C.

Joe D. Conerly
Deputy Director
Systems Research & Development Service
Federal Aviation Administration
Washington, D.C.

C. Stark Draper
Director, Instrumentation Laboratory
Massachusetts Institute of Technology
Cambridge, Mass.

F. Ray Edgin
Technical Director
Air Weapons Surveillance and Control
Headquarters ESD, Hanscom Field
Bedford, Mass.

Frederick C. Frick
Massachusetts Institute of Technology,
Lincoln Laboratory
Lexington, Mass.

Richard M. Head
NASA Electronics Research Center
Cambridge, Mass.

A. L. Hedrich
Assistant Director,
Research and Development
Page Communications Engineers
Washington, D.C.

James Huntoon
Department of Aviation Affairs
Environmental Science
Services Administration
Rockville, Md.

Walter A. Jensen
Assistant Vice President
Operations and Engineering
Air Transport Association of America
Washington, D.C.

Newton Lieurance
Director of Aviation Affairs
Environmental Science
Services Administration
Rockville, Md.

George M. McSherry
Asst. General Manager for Planning
Los Angeles International Airport
Los Angeles, Calif.

Stanley Seltzer
Director, Air Navigation/Traffic Control
Air Transport Association of America
Washington, D.C.

AIRPORTS AND TERMINALS PANEL

Chairman
W. E. Leonhard
Senior Vice President
The Ralph M. Parsons Company
Los Angeles, Calif.

Merrill Armour
General Counsel
Association of Commuter Airlines
Washington, D.C.

Robert F. Bacon
Chief, Systems Planning
Federal Aviation Administration
Washington, D.C.

E. Thomas Burnard
Executive Vice President
Airport Operators Council
International, Inc.
Washington, D.C.

Charles W. Duke
President, Transport Systems, Inc.
Northport, N.Y.

William J. Ely
Vice President
Sverdrup, Parcel, and Associates, Inc.
St. Louis, Mo.

Joseph A. Foster
Vice President, Airport Facilities
Air Transport Association of America
Washington, D.C.

Colonel Floyd Irving, Jr., USAF
Chief, Transportation Support & Services
Dir. of Transportation
DCS/S&L, Hqs USAF
Washington, D.C.

Carl G. Johnson
ASD (ASZLE-20)
Wright-Patterson Air Force Base, Ohio

Keith Kahle
Asst. to Vice President-General Manager
LTV Vought Aeronautics Division
Dallas, Tex.

Frederick A. Koomanoff
Senior Associate
Planning Research Corporation
Washington, D.C.

Lt. Colonel John J. Logan
Headquarters, Military Airlift Command
Scott Air Force Base, Ill.

C. N. Moser
Systems Engineering Group
Wright-Patterson Air Force Base, Ohio

Forrest Six
Project Manager, Systems Engineering
Ralph M. Parsons Company
Los Angeles, Calif.

Robert B. Steans
Director Planning, Operations Group
Eastern Airlines, Inc.
Miami, Fla.

William S. Steele
Tracey, Brunstrom & Dudley, Inc.
Seattle, Wash.

Thomas M. Sullivan
Staff Consultant for
Aviation and Transportation
The Port of New York Authority
Washington, D.C.

Robert W. Williams
Seaboard World Airlines, Inc.
Jamaica, N.Y.

Robert B. Wilson
Division Vice President
Operations Planning
Eastern Airlines, Inc.
Miami, Fla.

John H. Yienger
Manager, Industrial Systems Division
Aerojet General Corporation
Frederick, Md.

MIXED-MODE AIRPORT COLLECTION AND DISTRIBUTION PANEL

Chairman
James O. Murcklen
Study Director, Air Transportation
TRW Systems
Washington, D.C.

Clarence M. Belinn
President, Los Angeles Airways, Inc.
Los Angeles, Calif.

George F. Brewer
Director, Marketing Research
Cessna Aircraft Company
Wichita, Kans.

Francis T. Fox
General Manager
Los Angeles International Airport
Los Angeles, Calif.

Bernhard H. Goethert
Director and Professor
University of Tennessee Space Institute
Tullahoma, Tenn.

David Highman
President
Air Dispatch, Inc.
New York, N.Y.

George M. McSherry
Assistant General Manager for Planning
Los Angeles International Airport
Los Angeles, Calif.

Charles ReVelle
Cornell University
Ithaca, N.Y.

Colonel Lewis Rice, USAF
Chief, Plans and Programs
DCS/Systems and Logistics, Hqs. USAF
Washington, D.C.

Howard R. Ross
Logistic Systems Research
Stanford Research Institute
Menlo Park, Calif.

William M. Spreitzer
Head, Special Products Department
General Motors Corporation
Detroit, Mich.

James Wallace
Special Products Department
General Motors Corporation
Detroit, Mich.

GOVERNMENT POLICIES AND TRENDS PANEL

Chairman
James T. Pyle
Director
Aviation Development Council
Flushing, N.Y.

Cochairman
Secor D. Browne
Professor, Aeronautics and Astronautics
Massachusetts Institute of Technology
Cambridge, Mass.

Arthur J. Fallon
Deputy Director for Aviation
The Port of New York Authority
New York, N.Y.

Colonel Francis K. Gerard
Director, Division of Aeronautics
New Jersey Department
of Transportation
Trenton, N.J.

David J. Goldberg
Chairman
Tri-State Transportation Commission
New York, N.Y.

Dorn McGrath
Office of Urban Technology & Research
Dept. of Housing & Urban Development
Washington, D.C.

William Ronan
Chairman
Metropolitan Commuter
Transportation Authority
New York, N.Y.

Irving Roth
Director, Bureau of Economics
Civil Aeronautics Board
Washington, D.C.

David D. Thomas
Deputy Administrator
Federal Aviation Administration
Washington, D.C.

Stuart G. Tipton
President
Air Transport Association of America
Washington, D.C.

Arthur Webster
Office of Assistant Secretary
for Policy Planning
Department of Transportation
Washington, D.C.

John R. Wiley
Director for Aviation
The Port of New York Authority
New York, N.Y.

COORDINATION STAFF

Staff Coordinator
Stephen G. Saltzman
Colonel USAF (retired)
Deerfield, N.H.

Joseph Angell
Director
AF Systems Command
West Coast Study Facility
Los Angeles, Calif.

Robert J. Goewey
Brigadier General, USAF (retired)
Belleair, Fla.

Frederick B. Mohr
Air Technology Division
Library of Congress
Washington, D.C.

Colonel Raymond Sleeper
Director, Foreign Technology Division
Wright-Patterson Air Force Base
Ohio

Henry R. Warden
Staff Advisor, Resources Council
North American Rockwell Corporation
El Segundo, California

CONTENTS

1 OVERVIEW   1

What Crisis? A Perspective   *1*
Sizing the Problem   *6*
Structuring the Problem   *7*
Some Options for the Planner   *9*

**2 SOCIOECONOMIC TRENDS AND THEIR
POTENTIAL IMPACT ON AIR TRANSPORTATION**   17

Introduction   *17*
Demographic Trends and Economic Growth   *19*
Patterns of Urban Growth and Airports   *26*
Air Transport Demand and Capacity:
The Role of Investment and the Role of Pricing   *32*
Future Peak-Hour Passenger-Flow Problems
in Relation to Airport Capacity   *49*
World Education Trends
and Their Potential Impact on Air Travel   *57*
The Impact of Leisure Time and Recreation
on the Air Travel Industry   *63*
Trends in Business and Military Distribution Policies
and Practices and Their Likely Effect on Post-1975 Demand
for Commercial Air Cargo Transportation   *69*
Governmental Regulatory and Promotional Policies   *83*
Governmental System for Regulation and Promotion
of Civil Air Transportation   *84*
Air Transportation Fiscal Policy   *130*
Intermodal Competitive Transportation:
High-Speed Common Carriers   *135*

Intermodal Competitive Transportation: Highways   *145*
Intermodal Competitive Cargo Transportation Trends   *150*
General Aviation Trends and Potentials   *155*
Conclusions   *168*
Recommendations   *182*

3 THE AIR VEHICLE   185

Introduction   *185*
CTOL Technology Forecast   *187*
CTOL Design Trends   *209*
General Aviation   *220*
STOL Technology Forecast   *223*
STOL Design Trends   *226*
VTOL Technology Forecast   *226*
VTOL Design Trends   *230*
Short-Haul Demonstration Projects   *248*
Conclusions   *261*
Recommendations   *264*

4 AIR TRAFFIC CONTROL   265

Introduction   *265*
Airspace Utilization   *270*
Atmospheric Environment   *275*
Aircraft Equipment   *281*
Navigation   *289*
V/STOL Traffic Control   *298*
Communications   *301*
ATC Facilities   *308*
Controllers   *319*
Airports   *323*
Conclusions   *331*
Recommendations   *333*

5 AIRPORTS AND TERMINALS   337

Introduction   *337*
Recent History and Perspective   *339*
Meeting the Challenge: By Evolution   *354*

Meeting the Challenge: By Developing New Airports   *385*
Alternative Regional Approaches   *396*
Special Technical Problems of Future Airport,
Terminal, and Facility Planning   *415*
Recommendations   *427*

**6 COLLECTION AND DISTRIBUTION
OF PASSENGERS AND AIR FREIGHT**   439

Introduction   *439*
Demand-Requirement Analysis   *442*
Development of Alternate Solutions   *452*
System Evaluation   *474*
Conclusions and Recommendations   *475*

7 GOVERNMENT POLICIES AND TRENDS   481

Introduction   *481*
Government Powers, Policies, and Practices   *481*
  At the International Level   482
  At the Federal Level   484
  At the State and Regional Levels   490
  At the Local Level   492
Conclusions   *493*
Recommendations   *495*

BIBLIOGRAPHY   497

GLOSSARY   505

INDEX   507

1. OVERVIEW

WHAT CRISIS? A PERSPECTIVE

The United States is a dynamic society historically committed to change, to economic, social, and political progress, and, even more firmly, to the preservation of its freedoms.

The people of our nation enjoy a degree of personal mobility unmatched anywhere in the world. This freedom of movement is regarded, and properly so, as a right and not a privilege. It is a social value woven so deeply into our lives that many would fight if deprived of it. The freedom to travel and to trade without barriers is the basis of the mass production and marketing that have given us the highest standard of living man has known. Unless we plan now for the future and begin to take the steps required of our transportation systems to meet the demands of the future, sheer growth in population and the accompanying economic demands could so saturate our transportation system, especially the air system, that mobility could become a premium service instead of a routine accommodation. If we are forced to pay too heavily from the quality of our lives for improving our mobility, the price may be too high. Noise, pollution, congestion, delays, high cost, and a landscape overlaid by concrete are some of the prospects that may limit the growth of the systems that give us our cherished mobility. This is a major part of the nature of the transportation problem facing the United States today.

The upward trends in population and economic growth during the next two decades will pose a series of challenges to the viability of our philosophy of living. At the same time, these challenges will offer almost unlimited opportunities for the kind of creative planning that will ensure an equitable balance between private rights

1

and public needs, between competition in a free society and increasing political controls.

The burgeoning social and economic demands of people at home and abroad will lay heavy requirements on world markets for goods and services. These, in turn, will force an accelerated upsurge in demand for the transportation of people and things. Common carriers — land, sea, and air — will continue as the vital link between producers and consumers, and air transportation is expected to expand further its share of the market in the movement of passengers both domestically and throughout the world. Moreover, all indicators point to annual increases in air cargo shipments that will even outstrip the gains in passenger traffic.

Failure to meet these demands for mobility would exact severe penalties from our society. Unless we preserve our freedom of movement we are destined to become growth-limited, a frightening prospect for an economy whose health depends on growth.

A brief review of the factors of growth and the elements that may impede that growth is prerequisite to understanding the problem faced by the air transportation system today.

THE FOUNDATIONS OF GROWTH

In 1966 air transportation accounted for 66 percent of common carrier passenger miles, as compared to 13 percent in 1950. While speed and convenience have been the basic qualities attracting passengers to air travel, the growth experienced would not have occurred except for the maintenance of an excellent economic climate as measured by gross national product, high disposable income and virtually full employment, and declining overall fares. Looking to the future, the GNP is forecast to grow at an average real rate of 4.25 percent per year, while average airline fares are forecast to decline in real terms at a rate of 2 to 3 percent per year. Disposable income is expected to increase, and the population is forecast to reach 250 million by 1980. These factors in combination augur a growing demand for air travel and for shipment of goods by air.

Coincident with a rise in discretionary income, a fleet of even more economical, high-payload aircraft is coming into service. There are predictions that fares to Europe may be as low as $99. Persons who never before were attracted to air travel are suddenly going to find bright new potentials opening to them. A weekend trip to attend a family wedding will be in the realm of possibility for persons who previously would have merely sent their congratulations by telephone or letter. Distant points in the United States and other continents will become vacation goals. Lowered fares will increase the proportion of nonbusiness travelers on domestic passenger lists and will have an explosive effect on demand. New vistas for trade and commerce will open as air freight and air cargo rates drop.

Still other factors will stimulate the growth of air transport. More people will have more leisure time; some of it will be used for travel. The number of retired persons will increase, and they will wish to travel more. A higher percentage of our population will be more highly educated, and past experience shows that as level of education increases, so does the tendency to travel. Many people in today's travel market still cling to an old-fashioned fear of flying, which helps account for the fact that, as of 1964, only 39 percent of Americans had ever taken a trip by air. The generations coming into the air travel market will not bring a fear of flying with them, and this will expand the market even further.

These factors of growth lend credence to median forecasts that by 1980 the number of domestic revenue passengers carried by airlines will grow four times over current levels and that air cargo will grow as much as ten times. However, serious hurdles face those who are charged with preparing the facilities to permit this growth to take place.

SOME INHIBITIONS TO GROWTH

Any casual air traveler or shipper recognizes signs of trouble in the delays and congestion that have become the norm. Up until now, the growth of air travel has been unhampered by capacity restrictions in such system elements as runways, terminal facilities, and surface access between city centers and airports. As the demand grew, the system could grow to satisfy it. And, as the service improved, the demand grew larger. But these favorable conditions are fading rapidly. Most of our hub airports are reaching a saturation point, and saturation equates with costly delays — costly in terms of the ill will of inconvenienced passengers and costly in operating dollar losses to airlines. The Air Transport Association estimated the direct cost of operating delays in 1965 at $41 million, no small economic drain, yet relatively insignificant when compared to the potential delay costs in the coming decades. Serious new problems will be introduced when the large subsonic jets and the SST's are introduced into the inventory. Estimates indicate that by 1975 20 aircraft of the C-5, B-747, or SST type will land or depart within one hour at primary airports during peak times. This indicates a need to accommodate up to 10,000 passengers per hour at these locations.

Any given set of facilities has a finite capacity beyond which it cannot handle the load. We are already experiencing frequent and serious congestion at our major hub airports during peak traffic hours, and we cannot avoid worse congestion and longer delays if we keep looking to that fixed capacity to handle still heavier loads simply by projecting today's environment forward. We can improve and add to our present facilities, which we are doing. But we cannot expect to generate substantial new facilities in time to avoid further stoppages such as that experienced in the summer of 1967 when ground traffic was tied up at Kennedy International Airport for two hours. It is difficult to predict what will finally limit the capacity of individual airports. It could be airport access and egress. It could be the ability of the air traffic control system to handle arrivals and departures. It could be the terminals themselves — the number of people that can flow through them in a given period. It could be the ground-handling facilities for airplanes. Each airport is unique, each has unique problems. But delays at any of the major hub airports back up to cause system-wide delays as equipment fails to arrive on time and schedules deteriorate.

The factors that may do most to limit the ability of the air transportation system to meet demand are the most difficult to evaluate and to correct.

Growth of General Aviation

One factor threatening to limit system growth is paradoxical. General aviation — the air taxis, fixed-based operators, company and private airplanes that play a key role in supporting the industrial and service bases that make our air transportation system possible — is growing at a rate that, alone, will absorb anything short of extraordinary expansion of air traffic control and ground-handling facilities. The scheduled air carriers predict that by 1980 their nearly all-jet fleet of 3600 aircraft will have to vie for air and airport space with a forecast 210,000 general aviation aircraft, more than double today's fleet.

Noise and Pollution

It was the jet engine that made large and efficient aircraft possible, and we are committed to the jet engine until another form of propulsion is invented. Jet engines, unfortunately, make noise. No solution to the noise problem is yet in sight. Jet engines also pollute the air. Fortunately, this pollution is not as serious as would appear from the smoke trails left by jets, but it is serious enough to make people complain. As antipollution devices become more common and begin to reduce the pollution from such offenders as cars and factories, the atmospheric pollution contributed by today's aircraft will assume a proportion of the total that will attract increased attention. Noise and pollution will lend pressure — emotional but perhaps unbearable pressure — to move airports farther from our cities. They will force the imposition of noise-abatement flight procedures which are even more restrictive than the ones that are already shrinking critical airspace and raising operating costs. Financing the building of new airports is going to offer a major challenge if noise and pollution force the issue. Locating suitable real estate is going to present another problem.

Jurisdictional Complication

Another inhibition to growth is indicated by the comment that on a clear day from the top of the Empire State Building one can see 1300 separate political jurisdictions. When a community is forced by congestion to the decision to build a new airport, that new airport will most probably have to be built on land belonging to another community. Roads and other access systems to the new airport will generally have to cross real estate controlled by several other communities. The resulting jurisdictional problems can create years of delay before concrete is poured, and they can force compromises that must inevitably result in less than optimum facilities. The delays occur as a function of local prerogative. The compromises are a consequence of the fact that airport planners employ criteria that differ from those used by urban and highway planners, and planning for these seemingly diverse but actually interrelated ends is being conducted for the most part by men working in isolation from each other. Taken together, these problems may completely block the building of badly needed new facilities.

Federal Fiscal Policy

By far the most difficult growth constraint facing the air transportation system is that of financing. At a point in time when U.S. airlines are committed to the purchase of $10.5 billion in new equipment through 1971, austerity programs are forcing adoption of a federal fiscal policy that passes to the users the responsibility for paying for a greater share of the system. The airlines have been told, in effect, to make the service fit existing fiscal policy rather than to expect fiscal policy to evolve to permit development of the desired service. Safety requirements in a climate of austerity will force even greater air and ground delays than those now being experienced, as inadequate traffic control facilities and overburdened controllers try to shoulder heavier traffic loads. New airports and improvements to airports must be planned against lowered federal assistance. New access systems to move people and goods to airports are needed and are also expensive. Because of the nearness of the crisis and the lead times for constructing new facilities, austerity measures could not have come at a worse time for the air transportation system. Policy changes tend to lag behind changes in the climate that occasioned the policy change in the first place, a factor that suggests that the system will have to live with austerity for a critical period of time to come.

This brief review has identified some of the factors that will create heavier demand for air transportation and some of the problem areas standing in the way of satisfying that demand. In addition to this system-wide perspective, it is felt that understanding of the problem may be enhanced by focusing on the size of one aspect as it appears to an airport planner.

SIZING THE PROBLEM

Historically, U.S. commercial air traffic has been highly concentrated. FAA studies show that in 1965 the 21 major metropolitan areas that have been identified as large hubs accounted for 66 percent of the total airline passenger enplanements and 48 percent of all air carrier operations at U.S. airports. As a group, these large hubs have, over the years, increased their share of the total U.S. air traffic for both air carrier and general aviation activities. This trend is forecast to continue. Projections indicate that by 1980 these hub airports will account for approximately 70 percent of all U.S. enplaning passengers.

In 1965 only three large hubs, New York, Chicago, and Los Angeles, generated more than six million enplaned passengers each. By 1980, 20 of the large hubs will generate this number annually, according to FAA forecasts.

The number of air carrier operations is also expected to increase markedly, but, because of the shift to larger aircraft, these increases will not be proportionate to the gains in passenger volume. Between 1965 and 1980, air carrier operations at the 21 major hubs are expected to increase 143 percent and passenger enplanements 444 percent. Furthermore, general aviation aircraft operations will increase twice as fast as those of the air carriers at the major hubs, demanding three times the aircraft parking and servicing areas required by the carriers.

Translated to show their effect on one of the major hubs, Miami, data like these illustrate the magnitude of airport facility problems confronting the system today.

In 1965 the seven airports that form the Miami hub accounted for about three million enplaned passengers. By 1980 airports in the Miami area must be ready to handle nearly 19 million enplaning passengers. To accommodate this growth, Miami will need five times the total air carrier terminal space it has now. It will also require four times the amount of apron area for carrier aircraft, four times the present cargo building space, and six times the amount of existing cargo apron area. The projections for the other large hubs are similarly dramatic. For example, FAA forecasts indicate that the New York hub's present 4,213,000 sq ft of gross terminal area (including the expansion at Newark) must grow to 8,864,000 sq ft plus 500,000 sq ft for international travelers; Chicago's 1,788,000 sq ft will have to expand to 6,792,000; and Atlanta will have to find ways and means to build 2,375,000 extra square feet of terminal building to process its forecast traffic.

Similar requirements exist for all the major hub areas, a fact that indicates the extent of the terminals portion of the problem. The airports themselves face comparable problems and must be expanded so they will be able to accommodate the number and size of aircraft that will be operating in the future and turn these expensive machines around quickly for departure with fuel, maintenance, passengers, and cargo.

The prospects for getting passengers and cargo to and from airports through urban distribution systems that are becoming less adequate each year are even more dismal. And there is also the problem of how to control the growing numbers of aircraft that will be occupying the airspace, including takeoff, routing, and landing, within acceptable standards of safety, noise, and pollution.

As has been noted, it is difficult to determine what will be the limiting factor. A recent study by the general manager of Los Angeles International Airport indicates that that airport's capacity will finally be limited not by terminal, runway, ramp, or parking facilities but by the capacity of the external road system that brings passengers and cargo to the airport and carries them away.

STRUCTURING THE PROBLEM

In attempting to achieve an understanding of the air transportation problem it is helpful to reduce the system to its key subsystems and to examine each of these in depth. Basically, the air transporta-

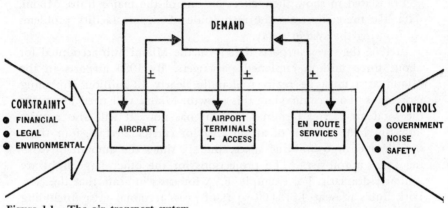

Figure 1.1. The air transport system.

tion system (Figure 1.1) contains three subsystems — the air vehicle, en route services (airways, navigation, approach control, meteorology, and radiation monitoring), and the airport/terminal with its access and egress systems.

User demand rises or falls as the system provides or fails to provide service that is economical, fast, dependable, comfortable, and safe. The subsystems are interdependent, and deficiencies in one subsystem affect all the rest. One can see how easily this complex system can get out of balance. As a result of improved technology, the flow of aircraft down the production lines and into service occurs in an orderly progression and at a rate that is almost a pure function of market-place decisions. However, the two supporting subsystems, the en route services and the airport with its collection and distribution complex, lag behind. The hardware technology is as available to meet the requirements in these latter areas as it is in the case of the aircraft. However, there is a shortage of what might be termed a technology of decision-making as it relates to such matters as financing, land use, urban planning, jurisdictional roadblocks, and policy.

The air transportation system operates in a dynamic environment composed of people and their economy. This environment influences and shapes the demands that will be made on the system, simultaneously offering both opportunities and constraints. On the one hand, the burgeoning of population, industry, leisure, education, and disposable income creates new and expanding markets for the air transport industry. On the other hand, factors such as noise, pollution, and legal, financial, and jurisdictional problems act to restrain its growth. The socioeconomic environment is both an expanding and a limiting factor; as yet the influence of the social effects of transportation are not understood sufficiently well for planners to know how to react to them or to influence them. The need to learn more in this area is in itself a vital part of the problem.

Finally, there are policy considerations that, operating in the public interest, serve to control demand. Badly drawn policy inhibits the air transportation system; well conceived policy nurtures growth and provides for orderly progression toward a system that will serve society. Policy affecting air transportation slices a crazy quilt of authority, city, county, state, regional, federal, and foreign, in a maze that seems to defy clarification. Antitrust and other regulatory legislation created in response to the development of the various segments of the national transportation system — water, highway, rail, and air — affects all modes of transportation. It has led to a situation in which airline management cannot even sit down with its counterparts in the bus and rail areas to discuss possible cooperation or merger without violating antitrust legislation. Questions like these affect the structure — and structuring — of our society. They demand that we reexamine the sources of our society's vitality and its ability to respond to the challenge of a technology that drives our world exponentially faster.

These brief comments on future growth and future problems give only a fleeting glimpse of what lies ahead. Together with the comments on the size of the problem and on the notion of structuring the system, they form a perspective for addressing a solution.

SOME OPTIONS FOR THE PLANNER

Although no one yet knows specifically what steps should be taken to optimize the performance of our air transport system while adequately protecting other segments of society, it is nonetheless possible to outline some system-oriented options for the planner and some recommendations that point the way to further study efforts. A few of the options and recommendations considered by the panels are highlighted here for the purpose of lending emphasis to their more detailed consideration in the following chapters.

THE AIRPORT PROBLEM

The projected increases in air passenger traffic lead one to conclude that even if concurrence had been achieved among the jurisdictions involved, if plans had been approved, and if financing were in hand, new terminal facilities could still not be constructed soon enough to forestall peak-hour congestion of epic proportions. Consequently, the near-term solution must be found in increasing the flow of passengers through today's facilities and along the access routes to them. Fortunately, considerable early relief is available, although achieving it would require abandonment of traditional ways for processing passengers.

Passenger-Processing Satellites

Coordinated, system-wide adoption of automated ticketing and baggage processing, which are within the present state-of-the-art, would go far toward eliminating a major bottleneck in passenger flow through terminals. This in itself would offer relief, but if such a system were incorporated in a complex of passenger-processing satellites strategically located within and close to urban complexes, a large part of the terminal congestion problem would disappear. Passengers and their luggage could be completely processed upstream in the flow and moved as directly as possible to aircraft loading areas and then discharged downstream near their ultimate destinations. Automobiles would not have to be driven to the airport but could be parked at the satellite. Well-wishers would not have to accompany passengers to the airport or go there to greet them. Transferring the passenger and his baggage from the satellite to the airport would remain a problem, but it could be handled on an evolutionary basis, beginning with standard large-capacity buses, limousines, and taxis. If satellite locations were planned with the airport access problem in mind, e.g., along existing or planned rights of way, such a primitive system could evolve to a point where special cars on ground transit systems could carry the passenger to the airport and, in follow-on refinements, to a system that would bring them directly to the skin of the aircraft. While such a plan might be distasteful to air travelers who have been conditioned to expect fancier treatment, the alternatives, with their delays and frustrations, may prove to be even more distasteful.

The plan has other advantages. An airport that did not have to devote so much space to terminal buildings with their classical passenger facilities — ticket counters, circulation areas, concessions, public conveniences, waiting rooms — could then devote more space to the proper business of airports: landing, maneuvering, servicing, and loading airplanes, and getting them airborne. An airport that did not have to devote so much space to car parking might find room for extra gates, ramps, taxiways, and in some cases for a parallel runway that would nearly double the acceptance rate for landings and takeoffs.

Carrying such a plan to its logical end, other typical airport functions could be moved off-airport. This would include cargo-processing functions such as containerization, palletization, and break-bulk operations, as well as heavy aircraft maintenance and overhaul.

New Concepts of Financing

The implementation of such a plan will undoubtedly run into serious opposition on the grounds that large investments already exist in support facilities at airports and the income from these supports the principal functions of the airport to a significant degree. Consequently, the development of a system of satellite collection-distribution points will require development of a new view toward airport financing. Such a scheme would also benefit materially from agreement by the major airlines to a standardization of passenger- and baggage-processing methods and to the use of compatible automated equipment. This agreement may be difficult to obtain in view of the competitive aspects of air travel. However, securing it would be in the best interests of the passengers and consequently, in the long view, of the airlines. While study is needed before such a plan could be put into operation, the obvious merits of the plan warrant study. This plan would offer near-term relief from congestion and would deflate the staggering estimates of terminal space required in the future. Compared to requirements for the construction of new airports, satellite-system requirements are not immoderate; satellites could probably be in operation sooner and at lower cost. Adopted as a standard for future airport planning, satellites could end the traditional ways of thinking about airports, which otherwise will continue to create periodic crises in the air transportation system.

DEMONSTRATIONS

Jumbo jets, supersonic transports, and large-capacity cargo aircraft will probably accommodate the anticipated passenger and cargo growth. However, present ground facilities at hub airports are at or near saturation during peak hours, and further traffic increases will only aggravate air traffic control, congest the airport complex, and clog the access road systems.

Generally speaking, public roads leading to airports are inadequate, especially at the peak hours of movement of passengers, airport employees, and visitors. Furthermore, it is interesting to note that not a single hub airport is directly connected to the central city by a fast subway or railroad system. Numerous hardware proposals have been put forth but have not been implemented because of the problems of obtaining the required political acceptance and financial backing. We have reached the point where live demonstrations of some of the new hardware ideas are essential. The benefits flowing from these experiments would be multiple and would point the way to solution of one phase of the air transportation problem. Properly designed, they will alleviate the crush at some of the airports and will provide data on their social and political feasibility that simply do not exist and that are needed as a basis for future planning. A system of off-airport satellites such as that discussed previously would lend focus to the implementation of ground and air system demonstrations, serving as station stops for ground systems and as landing pads for V/STOL and advanced helicopter systems.

NOISE ABATEMENT

The noise problem associated with the operation of jet aircraft is a difficult one and, short of an unforeseen breakthrough, a quiet engine is not on the horizon. Despite the considerable attention industry and government groups have devoted to attenuation of this problem, their proposals probably will not resolve the issue.

In time a set of acceptable noise standards will be established, and compatible land-use plans to attract industrial rather than residential development to the periphery of airports will gradually be evolved. These steps and the imposition of restrictive noise abatement aircraft routing procedures will help. Nonetheless, mounting opposition can be expected from those citizens who live within the high-noise patterns of airports, perhaps forced to do so by other considerations. Any approach to the noise problem must weigh the considerable economic contribution of a hub airport against the relatively small number of citizens who are affected. The alternatives are not attractive, for they involve either placing further restrictions on an already congested system or building a new system of airports. It is clear that we are not going to stop flying, but it is equally clear that we could attach so many penalties to investment in commercial aviation that it would cease to attract investors. This whole problem area must receive a great deal more attention.

GENERAL AVIATION

The impact of general aviation cannot be regarded lightly. Whether for business, pleasure, industrial use, or as an air taxi service, these aircraft carried nearly 40 million passengers during 1966. They accounted for 16.2 million aircraft operations at airports with FAA traffic control services, as against 8.2 million operations by the commercial airlines. The FAA forecasts that by 1977 general aviation will generate 54.9 million operations, as compared to the carriers' 16.9 million. Even these cursory figures make it clear that neither the airlines nor general aviation should seek solutions to their problems in isolation. The solution appears to lie in the area of providing equal but separate facilities for general aviation aircraft at reliever airports in hub areas, a solution that takes into account both the traditional freedom to fly and the fact that it is not in the public interest for a private airplane with two persons in it to delay a commercial aircraft carrying perhaps 500 passengers. It also takes into account the fact that, while rising general aviation activity will certainly affect congestion in the air, its major impact on the ground will be felt at only a small percentage of the 10,000 airports in the United States.

AIR TRAFFIC CONTROL

If air traffic is to grow with the national economy, the airspace must be treated as a national resource. At present, however, passenger and cargo growth is increasing faster than the improvements and modifications that are being made to keep the air traffic control system properly responsive. Progress toward solutions to some of the ills plaguing air traffic control require primarily decisions as to what should be done. Unfortunately, these decisions must be delayed until planners present policy-makers with the range of alternatives and the arguments for and against each alternative. For example, a decision to require general aviation aircraft to install adequate avionics packages or be restricted is obviously difficult to make. Similarly, it is not easy to decide to impose requirements such as minimum speeds and pilot proficiency standards on general aviation, yet there seems to be no alternative if we are to avoid unsafe conditions and delays in the airspace. Our system, although recognizing every citizen's right to use the national resources, also contains precedents for restricting that right in the public interest. These questions demand resolution, and action is required on the decision-making level.

The remaining critical problems in air traffic control also require primarily decisions. They differ from the problems just discussed in that they also require the commitment of public funds. Technology is ready to computerize and combine the meteorological, navigation, communication, and control data fed through the air traffic system; realization of this objective would go far to improve safety and to relieve the nerve-wracking burden shouldered by air traffic controllers. A new traffic control system will have to be developed to augment and perhaps eventually replace the present radar-based system, which will be inadequate for the anticipated traffic. However, data are required on which system to adopt, when and how to phase it into the existing system, and how to fund the purchase and installation of the required equipment. Once again, development of these data requires study, as does the problem of new work and pay standards for controllers and how to recruit persons for this difficult vocation.

AIR FREIGHT AND CARGO

The rosy forecasts for the growth of air freight and cargo probably disregard a great many hurdles that must be cleared before these levels are attained. Many potential shippers do not understand air logistics as a means of increasing sales and profits by enlarging market areas, increasing the length of time perishables and style-obsolescent products can be on the market, lowering inventory costs, and reducing the time between shipment and payment. Computer-aided analyses of distribution costs have not been made available to industry and commerce on a sufficient scale. The advantages of containerization have not been made apparent, nor has the requirement to develop containerization that is compatible for all modes. (Efforts to require certification of air containers may preclude or delay container standardization and may straddle shippers with one set of containers for air and another set for other modes.)

Spectacular potentials for domestic and world trade are available with the high payload, low ton-mile-cost aircraft that are coming into service. These potentials may be lost unless cooperative planning can reduce the cost of air cargo service, encourage potential shippers to organize for total distribution cost management, standardize containers, reduce the paperwork required for air commerce, and develop suitable air cargo facilities and equipment. This order of planning will demand the combined efforts of shippers, airport operators, air carriers, aircraft manufacturers, and government planners.

FISCAL POLICIES

Tremendous sums will be required for financing the expansion of airport and terminal facilities, the introduction of new air traffic control systems, and the construction of new and improved access means. It is evident that no single sector of the economy will underwrite these requirements *in toto*. It is equally apparent that a systematic approach to financing cannot be developed until data on the operation of the total system can be assembled and reviewed. Unfortunately, fiscal operations in the air transport area are so fragmented that it is essentially impossible to assemble consistent data. Furthermore, estimates of future costs show such divergence that they do not provide an adequate base for decision-making.

Future developers will look to the federal and state governments for assistance in the form of grants, loans, and tax incentives. The private investment sectors, and the users too, must assume a share in the financing to ensure that free competition is not replaced by excessive governmental restraint. However, unless and until adequate data are developed and organized, the prospects for articulating an effective fiscal policy are not bright.

PLANNING

At the present time, planning — both short and long-term — for the development of our national transportation system is fragmented throughout government, industry, research corporations, and universities. There has as yet been little attempt to integrate the results of these multiple efforts. However, the national trend toward regionalism may hold promise as a mechanism for facilitating transportation planning. Regional planning commissions offer a structure under which urban, highway, and airport planners can sit down together and develop a common set of objectives and criteria.

One conclusion stands out, unmistakable and incontrovertible. There is an urgent need for organized planning oriented toward the total air transportation system of the future. None of the options can be initiated with confidence without further study to close the gaps in data and knowledge. They represent at once opportunities and problems. The selection of best options and the solution of other problems facing the air transportation system argue for immediate initiation of a concerted planning effort. How to organize to do the planning needed becomes a critical target for attention.

TRANSPORTATION POLICY

Utopia does not lie ahead. This became clear in the Workshop's review of problem areas. It is not likely that technology, for all the blessings it may bring, will give us a world free from noise, pollution, traffic jams on the ground and in the air, delayed trains and planes, irate travelers, jurisdictional quarrels, or selfish public and private interests. Consequently, modern policy guidelines must be established under which our transportation system can develop. Many of our present policies have been articulated over a period of two centuries against the push and pull of public and private interests. Our problems now are taking on a new dimension as well as becoming more complex, with the result that today the crux of the policy question lies not in the realm of what technology can do but rather in what we want it to do. We must cope with expansion not simply in terms of dollars, physical plant, and technology but also within the limits of social acceptability. If we can enunciate a policy that will encourage the development of transportation systems that serve the society in which they will operate, and in the best interests of that society, then American technology and American industry can provide the systems. The technological base is adequate to any transportation task levied against it. Designing to policy could be, in the long run, far more effective than designing to marketplace decisions.

2. SOCIOECONOMIC TRENDS AND THEIR POTENTIAL IMPACT ON AIR TRANSPORTATION

INTRODUCTION

Before the end of 1967 the population of the United States passed 200 million and, according to the Census Bureau's projections, we are likely to add another 100 million before the end of this century. Not only is population growth creating additional demands for transportation of both people and goods, but these demands are growing far more rapidly than the population.

Since 1940 there have been large increases in America's per capita consumption of both freight and passenger transport. Population grew 48 percent, from 133 million to 197 million, between 1940 and 1966, but total intercity ton-miles of freight, mail, and express traffic grew 185 percent, from 618 billion ton-miles to 1,767 billion ton-miles. During the same 26 years, total intercity passenger-miles in private automobiles and aircraft and all types of public carriers increased 200 percent, from 330 billion to 933 billion passenger-miles.

As shown in Table 2.1, in 1966 the people of the United States were consuming twice as much intercity passenger transport and nearly

TABLE 2.1. U.S. PASSENGER AND CARGO TRANSPORT CONSUMPTION

Year	Passenger-miles per capita	Freight ton-miles per capita
1940	2,500	4,600
1950	3,300	7,000
1960	4,600	7,300
1966	5,000	9,000

SOURCE: Computed from Transportation Association of America, *Transportation Facts and Trends* (4th Edition, April 1967), p. 7 and census data.

twice as much cargo transport per man, woman, and child as they did a quarter of a century earlier.

In relation to the total mobility market of the United States, air transport is still in its infancy and commands a relatively modest share of the total passenger and freight traffic. While the private automobile still carries the vast bulk of short-run intercity passenger transport, the airlines by 1966 had captured 62 percent of all passenger movement by common carriers.

Despite excellent "percentage gains" in air cargo transport during recent years (342 percent from 1956 to 1966), the airplane in 1966 was only moving 0.12 percent of all the intercity freight, mail, and express traffic in the United States. With air freight rates (airport-to-airport and not including door-to-door pick-up and delivery) averaging more than 20 cents per ton-mile, air transport was unable to compete with trucks averaging $6\frac{1}{2}$ cents per ton-mile door-to-door, or with railroads, whose overall freight rates in 1966 averaged only $1\frac{1}{4}$ cents per ton-mile. Still, air cargo was gaining more customers daily on the basis of trade-offs between higher transport costs and savings in inventories, warehousing, packaging, and other distribution costs and by extending the market areas and market life of many commodities.

It is obvious to anyone familiar with the rapid growth of air transportation during the past few years that the economic dimensions of the aeronautical system will need continual upward revision. In the New York metropolitan region, for instance, as of June 1967, there were 50,200 persons, earning a total of $446.5 million a year, who were directly employed at Kennedy International and LaGuardia airports in New York and at Newark and Teterboro airports in New Jersey. This compared with 41,944 people earning $349 million at these four airports at the end of 1964.

The Aviation Development Council, the source of the preceding data, estimates that air transportation in June 1967 was already a billion dollar payroll business in the New York metropolitan area, employing approximately 180,000 people. Obviously, a growth industry of this magnitude provides economic benefits to many communities and to far more people than are included on the passenger lists of the commercial airlines.

AIR TRANSPORTATION AND SOCIOECONOMIC TRENDS

There is a two-way relationship between air transportation and socioeconomic trends. Air transport as a dynamic force in human affairs exerts its own impacts on the economy and on the environment.

A study of such impacts would be valuable but is not the immediate task of the Workshop. Instead, this section of the Workshop's report has identified what are believed to be some of the most significant social and economic trends for analysis and evaluation of their potential impact on air transportation within the next 10 or 15 years. This begins with a consideration of demographic trends, economic growth, and patterns of urban growth, followed by an evaluation of air transport demand and capacity data and future peak-hour passenger flow problems. Trends in education, recreation, and use of leisure time are analyzed; then business and military distribution policies are discussed in relation to air cargo transportation. There follows a detailed matrix analysis of the governmental system for regulation and promotion of civil air transportation and consideration of the possible impacts of government policies.

The next section deals with the vital question of ways and means, or fiscal policies, which must necessarily receive careful attention as rapidly growing demands press upon limited resources. High-speed ground transportation and other competitive transportation developments are then assessed with respect to their potential impact on air passenger and air cargo transportation. Finally, general aviation trends and potentials are considered.

DEMOGRAPHIC TRENDS AND ECONOMIC GROWTH

The population of the United States continues to grow at a rate which could add another 100 million people between 1967 and the end of the century. Since production and consumption, not only of the products of aviation but of all other goods and services, depend first of all on population trends, such trends are properly the first to be considered.

POPULATION GROWTH

The total population of the United States, including the armed forces abroad, reached almost 197 million in 1966 according to the Bureau of the Census. The increase from 1965 was 2,150,000, or only 1.1 percent, which was the lowest growth rate since 1945. The average annual growth rate was 1.7 percent from 1950 to 1959, and 1.4 percent from 1960 to 1966.

The Bureau of the Census has made four different projections of U.S. population for the period 1970-90 (see Table 2.2). The differences are due to differences in assumed fertility rates, i.e., the average number

TABLE 2.2. U.S. POPULATION PROJECTIONS

	Series A	Series B	Series C	Series D
1970	209 million	207 million	206 million	205 million
1975	228	223	219	215
1980	250	243	235	228
1985	275	265	253	242
1990	300	287	271	256

SOURCE: U.S. Bureau of the Census, *Current Population Reports*, Series P-25.

of children per 1,000 women at end of childbearing. Series A is based on the assumption that the approximate average level of fertility in the 1962-66 period will persist through 1990 (fertility rate, 3,350). Series B, C, and D are based upon rates of 3,100, 2,775, and 2,450, respectively.

While population growth will affect the future demand for air transport, it is obvious that growth in the labor force will be even more significant. The Bureau of Labor Statistics predicts that the total labor force will increase from 78 million in 1966 to 86 million in 1970, 94 million in 1975, and 101 million in 1980. The American economy is now feeling the effect on the labor force of the wartime baby boom. By 1970 there are expected to be more than 20 million persons under 25 years of age in the labor force — about 24 percent of the total.

It is significant from the standpoint of future air transport demand that the 18-24 age group will be growing throughout the 1970's but will be declining during the 1980's. Over one-fourth of the growth in population from 1966 to 1975 will be concentrated in this age group, which in 1967 represented only 11 percent of the total. This group includes the college students and those seeking first jobs and finding careers, as well as the young married couples, whose family incomes should average considerably higher than in the past as wages increase and with the growing tendency for both husband and wife to work.

In their report accompanying the *Economic Report of the President*, January 1967, the Council of Economic Advisers reported that the number of persons unemployed was about 2 million lower than it was in 1960. The civilian unemployment rate was then 3.9 percent — the lowest since 1953. Nevertheless, unemployment was still high among nonwhites, teenagers, and, in particular, unskilled workers.

With the labor force increasing by $1\frac{1}{4}$ percent to $1\frac{3}{4}$ percent annually, longer vacations and shorter workweeks (plus relatively full employment) should permit an annual growth in total productive man-hours of about $1\frac{1}{2}$ percent per year. In addition, labor productivity in the economy has been growing at a rate of about $2\frac{1}{2}$ percent a year. With gross national product per man-hour increasing at that rate and total man-hours at $1\frac{1}{2}$ percent, the potential output (GNP) of the country advances at a rate of about 4 percent per year.

Gross National Product

The GNP measured in current dollars increased from $284.8 billion in 1950 to $739.6 billion in 1966. Measured in constant (1958) dollars, the increase was from $355.3 billion to $647.8 billion, representing an average annual compounded growth rate in "real product" of 3.8 percent during the period 1950-1966.

Figure 2.1 indicates the considerable range in GNP projections made by various agencies and private groups for the period 1963-1980. While there are major differences of opinion with respect to future rates of growth, every projection assumes that the future rate will considerably exceed the average long-term growth rate of less than 3 percent from 1900 to 1963. Most forecasters expect a future growth rate even exceeding the postwar average growth of 3.4 percent annually from 1947 to 1963.

Of greatest significance in relation to the demand for air travel (as well as for other products of aviation) is the gain that has been taking place in real disposable income per capita, which is considered to be the best single measure of consumer welfare. Such income rose 24 percent during the six years preceding 1966, matching the increase during the previous 13 years. Despite a 3 percent rise in the level of consumer prices from 1965 to 1966, real disposable income per capita increased by 3½ percent.

The trend over the period 1950-1966 is shown in Table 2.3 for real disposable income per capita and for the principal categories of personal consumption expenditures, all expressed in terms of constant (1958) dollars:

TABLE 2.3. DISPOSABLE INCOME AND EXPENDITURES

	Per capita disposable income	Expenditures (per capita) for		
		Durable goods	Nondurables	Services
1950	$1,646	$229	$752	$539
1955	1,795	261	797	601
1960	1,883	248	828	673
1965	2,214	341	916	779
1966	2,294	359	945	806

SOURCE: U.S. Department of Commerce, Office of Business Economics, *The National Income and Product Accounts of the United States, 1929-1965*, and *Survey of Current Business*, February 1967.

Disposable income is the income remaining to persons after deducting personal tax and nontax payments to general government. It is the personal income available for spending or saving. As shown in the table, U.S. citizens (each man, woman, and child) had an average of $648 more in constant (1958) dollars to spend or save in 1966 than they

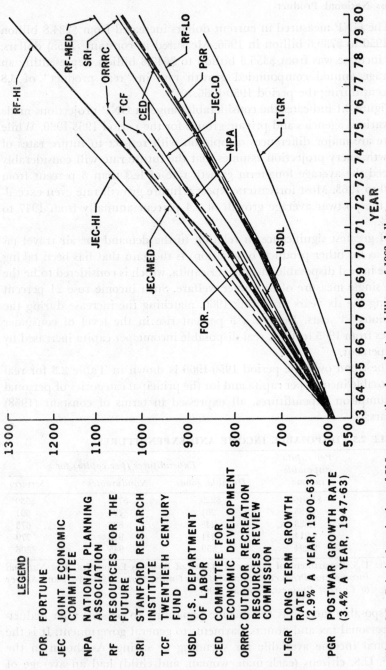

Figure 2.1. Principal projections of U.S. gross national product, in billions of 1963 dollars.
SOURCE: National Industrial Conference Board *Record*, July 1964.

LEGEND

FOR.   FORTUNE

JEC   JOINT ECONOMIC
       COMMITTEE

NPA   NATIONAL PLANNING
       ASSOCIATION

RF   RESOURCES FOR THE
       FUTURE

SRI   STANFORD RESEARCH
       INSTITUTE

TCF   TWENTIETH CENTURY
       FUND

USDL   U.S. DEPARTMENT
       OF LABOR

CED   COMMITTEE FOR
       ECONOMIC DEVELOPMENT

ORRRC OUTDOOR RECREATION
       RESOURCES REVIEW
       COMMISSION

LTGR   LONG TERM GROWTH
       RATE
       (2.9% A YEAR, 1900-63)

PGR   POSTWAR GROWTH RATE
       (3.4% A YEAR, 1947-63)

had in 1950, a gain of nearly 40 percent in spending and saving power during the 16-year period. The individual consumer increased his annual expenditures for durable goods by $130 (almost 60 percent), and for nondurable goods, by $193 (26 percent); he spent an average of $267 more per year for various services, including transportation services (an increase of approximately 50 percent). Personal saving (which tends to average about 5 percent of disposable personal income) also increased somewhat during the period.

In the light of the preceding considerations, it is obvious that air transportation is in an attractive position for continued rapid growth if it can compete with other goods and services available to the consumer. In 1965, for instance, the total passenger service sales of all U.S. scheduled domestic and international airlines amounted to approximately $4 billion. Yet in 1965 personal consumption expenditures for recreation (products and services) amounted to more than $26 billion, representing a sixfold increase since 1940 (see Table 2.4). Of this amount,

TABLE 2.4. CONSUMER EXPENDITURES FOR RECREATION

1940	$ 3.8 billion
1950	11.1
1960	18.3
1965	26.3

SOURCE: U.S. Dept. of Commerce, *Statistical Abstract of the United States*, 1967, p. 212.

$7 billion was spent for radio and television sets and their repair, records, and musical instruments. Nearly $5 billion was spent for magazines, newspapers, books, maps, and sheet music, and nearly $3½ billion for "nondurable toys and sport supplies." "Wheel goods, durable toys, sports equipment, boats, and pleasure craft" attracted nearly $3 billion, and "admissions to spectator amusements" (movies, theatre, sports, etc.), nearly $2 billion.

PUBLIC EXPERIENCE IN AIR TRAVEL

In spite of the growing availability of funds for travel, there still remains the question whether consumers will elect to travel by airplane.

Since 1955 the University of Michigan Survey Research Center has conducted a series of national travel surveys based on interviews with people about trips they and their families have taken 100 miles or more from home. Curiously, a survey taken as recently as 1962 revealed that one-third of the adult population had made no trips of 100 miles or more during the preceding year. Most of the two-thirds who did travel went by automobile. Only 11 percent had taken an air trip, 9 percent a bus trip, and 7 percent a railroad trip.

Airline people often express dismay at the discovery that the majority of the adult population have never taken an air trip, and it is true that as recently as 1964 more than 60 percent of the adult population surveyed by the University of Michigan group were without air travel experience. However, the adult population is rapidly gaining experience in air travel (see Table 2.5). The proportion of adults who have

TABLE 2.5. PROPORTION OF THE ADULT POPULATION WHO HAVE TRAVELED BY AIR

1955	23%	1960	28%
1957	27%	1962	36%
1958	29%	1964	39%

taken at least one airplane trip has been rising at about 1.8 percent per year since 1955, and it is clear that the appeal of air travel has been noticeably greater since the advent of jets.

ELECTRONIC COMMUNICATIONS VERSUS TRAVEL

Another question frequently raised is whether trends in the development and use of electronic communication techniques might increasingly provide a substitute for travel by airplane. Little evidence is available to substantiate this possibility.

Professor John B. Lansing reports that an attempt was made in 1960 by the University of Michigan Survey Research Center to evaluate this possibility with respect to business travel. It was learned that most business travelers either meet with a group of people or have several appointments. Few trips are made just to talk to a single person. Thus the purposes of the trip could not be served by a system of communication designed for conversations between only two persons, one in each location. Also, it is unusual for the time spent at appointments on business trips to be short. Only a minority of business travelers spend less than six hours with their appointments. Most spend periods of 12 hours and over. Thus, according to Lansing, any new means of communication would have to be suitable for long periods of use in order to substitute for a business trip. He concludes that "business travel is not likely to be replaced by new methods of communication. An alternate possibility is that new methods of communication might complement rather than supplant business travel."

However, John R. Pierce, of the Communications Science Division of Bell Telephone Laboratories, told a Chicago audience in June 1967, that he believes that "increasingly, we will confer by electrical communication rather than by traveling." Certainly if the quality of communications improves and if the quality of travel deteriorates (because of inadequate capacity of the system to accommodate rapidly growing demands), he might be right.

AIR TRANSPORTATION IN THE ECONOMY

Electronic communications and aviation have a common characteristic in that they are both "growth industries," and as such they may be expected to contribute increasingly to the national economy in terms of employment and payrolls.

The U.S. aeronautical system — including aircraft, engines and parts manufacture; airlines, airports, and general aviation; military aviation; and a number of federal agencies (FAA, CAB, Weather Bureau, and NASA aeronautical services) — was estimated to employ more than two million persons and contribute about $24 billion, or 4 percent of the GNP in 1964. Civil aviation accounted for about $7.4 billion of this amount and employed nearly 500,000 persons. Table 2.6 indicates how employment and GNP contribution were divided among the various activities involved.

TABLE 2.6. ECONOMIC DIMENSIONS OF THE AERONAUTICAL SYSTEM

Activity	Employment (thousands)	GNP contribution (millions)
Civil:		
Aircraft manufacture	76.25	$1,010
Airlines	230.40	3,500
Airports	16.90	218
General aviation	122.40	1,870
FAA	45.00	729
CAB	.80	8
Weather Bureau	1.00	15
NASA (aeronautical only)	1.70	48
Total civil aviation	494.45	$7,398
Military:		
Aircraft manufacturing plus research, development, test, and evaluation	556.01	$7,370
Dept. of Defense payroll	1,000.00	7,430
Dept. of Defense purchases	100.00	1,500
Total military aviation	1,656.01	$16,300
Grand total	2,150.46	$23,698

SOURCE: U.S. Senate, Committee on Aeronautical and Space Sciences, *Policy Planning for Aeronautical Research and Development,* Staff Report prepared by the Legislative Reference Service, Library of Congress, Document No. 90, 89th Congress, 2nd Session, May 19, 1966, p. 89.

PATTERNS OF URBAN GROWTH AND AIRPORTS

Airports are not merely adjacent to the city; they are functionally and spatially important in themselves. They are sensitive to the ways in which the city may change, and in turn they influence these changes. The physical interface between airport and city is never likely to be felicitous. All of this means that wise planning for airports requires foresight of the order of, at least, a decade, and the continuing participation of public agencies.

AIRPORTS AND CITIES

There is more than one kind of airport, although usually the one that comes to mind is that which serves as the airlines terminal. It is generally thought of as a large amorphous tract, vaguely distant, difficult to get to, a necessary nuisance, peripheral not only in location but also in its relations to the city. Except for the last, all these impressions are accurate — a fact which makes them all the more unfortunate.

It is true that at one time the airport was spatially, functionally, financially, and administratively marginal to the city. However, it has now come to bear approximately the same relation to the city that the central railroad terminal did some 40 years ago. Although automobiles rather than airplanes have preempted most of the railroad passenger traffic, the increase in the urban population and the fact that a larger percentage travels combine to make the airport as intensively used as was the railroad terminal.

Unlike the railroad terminal, the airport's principal nuisances — its requirement for long clear approaches and the noise generated along these lanes — are difficult to disguise or ameliorate. They lead in turn to the effort to plan and locate the airport so that it is isolated from the city. This effort has clearly failed in some places, and it is quite likely to fail in others on two counts: (1) the rate and manner in which cities are growing make their boundaries short-lived, and (2) the airport is itself not a passive component but a force that attracts development in its direction. Both of these are consequences of the forces which influence the kind and pattern of urban growth.

PATTERNS OF URBAN GROWTH

The form of the city describes the activities of its citizens and the places at which these occur. It describes where they live, work, and play; the location of the offices of government, of markets, industries and warehouses, of parks, schools, and museums; and the modes and routes by which they travel between these places.

A city can grow in different ways: by filling in and by rounding out, in layers, in sectors, along particular directions, or by combinations of these. And for any given pattern, the growth can be isotropic or disjointed.

The city was conventionally thought of as a dense core, the central business district, surrounded by residences arranged in layers of progressively lighter density. And the ebb and flow in the city was pictured as polarized between core and residential layers. At its best, this view was simplistic. It is now badly mistaken and becoming steadily more so, for it is a fundamental fact of cities that they are comprised of a complex mosaic of activities that is further complicated by the unequal rates of growth of its parts. The income and population, and the concentration of housing, industry, and commerce, for example, are increasing much faster in the suburbs than in the central city.

In effect, the metropolis is turning outward and streaming toward its periphery. It is unlikely that the central cities will be undone — at least not within the next two decades. It is also unlikely that they will ever recover the centrality they once had. This pattern of growth is not a recent event, but it is only recently that the accumulated changes and their consequences have shown markedly.

It is worth a moment to consider the sources of these changes. There are several and they have acted in concert. Cities had to grow, simply because the population generally increased and a large fraction of the people elected to move to the cities. Increasing incomes and the automobile, abetted by the federal policy that built roads and guaranteed home mortgages, made possible the home in the suburbs. Retailing always follows the movement of its market, and therefore the rise of the suburban shopping center.

The same roads also made extensive trucking possible, which removed the railroad siding as a condition of industrial location. And the roads also made it cheaper to move warehouses and terminals outside of the city, since these also required space, and land inside the city is still expensive. The space requirements of the new technologies of production also brought factories outside the central city. And because the suburbs had grown, they could find their labor locally.

Technology frees us of constraints, including that of assigned location. It is not surprising that most technological developments contributed to the motility of people, industry, and commerce that has marked the changes in the city during the last two decades.

THE AIRPORT IN THE CITY

In the course of its growth, then, the city would stream past the airport even if there were no especial attractions in that direction. In fact, there are. The airport is itself a large source of employment. In addition to the labor necessary merely to operate the airport and the airlines, consider the complex of auxiliary services that attend passengers and cargo before departure and upon arrival. Then there are hotels, restaurants, and entertainments; a substantial number of trips are made to the airport for recreation. Finally, there are the commercial and industrial activities that gather in the vicinity because they need easy access to the airport, or because the vicinity is a lively place. All these support the analogy of the airport to the railroad terminal.

Since the airport is or will soon be a part of the city, its nuisance will be felt more keenly by more people. Noise is the principal complaint. The problem has been examined by the Jet Aircraft Noise Panel, arranged by the Office of Science and Technology. Their report, *Alleviation of Jet Aircraft Noise Near Airports,* is dated March 1966. Nothing has yet occurred that might make it obsolete. Two difficulties emerge: (1) there is no satisfactory measure of noise tolerance, and (2) whatever the measure, it is not likely that much can be done technologically about the noise. Those of the panel's conclusions and recommendations that have especial relevance here are quoted below.

Conclusion 9

In spite of extensive industry- and government-sponsored research, there appears to be no technical avenues for achieving major improvements (i.e., no "breakthrough" in engine noise suppression along lines which now appear economically feasible and early enough in achievement to provide practically important assistance to communities where aircraft noise problems either already are, or are shortly expected to become, acute.

Conclusion 15

At many airports, land development has not been completed, and at others land is in the process of development. Under these circumstances, a number of federal agencies in addition to the FAA can influence the course of land development in the vicinity of airports, namely those concerned with housing, public roads, urban renewal, area development, mass transportation, and so on. However, no action has yet been taken at the top federal level to insure that such agencies have coordinated their programs and work together near airports in the interest of noise abatement.

Conclusion 16

Although it has been often argued that condemnation proceedings to insure that land is more compatibly used in the vicinity of airports may be extremely costly (i.e., "billions of dollars" might be involved), the point has seldom been made that eventual resale of the formerly residential land for later more compatible uses might actually result in final profits to the condemning jurisdiction. Accordingly, careful exploration should be made of the possibilities for condemnation or direct purchase followed by resales at various airport problem areas to obtain more realistic estimates of the long-term financial risks to the jurisdictions involved. It is to be recognized, of course, that the use of condemnation proceedings may be legally and politically difficult, if not impossible. Some airports with the most acute current problems and large intensively built-up areas would, in any event, present serious economic and sociological problems. On the other hand, it is reported that the authorities in charge of one of the nation's largest airports are in the process of acquiring residential land by purchase in areas where the PNdB [perceived noise decibel] level is, or is expected to be, higher than 105 and hope eventually to resell such property without incurring a net financial loss.

Conclusion 17

In view of the general pessimism as to how much near term noise reduction can be achieved by further R&D focused on the engine and aircraft, or by additional modifications of flight procedures in the vicinity of airports, and, because of the apparent general inadequacy of zoning authorities, police powers, program controls and/or financial assistance by federal and state governments will need to be devised for attacking the aircraft noise problem, particularly in those communities where it is rapidly becoming more acute.

The Jet Aircraft Noise Panel also made certain recommendations, of which we reprint the following:

Recommendation 8

A federal task force, representing all major federal agencies having the regulatory or financial capability to influence the course of community real estate development near airports and military bases, should be established to undertake a study of the practicable approaches to a coordinated, federally managed and financed program for stimulating airport community development in directions which would tend to anticipate or ameliorate community aircraft noise problems. This study should provide clear administrative guidance and practicable alternative programs that take into account agency authorities now legally available and those new authorities which would be needed to undertake practically useful programs at the earliest possible dates.

THE DEMANDS OF THE AIRPORT ON A CITY'S TRANSPORTATION SYSTEM

The intimacy between the city and the airport is nowhere more clearly exhibited than by the channels of travel that connect them. There are two classes of travelers to the airport: those who intend to board a flight and those who have other purposes. Of the latter, by far the largest fraction comprises airport employees, most of whom make relatively short trips.

The distances traveled for the purpose of making a flight differ much more markedly. Most cities still have a single airport, and air travelers' places of origin are widely dispersed. The largest part of such trips originates in the central business district, but that fraction is rarely as large as a half and will decrease as cities grow more diffuse. The remaining trips are almost uniformly dispersed over the metropolis. Transportation to the airport will not be solved simply by special links to the central business district. It is not even clear that the density of traffic would, by itself, be sufficient to support such a special link.

Taken as a lumped parameter in the metropolitan circuit, the airport displays some of the properties and problems of the central business district. Like the central business district, it contains a variety of activities in a small place. Its uses are therefore intense. And also like the central business district, it is a node and a nexus. Considered either as a lumped or as a distributed parameter, i.e. taken in the large or in detail, systems of transportation that work for the central business district are likely to be useful also for the airport.

A large-capacity link to the airport seems indicated. That is the easy part of the problem, but by itself it is likely to fail. It must be coupled with another system that can disperse passengers to (or collect them from) places close to their ultimate destinations. And the coupling must also be easy. The new system must, in effect, match the convenience of the automobile at its best, if the automobile is to be displaced as the predominant mode of transportation to the airport.

AIRPORT OR AIRPORTS?

There seem to have been no attempts to determine the airport size beyond which large-scale economies become negative. Even if no upper limit exists with respect to airport operation, there may be a maximum size with respect to its interface with the city. It may become an intolerable nuisance or it may simply run out of space to expand. The latter circumstance exists now in several cities. It is reasonable therefore to ask how a network of airports might work, and whether it might have positive advantages over a single larger airport.

An airport with fewer flights is not as noisy. One that occupies less land will mix better and be a more congenial neighbor. If the traveler could choose between airports, getting there might be easier. With a system of airports, the approaches and therefore the air space can be allocated exclusively. Mid-air collisions would be less likely. These appear to be some of the advantages.

The major requirement that a system of airports must meet is that they act as if they were in close proximity, which is to say that it must be easy to transfer goods, people, and baggage among them. Twenty minutes seems a generous specification of "easy."

Goods would require standard containers. People and baggage are more difficult to package. If transportation is provided from airlines terminal to airlines terminal, the passengers might convey their own baggage. This condition suggests a ground transportation system, but the 20-minute transfer suggests air transportation. Whatever mode is used, it should be made part of the intrametropolitan trip network, to increase its use and decrease its cost.

AIRPORTS OTHER THAN THOSE OF SCHEDULED AIRLINES

Of the approximately 10,000 airports in the country, about 550 are licensed to serve the airlines (and of these 142 account for 96 percent of all the passengers). In other words, the extent of aviation outside the domain of the airlines is substantial, and as the diffusion of the city increases it will become more substantial. If one adds to "general aviation" the potentials of aircraft that can take off and land either vertically or in very short distances, the problems of sorting, accommodating, and absorbing these activities into the metropolitan mosaic become rather more than merely complicated.

The influence of general aviation airports is no more local than the flights that originate and terminate there. Taken as a network, they should remain a local function, but the allocation of airport resources and functions should be made from a larger geographical base. Whether this base is a state, or a group of states will depend on the extent, the intensity, and the kinds of flying.

Accessibility

Obviously, all airports should be accessible. It is not likely that general aviation airports can now be located close to areas of intense activity, although in time they may generate such neighborhoods. Even then, the total of these activities will probably not be sufficient to justify special public-transit rights of way. In any case, the high-capacity line may not help much because the users of airports will arrive from all directions — a restatement of the increasing diffusion of the city. This circumstance applies as well to all other modes of line-haul travel. The condition of the subsystems that collect and carry away passengers is more important than the centrality of the terminals — unless, of course, the terminals are too far from any point in the city. The siting of airports intended for short trips is therefore a fussy affair.

The principal access, then, is likely to be provided by the automobile — or, if the traffic justifies, an automated highway (in any case, an automobile-like vehicle). Then access becomes a minor constraint on the location of the airport, because the ease of highway travel is now rather uniformly distributed and is becoming more so.

Aircraft as Feeders

If the distribution systems become sufficiently good, V/STOL aircraft may also provide intrametropolitan travel. They are not suited to the range from zero to ten miles, and during the next decade, at least, most city trips will fall in that interval. But the metropolis is expanding, and the number of long trips will increase even though their part of the total remains small. Aircraft seem particularly suited for those trips for which another airport is a link or an end.

If aircraft are to be used for intrametropolitan travel, the location of terminals becomes important. In order that the time needed for the trip be substantially less than by automobile or other public transportation, the aircraft must deliver passengers close to their destination or close to the transportation means that can finish the job. There will be places in the suburbs where the touchdown site is also the destination. That is much less likely in the central cities. Aircraft are not likely to work well as an urban mode of travel unless they are closely coupled with pervasive transportation systems.

Landing and takeoff sites will be no difficult problem in the suburbs. They will be difficult within the denser parts of the city. In addition, special terminal structures will probably be needed. However, none of these problems are worth a second thought if the noise remains intense. It would appear that for the present the noise problem is sufficient to write off aircraft as local carriers.

AIR TRANSPORT DEMAND AND CAPACITY: THE ROLE OF INVESTMENT AND THE ROLE OF PRICING

The United States domestic air transport industry grew at an extraordinary rate between 1945 and 1965. Revenue passenger-miles of trunk and local carriers increased from 3,337 million to 51,480 million, an annual average rate of growth of more than 15 percent. Between 1955 and 1965 cargo traffic increased from 453 million to 1,848 million revenue ton-miles. This section reviews the factors that have contributed to the industry's growth and considers what its growth rate may be in the next 15 years or so. The section is divided into three parts. First, trends in air travel as forecast by several recognized authorities are discussed. Second, some alternative projections of demand for air transport and air cargo are presented and the techniques underlying a few of them are discussed. Third, the role of public investment and pricing policies are considered. An argument is also presented for the role of peak load pricing as a *partial* alternative to investment in additional airport capacity.

TRENDS IN AIR TRAVEL

While air freight, mail, and express traffic of the U.S. scheduled airlines seemed to be looking forward to the potential rate reductions which could be achieved by high-capacity, low-unit-cost aircraft soon to be delivered, there was little evidence in 1966 that passengers were being much restrained by the prevailing levels of fares.

The total number of revenue passengers carried by all U.S. scheduled airlines increased from 58 million in 1961 to 109 million in 1966. The impact of such growth in passenger traffic on airports, air traffic control, and other essential facilities can be more readily appreciated when the net annual gains in passengers handled are reduced to average daily increases. As shown in Table 2.7, the average increase of 40,000 passengers per day boarding the planes of U.S. scheduled air carriers in 1966 compared with a gain of only 14,000 passengers per day in 1962.

TABLE 2.7. REVENUE PASSENGERS CARRIED BY U.S. SCHEDULED AIRLINES

	Passengers carried	Yearly increase	Average increase per day
1961	58 million	—	—
1962	63	5 million	14,000
1963	71	8	22,000
1964	82	11	30,000
1965	95	13	36,000
1966	109	14	40,000

SOURCE: Computed from Air Transport Association of America, *1967 Air Transport Facts & Figures*, p. 41.

If such growth in passenger traffic were evenly spread over the 527 U.S. communities served in 1966 by domestic scheduled airlines, it might have been relatively easy to accommodate the net growth of fewer than 100 additional passengers per day at each point. But U.S. airline traffic is heavily concentrated at 22 communities classified as "large air transportation hubs," each generating 1 percent or more of the total scheduled air carrier domestic passengers enplaned.

These large hubs in 1965 collectively accounted for 68 percent of all domestic passengers enplaned and 79 percent of all domestic air cargo carried by U.S. scheduled airlines. The traffic was still more concentrated at the first 10 of these hubs, which generated over half of all the scheduled air passenger trips, and at the first four — New York, Newark,

Chicago, and Los Angeles — which together accounted for more than one-fourth of all the 1965 passenger enplanements in the country.

The Federal Aviation Agency, the source of this information, reports that any one community's share of the U.S. airline passenger market has proved relatively stable from year to year, and therefore concludes that most of the future requirements for public airport facilities in this nation are encompassed by large hub forecasts. Having reached this conclusion, the Agency's staff apportioned FAA forecasts of total U.S. scheduled air carrier traffic in 1970, 1975, and 1980 to each of the 22 large hubs as shown in Table 2.8. The magnitude of the expected increases may be more easily visualized in terms of average daily enplanement of passengers at individual hubs. New York's airports, for instance, which were originating an average of about 32,000 passengers per day in 1965, must be prepared to handle 58,000 per day in 1970,

TABLE 2.8. FAA FORECAST OF SCHEDULED AIR CARRIER PASSENGERS TO BE ENPLANED AT LARGE AIR TRANSPORTATION HUBS IN 1970, 1975, AND 1980

		(Millions)			
		Base year 1965	Forecast 1970	Forecast 1975	Forecast 1980
1	New York*	11.6	21.1	36.2	61.0
2	Newark				
3	Chicago	8.7	16.0	27.4	46.2
4	Los Angeles	6.1	11.0	18.8	31.8
5	Washington, D.C.	4.4	8.0	13.8	23.5
6	San Francisco	4.1	7.7	13.2	22.3
7	Atlanta	3.4	6.9	11.9	20.0
8	Miami	2.9	5.5	9.4	15.9
9	Dallas (and Fort Worth)	2.6	5.0	8.6	14.8
10	Boston	2.6	4.8	8.2	13.8
11	Detroit	1.9	3.4	5.8	9.8
12	Pittsburgh	1.7	3.1	5.2	8.8
13	Philadelphia	1.6	3.1	5.2	8.9
14	Denver	1.5	2.9	5.0	8.5
15	Cleveland	1.5	2.8	4.8	8.1
16	St. Louis	1.5	2.7	4.7	7.9
17	Minneapolis-St. Paul	1.3	2.4	4.2	7.1
18	Kansas City	1.2	2.2	3.8	6.4
19	Houston	1.2	2.2	3.8	6.5
20	Seattle	1.2	2.3	4.2	7.1
21	New Orleans	1.1	2.1	3.6	6.0
22	Cincinnati	.8	1.7	2.8	4.8
	Total 22 hubs	62.9	71.4	200.6	339.2

(440% increment 1965–1980)

* These two large hubs are combined in one forecast.

SOURCE: FAA, Advisory Circular No. 150-5040, Airports, *Aviation Demand and Airport Facility Requirement Forecasts for Large Air Transportation Hubs Through 1980*, August 1967.

100,000 per day in 1975, and about 167,000 per day by 1980. Chicago's airports, which were enplaning passengers at a rate of 24,000 per day in 1965, must anticipate about 44,000 per day in 1970, 75,000 per day in 1975, and more than 127,000 per day in 1980. Of course, daily average calculations such as these considerably understate the actual requirements, since airline passenger traffic is not evenly balanced from day to day but is characterized by peak-hour movements on certain days and in certain seasons of the year.

FORECASTS OF SCHEDULED AIRLINE PASSENGER TRAFFIC

Before considering economic and social trends which influence air transport development, brief attention should be given to the pattern of recent forecasts of future scheduled airline passenger traffic.

Since reference has already been made to the large air transport hub projections of the Federal Aviation Agency, it is worth noting that the Agency's 10-year forecast (1967-77) anticipates that the total revenue passenger-miles of U.S. domestic and international scheduled airlines will grow from 76 billion in 1966 to 266 billion by 1977. Further, since much air facility planning is concerned with passengers rather than passenger-miles, the Agency arrives at the following forecasts of total U.S. air carrier passenger enplanements in the future as compared with actual volumes in the base year 1965.

TABLE 2.9. FORECASTS OF U.S. AIR CARRIER PASSENGER
ENPLANEMENTS

Fiscal year	Domestic carriers	International carriers
1965 (actual)	84.6 million	10.0 million
1970	150.8	17.2
1975	258.0	28.5
1980	435.5	46.5

SOURCE: FAA, *Aviation Forecasts, FY 1967–77*, revised to 1980 by the FAA's Office of Policy Development, April 14, 1967.

Forecasts of the Port of New York Authority, like most others, have required upward revision in recent years.

The Port Authority's December 1966, study *Airport Requirements and Sites*, pointed out that annual air passenger demand for the New York region (three airports) is expected to increase from 25.8 million air travelers in 1965 to 53.5 million in 1975 and 65 million in 1980.

In January 1957, the Authority's *Forecast of the United States Domestic Air Passenger Market 1965-1975* had predicted 21.0 million air travelers in 1965 and 38.0 million in 1975. It must be realized that this was a prejet-age projection, looking ahead from 1955, when the actual number of domestic air passengers originating or terminating at the Port Authority's airports was only 9.5 million.

In view of the conservatism of the Port Authority's earlier forecasts, observers such as the economist of the First National City Bank of New York have expressed alarm over the estimate by the Authority that whereas the present maximum peak-hour combined capacity of the three airports is 185 plane movements per hour under instrument flight rules (IFR), future peak-hour demand is forecast at 213 plane movements in 1970, 247 in 1975, and 302 in 1980, "frighteningly in excess of the maximum capacity." In this connection it should be mentioned that the FAA's August 1, 1967, forecast of busy-hour operations for the New York hub was 213 plane movements in 1970, 277 in 1975, and 372 in 1980 for scheduled air carriers. In addition, the FAA projected peak-hour general aviation plane movements would increase from 1,130 in 1965 to 1,962 in 1970, 2,923 in 1975, and 4,365 in 1980, but pointed out that general aviation's peak hour is not the same as that of air carriers.

World scheduled airline passenger traffic (measured by the combined traffic of carriers of member countries in the International Civil Aviation Organization) grew at an average rate of 14.2 percent annually from 10 billion passenger-miles in 1946 to 123 billion in 1965, a twelvefold increase. U.S. domestic traffic during the same period grew from 6 billion passenger-miles to 52 billion, nearly a ninefold increase.

The postwar growth of ICAO world and U.S. passenger-miles from 1946 to 1965 at approximately 5-year intervals is shown below:

TABLE 2.10. ICAO WORLD AND U.S. SCHEDULED AIR PASSENGER-MILES

	ICAO world	*U.S. domestic*
1946	10 billion	6 billion
1950	17	8
1955	38	20
1960	68	31
1965	123	52

Growth has generally exceeded the forecasts that have been made from time to time. Besse and Desmas of the Institut du Transport Aerien compared eight published forecasts with actual world air passenger-miles in 1965 and discovered that they underestimated the actual growth by 6 to 21 percent. Eight forecasts of actual U.S. domestic passenger-miles for 1965 undershot the mark by 15 to 20 percent. According to Besse and Desmas, the reason seems to be that forecasters are prone to be too strongly influenced by the trend during the most recent years.

If this is the case, current forecasts for the period 1970-1980 could quite easily be too high, since annual traffic growth during the past few

SOCIOECONOMIC TRENDS

years has been exceptionally rapid when compared with year-to-year
gains even over the past decade (see Table 2.11). When 1966 results are
adjusted upward to what they might have been except for the general
airlines strike in 1966, a growth rate from 1965 to 1966 of 23.1 percent

TABLE 2.11. REVENUE PASSENGER-MILES FOR DOMESTIC
OPERATIONS OF THE DOMESTIC
TRUNK AIRLINES

Calendar year	Revenue passenger-miles (billions)	% Increase over previous year
1956	21.6	12.7
1957	24.5	13.2
1958	24.4	− 0.3
1959	28.1	15.1
1960	29.2	3.9
1961	29.5	1.0
1962	31.8	7.8
1963	36.4	14.3
1964	41.7	14.5
1965	49.0	17.6
1966	56.8	15.9

SOURCE: CAB, *Forecast of 1967 Scheduled Domestic Air Passenger Traffic for the
Trunk Carriers.* (Research Study)

appears to have been achieved. To expect such high yearly growth rates
to continue would ignore the fact that four times during the past
decade growth was under 10 percent, and in one year (1958) traffic
actually fell below that of the previous year.

A similar pattern of ups and down in the annual growth rate of
scheduled airline passenger-miles is found in the case of ICAO world
traffic, 1956-1965:

TABLE 2.12. PASSENGER-MILE GROWTH, ICAO WORLD TRAFFIC

	Percent
1955-56	16
1956-57	14
1957-58	5
1958-59	15
1959-60	11
1960-61	7
1961-62	11
1962-63	13
1963-64	16
1964-65	16

Here again concentration on the 16 percent growth rates achieved in
1964 and 1965 would overlook the fact that the average annual increase
was considerably less, and that similar ups and downs might very well
temper future growth rates as well.

Looking into the immediate future, the ICAO forecasts for 1965-
1970 a range between a maximum growth rate of 16 percent and a
minimum of 10 percent. ICAO's maximum assumes a 3 percent reduction in fares every year and assumes that the price elasticity of demand
is 2 (i.e., that a 1 percent reduction in fares will result in an additional
2 percent increase in traffic). For the period 1970-1975, ICAO forecasts
again suggest a growth rate ranging from 10 to 16 percent.

In the spring of 1967 a number of air transport people representing
several domestic trunk airlines, aircraft manufacturers, and airport
operators met in New York to discuss forecasting methods and compare
their projections as far into the future as 1975 and 1980. While some of
the individual forecasts were not released for publication, it is possible
to state the range of their predictions of U.S. domestic trunk revenue
passenger-miles as compared with the actual volume of 57 billion
revenue passenger-miles carried in 1966 and 70 billion estimated for
the calendar year 1967.

TABLE 2.13.   FORECASTS OF DOMESTIC TRUNK AIRLINES
              REVENUE PASSENGER-MILES

Year	Airline forecasts	Aircraft manufacturers' forecasts	FAA forecasts
1970	92-101 billion	94-100 billion	90 billion
1975	150-175	144-185	163
1980	220-290	200-295	230
1985	N.A.	260-400	N.A.

It is clear that knowledgeable people in the air transport industry
anticipate a continuation of rapid growth rates. Similar rates are likewise predicted by the Federal Aviation Agency. If such predictions are
correct, it is obvious that present airport capacity, air traffic control,
and ground connection capacity will need to be greatly expanded.

ALTERNATIVE PROJECTIONS OF DEMAND

Figures 2.2, 2.3, and 2.4 present the projections of passenger traffic
made by a number of airframe manufacturers, carriers, and agencies
of the federal government. The projections shown, as well as almost
any others that might be presented, are in broad agreement as to methodology. They all tend to take into account such factors as changes in
population, level and distribution of per capita income, and, explicitly
or implicitly, the character of the air transport industry, including
fares and quality of service offered.

The forecasters also agree that the industry will continue to grow,

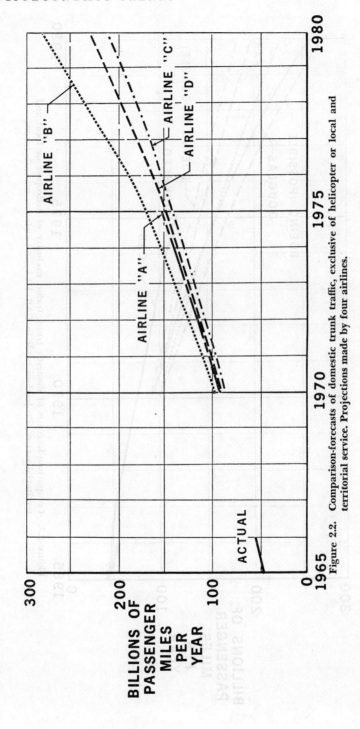

Figure 2.2. Comparison-forecasts of domestic trunk traffic, exclusive of helicopter or local and territorial service. Projections made by four airlines.

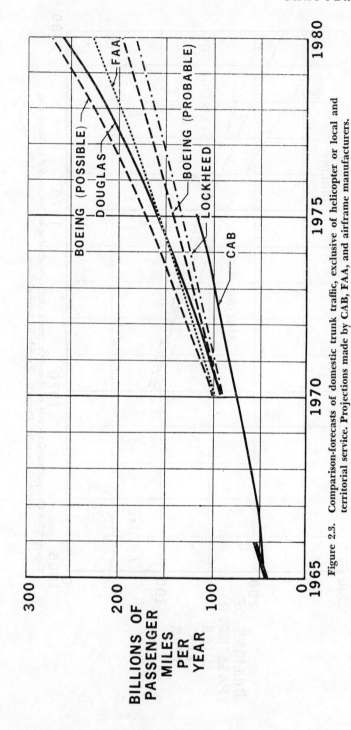

Figure 2.3. Comparison-forecasts of domestic trunk traffic, exclusive of helicopter or local and territorial service. Projections made by CAB, FAA, and airframe manufacturers.

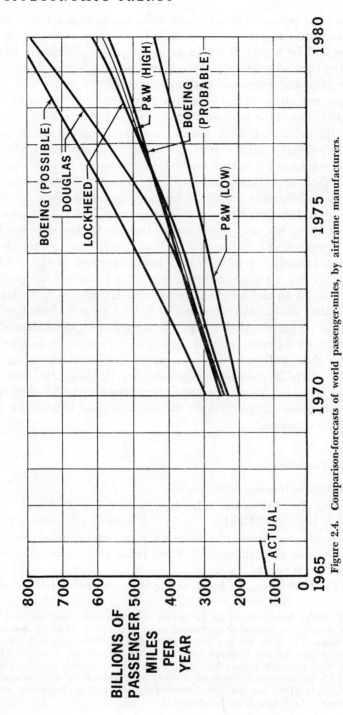

Figure 2.4. Comparison-forecasts of world passenger-miles, by airframe manufacturers.
SOURCE: International Civil Aviation Organization.

although their projected growth rates differ owing to differences in assumptions concerning rates of investment in aircraft and airport capacities. It would be highly desirable to investigate in detail the factors underlying these differences and to choose the most reasonable projection for planning purposes, but unfortunately the projection techniques are not always stated in quantitative terms. Thus, while it is known that most of the forecasts take changes in per capita income into account, the precise influence of such changes on demand is not stated, at least in publicly available sources. Two of the groups, the CAB[1] and the FAA,[2] use formal statistical methods in developing their projections and state their assumptions, although they do not always explain and justify them. Before discussing the forecasts, it should be said that by a happy coincidence the two offer a good contrast. The CAB forecast is the least bullish, but not greatly unlike the low Lockheed projection. The FAA projection is in the medium-high range, being almost identical to that of Douglas up to 1975. Both forecasts appear in Figure 2.3.

The CAB and FAA projections are similar in overall conception. They are based on the belief that significant factors can be identified which, if they do not fully determine, at least strongly influence the demand for air travel. After identifying these factors, the independent variables, both agencies employ multiple regression techniques to determine their influence in a past period. Projected values for the dependent variable, revenue passenger-miles (RPM's), are then obtained by choosing values for the independent variables that seem likely. As in almost all projections, the results depend to a great extent on the values chosen.

The CAB Projection

The CAB's estimating equation is

$$\Delta \log Q = .085 - 1.28 \, \Delta \log F + 1.16 \log Y - .04 \log T,$$

where Q is per capita RPM's; F is fare or revenue per passenger-mile deflated by the consumer price index; Y is per capita income deflated by the consumer price index; and T is a trend variable, a value being assigned to each year of the data.

Thus the CAB approach involves five independent variables: popu-

---

1 The CAB has three forecasts for the period ending in 1975 — low, medium, and high. The three differ because of alternative assumptions made as to the downward trend of fares. The high forecast involves the greatest reduction. It is the one depicted in Figure 2.3 and is drawn from the study *Forecasts of Passenger Traffic 1965-1975*, Staff Research Report No. 5, Civil Aeronautics Board, September 1965.

2 The FAA projection is based upon a study by its consultant, the Institute for Defense Analysis (IDA). See *Demand Analysis for Air Travel by Supersonic Transport*, Volume 2, Appendix A, N. J. Asher et al.

lation, fare, disposable income, trend, and the consumer price index.[3] The equation was estimated for the first differences of the above variables, a procedure that the CAB is mistaken in believing eliminates the problem of correlation between two of the independent variables, fare and income.

The CAB estimating equation explains a good deal of the variation in the dependent variable. The coefficient of multiple correlation is .79 and the coefficient of determination is .62. The signs of the two meaningful variables, fare and disposable income, are correct and statistically significant. The equation indicates that demand is slightly elastic with respect to price and income. That is, a 10 percent reduction in price would result in a 12.8 percent increase in demand. A 10 percent increase in income would increase demand by 11.6 percent.

The third independent variable, the trend, is difficult to justify conceptually and barely significant statistically. It is apparently a surrogate for such factors as long-run changes in attitudes toward air travel and improvements in aspects of service such as travel time. It would seem that the CAB should have included travel time as an independent variable and eliminated the trend variable, as in the FAA projection. Indeed, at least one member of the CAB research staff has included a variable called elapsed time (the sum of air and ground time) in an analysis of travel between city pairs.[4] In this study the coefficient attached to the time variable took on the correct (negative) sign and was statistically significant. Moreover, in one regression, demand was found to be more responsive to reductions in travel time than to fares.

In order to apply its estimating equation, the CAB had to specify values for each of the independent variables in the forecast period. It was assumed that population would increase to about 225 million in 1975, and that the consumer price index would increase about 1.5 percent per year. The projected increase in disposable personal income was 4.77 percent per year, the average for the decade 1953-1963. This rate of increase, together with the expected changes in prices and population, implies an increase in real per capita income of 1.91 percent per year. Finally, the CAB projection shown in Figure 2.3 assumes that fares will decline by 1.14 percent per year, the rate of change experienced in the period 1949-1957. This rate of change yields a real rate of 4.47 cents per mile in 1975.

3 A slightly different version of this estimating equation has recently been published. See CAB Research Study, *Forecast of 1967 Scheduled Domestic Air Passenger Traffic for the Trunk Carriers.*

4 S. L. Brown, "Measuring the Elasticities of Air Travel," Business and Economic Statistics Section, *Proceedings of the American Statistical Association,* 1965, pp. 278-285.

The FAA Projection

The FAA (IDA) study identified changes in per capita real income and population as having the greatest influence on air travel. Changes in fares and trip times were found to have important but smaller effects. The influence of these variables on RPM's was determined from data for the period 1950-1965 by multiple regression techniques. It was found that the best fit was provided by a linear equation in which per capita RPM's was the dependent variable, and real per capita excess income,[5] fare, and trip time were the independent variables. Although a linear equation was fitted to the data, the FAA's consultants then assumed that the results could be employed in a constant elasticity demand equation, i.e., an equation in log linear form. This procedure seems entirely unjustified. The projections obtained were based on the following equation:

$$\text{Log } Q = 1.0 \log Y - 1.5 \log F - 0.6 \log S,$$

where Q is per capita RPM's; Y is excess income; F is average fare deflated by the consumer price index; and S is speed. Again the variables all have the correct signs and the equation explains a considerable part of the variation in the dependent variable.

The CAB and FAA estimating equations involve somewhat different variables and were fitted to different data. It may, however, be instructive to note that the two equations do not differ greatly in their measure of the responsiveness of demand to income and fares. The CAB equation indicates a somewhat greater responsiveness of demand to income changes and a smaller responsiveness to fare changes. The greatest difference between the two equations is in their third variable. It will be recalled that the CAB trend variable had a very small coefficient statistically. The coefficient attached to the FAA speed variable is considerably larger.

The FAA elasticity estimates (i.e., the coefficients shown in their equation) were combined with estimates of the most likely values of the independent variables, to obtain projections of per capita demand. Real per capita income was assumed to grow at a compound rate of 2.5 percent, a rate that implies a 1.5 percent increase for the adult population. The latter figure is particularly relevant, the report argues, because population age 20 and over constitutes the largest market for air travel. The population in this age group can, moreover, be pre-

---

[5] IDA found that the demand for air travel tends to remain fairly constant for family incomes under $7500 and then begins to increase. The excess income variable is designed to reflect this pattern. It has been defined as the excess over $7500 for family incomes exceeding this amount, divided by the total U.S. population.

dicted with considerable accuracy to 1980. A Bureau of the Census projection was adopted in which this segment of the population was shown to grow at an annual rate of 1.5 percent.

Fares were projected to decline by 25 percent in the period 1966 to 1978. The speed variable, minutes per mile for overall aircraft miles, was projected to fall from 0.1691 in 1965 to 0.1326 in 1975.

The CAB and FAA projections for 1975 are quite different, the two figures being 119 and 170 billion RPM's respectively. As noted previously, the differences do not appear to be due to the fare and income elasticities. They are in part due to the fact that the FAA estimating equation has speed as a variable, that the coefficient of this variable is moderately large, and that the equation projects a fairly significant increase in speed over the projection period.

Differences between the two projections are also due to the fact that the CAB assumes per capita real income will grow 1.91 percent per year, whereas the FAA puts this figure at 2.5 percent.[6] Both projection techniques attach a great deal of weight to income. It is this difference in income growth that probably explains the greatest part of the difference in values that the two agencies project for 1975, and which could lead some to view the CAB projection as more realistic. The FAA growth rate was achieved in only one period in the postwar years, 1959-1965. It will be recalled that 1959 was a year of recession and 1965 a year of high economic activity, endpoints that would naturally produce a high growth rate. The CAB growth rate of 1.91 percent is, on the other hand, only slightly greater than the 1.69 percent growth experienced in the entire postwar period.

Air Cargo Projections

Many projections have been made for air cargo traffic. They cannot be evaluated, because the methodology on which they are based has not been stated in publicly available sources. The techniques used to project cargo appear to be much more primitive than those used for passenger traffic. Perhaps the main reason for their crudity is that until recently there has been no clearly stated and empirically tested theory of demand for the alternative modes of transport.[7] Forecasters have therefore been much less certain of which variables, aside from GNP,

[6] The reader should not be misled by the fact that the FAA projection emphasizes the adult population and the rate of growth (1.5 percent) of its income. The CAB rate of 1.91 percent for the entire population, if adjusted for the adult population, would show a somewhat lower figure.

[7] For one such effort, see L. N. Moses and M. Beuthe, "The Demand for Transportation," paper delivered before the Sesquicentennial meeting of the National Academy of Sciences, August 1967.

should be entered in any formal statistical model. Many of the forecasts are, as a result, largely based on the fitting of curves of one sort
or another to time series data and the projection of these curves into
the future. Thus, one group assumed that GNP would grow 3.5 percent
per year and that total intercity ton-miles would increase at a rate of
2.45 per dollar of GNP. Forecasts of the penetration of air cargo into
this total were obtained by fitting a Gompertz growth curve to past
penetration percentages. This procedure yielded the following results:[8]

TABLE 2.14. PROJECTED AIR CARGO GROWTH

Year	Revenue ton-miles (million)	Annual rate of growth for 5-year period (percent)
1970	3,861	15.9
1975	7,927	15.5
1980	14,670	13.1

The high rate of growth that the air industry has experienced in
the last 20 years is due to a number of classes of forces, some having
to do with the changing character of the U.S. economy, and others
with the changing character of the industry and its main competitors.
Increases in population and per capita real income are among the most
important forces in the former category, a fact that is recognized and
taken into account by all forecasters. Growth has also been due to
reductions in average air fares and improvements in the quality of
service, and to opposite trends among some of the air industry's main
competitors. In the last 20 years the cost of rail travel increased and
the quality of service decreased so far as to make this form of travel
no longer a serious competitor in the intercity passenger field. It seems
likely that the cost of intercity travel by private automobile, the main
competitor of air transport, has also risen quite strongly in this period.

The factors that operate through the economy at large will undoubtedly continue to increase the demand for air transport. While
forecasters differ as to the rate at which they expect the U.S. economy
to grow, none doubt that it will expand and with it the potential
demand for air travel. Whether or not the potentials implied in these
factors are realized seems to depend critically on the quality of the
service offered by the industry and the cost and quality of new methods
of high speed "ground" transport that are now in the developmental
stage.

The air industry is showing the effects of congestion. Thus, while
average speed of aircraft has continued to increase, door-to-door time

[8] Systems Analysis and Research Corporation, *Air Traffic Growth*, January 1967.

for air travel has not improved in the last half-dozen years. Congestion on routes leading to airports, in parking areas, and in terminal buildings has increased enormously. It is not an exaggeration to say that the overall time and convenience of an air trip have not improved at all in recent years. Congestion in air space is even more serious, since it has increased the number of near misses. It is not inconceivable that the accident rate might rise in the near future if appropriate steps are not taken. It seems clear that the future rate of growth of air travel will depend to a considerable extent on the ability of government and industry to alleviate the problems of congestion and thereby to improve the quality of air service.

INVESTMENT AND PRICING POLICIES IN RELATION TO CAPACITY

The FAA released a report on airport capacity that also bears on the problem of congestion.[9] The report projects needed expansions in airport capacities within 22 metropolitan areas. These areas are classified as "large hubs" because each generates one percent or more of the nation's domestic enplaned passengers. It maintains that a community's share of the passenger market tends to be quite stable and implies, therefore, that metropolitan area forecasts of enplaned passengers were obtained by multiplying national figures by these percentages. In order to arrive at estimates of required expansions in various types of airport facilities, the FAA then allocated projected passengers at each hub by type of user (scheduled air carrier, general aviation), type of activity (itinerant and local aircraft operations, busy hour operations), and type of aircraft. Table 2.15 summarizes the results for the 22 large hubs. (The hubs are listed, with their projected passenger increments, in Table 2.8.)

The techniques by which the FAA estimated needed expansions in capacity are complex. They are, however, the only comprehensive forecasts of their kind available and, representing as they do the judgments and knowledge of the nation's leading experts in the field, they must be taken seriously. If the FAA is to be faulted, it must be on the basis of certain omissions and the failure to consider alternatives to investment in additional capacity. Perhaps the most serious omission is the failure to attach a cost to the projected physical requirements. The agency has in effect indicated what the air industry will need in order to provide a certain level and quality of service, but it has not estimated what government will have to spend to provide these facilities.

[9] *Aviation Demand and Airport Facility Requirement Forecast for Large Air Transportation Hubs Through 1980*, FAA, August 1, 1967.

It is therefore unclear whether, from the viewpoint of society at large, it would not be preferable to formulate a less ambitious investment program and adopt measures that will contribute to the more efficient use of airport capacity. The most obvious such measure is the use of prices as a rationing device.

TABLE 2.15. SUMMARY OF LARGE HUB AIRPORT AVIATION ACTIVITY AND SELECTED AIRPORT FACILITY REQUIREMENT FORECASTS THROUGH 1980

A. *Airport aviation activities*	1965	%	1980	%	% *Increment 1965-1980*
Aircraft operations					
(millions)	20.3	100	74.6	100	269
Scheduled air carrier	3.8	19	9.1	12	143
General aviation	15.9	78	65.0	87	309
Military	.6	3	.5	1	(−21)
Enplaned passengers					
(millions)	69.5	100	370.6	100	433
Air carrier	62.8	90	339.2	91	440
Domestic	57.8	83	311.9	84	440
International	5.0	7	27.3	7	445
General aviation	6.7	10	31.4	9	367
Scheduled air carrier cargo tons					
(millions)	1.3	100	19.7	100	1,371
General aviation based aircraft					
(thousands)	20.3	100	50.0	100	146
Less than 12,500 lb	16.0	79	35.3	71	121
More than 12,500 lb	4.3	21	14.7	29	242

B. *Selected airport facilities*	1980 Requirements
Air carrier	
Passenger gate positions	2,253
Cargo gate positions	521
Public vehicle parking area (sq yd)	11.5 million
Terminal building area (sq yd)	5.8 "
Cargo building area (sq yd)	.9 "
Terminal apron area (sq yd)	19.4 "
Cargo apron area (sq yd)	4.4 "
General aviation	
Public vehicle parking area (sq yd)	3.3 "
Terminal building area (sq yd)	.4 "
Aircraft apron parking areas:	
Hangars (sq yd)	22.1 "
Open (sq yd)	45.3 "

Consider first the matter of parking facilities. Most air travelers arrive at their originating airport by private automobile. Such travel is more convenient than limousine. In addition, parking fees at most airports are so low that it costs less to park for three to five days than it does to make the round trip by taxi. As a result, the demand for parking and the resulting congestion continue to increase. Airport parking should probably be priced only slightly below the level of downtown parking. Then congestion on access routes would be reduced, as would the need for additional parking facilities.

Airlines have for some time used differential fares to even out demand. For example, excursion fares are not available on certain days and hours. This practice should be extended, since travel — particularly business travel — is highly peaked by hour of day. Airport capacity would be used more efficiently and less new capacity would be required if airport managers charged airlines higher landing fees during certain hours of the day, and airlines passed these higher fees on to passengers. A similar argument can be made for differential landing fees at different airports.

There is little doubt that growth of air travel will require additional airports in many major hubs in the next 20 years. The newer airports will probably be less conveniently located and may be underutilized while congestion at the older airports continues to grow. An obvious cure is to charge higher landing fees and premium fares at the more conveniently located airports. Finally, perhaps the greatest contribution to efficiency would be made by a system of pricing that had the effect of separating commercial and general aviation.

The purpose of this discussion has not been to dispute the fact that rather substantial expansions in airport capacities will be required in the next 15 years. It seems perfectly clear that they will be required. Rather, the purpose has been to suggest that the industry has not made the most efficient use of airport capacity in the past, and that proper pricing will increase this efficiency. Such pricing could reduce rates of needed investment below those projected by the FAA.

FUTURE PEAK-HOUR PASSENGER-FLOW PROBLEMS IN RELATION TO AIRPORT CAPACITY

When considering the passenger-flow problems related to multiple airport complexes of future time periods such as 1975-80 and 1980-85, one must project the interrelationships of passenger demand, aircraft population (and mix), and the capacity of the airports themselves. Merely projecting one of these factors and disregarding the others can be misleading.

PEAK-HOUR AIRCRAFT MIX

The use of dual independent runways is essential to achieving an IFR movement rate of around 80 aircraft per hour. This is a "mix" of 60 percent large jets, 20 percent medium jets, and 20 percent small jets or general aviation aircraft. The capacity declines as the "mix" is

changed to favor large aircraft. For example, the same configuration
of runways could handle around 110 movements per hour if the large
and medium jets constitute only 20 percent and 40 percent, respectively.
Expanded airports with three widely spaced parallel runways (with
good taxiway connections) have only recently been considered, and
here a possibility of up to 110 to 120 operations per hour with high
percentages of large aircraft seems possible.

The Boeing Company, in their report "Airport Activity Analysis"
(February 1967), suggests that for the 747 (jumbo) jets alone there will
be 198 daily passenger departures and 87 freight departures from New
York in 1976, the beginning of the two five-year periods discussed in
the report. In airport traffic analysis, "operations" are used as the basic
criteria. Since each departure is equivalent to two "operations," a landing and a takeoff, the Boeing figure is doubled. This provides a more
realistic figure for passenger movements, since arrivals and departures
combine to create total servicing demands. This would mean a total
of around 400 daily passenger operations of this large aircraft in the
New York multiple-airport complex. This same study suggests 87 SST
departures or a total of 174 operations per day. SST and big-jet daily
operations would be about 570 per day according to this projection,
based on a production estimate of about 300 passenger model-747 aircraft and 120 SST.

Assuming that the present general rule that says 8 to 10 percent of
the daily movements figure will continue to represent a peak-hour
figure, this would indicate 32 to 40 operations of big jets and 14 to 16
SST operations during a peak hour. One must further assume that the
average load factor in a peak hour is likely to range from 80 to 85
percent rather than the average monthly or daily figure of 50 to 60
percent. The reasons for the peaking of aircraft movements are the
same reasons that the load factors will be high. The travel demand
from 8:00 to 10:00 a.m. and 5:00 to 7:00 p.m. will probably continue
as at present, since most people desire to travel at these times. While
there is some tendency to spread these times somewhat and perhaps
add a third peak period in the middle of the day, it seems unlikely
that the 8 to 10 percent peak-hour factors noted above will change
much in the 1975 to 1980 period.

Thus, at this future date the peak-hour demand "mix" for service
at a major jet airport such as New York's J. F. Kennedy Airport might
be as shown in Table 2.16. Because of the servicing requirements of
large aircraft, there is likely to be a concentration of aircraft such as
the 747, but at only one airport of a multiple-airport complex.

The tendency to increase the percentage population of the larger
aircraft at the expense of the smaller aircraft is a natural turn of events

at a major airport, but the several other airports will still acquire most of this overflow traffic. The current, typical daily figures (rounded) for New York's three major airports are La Guardia, 800; Kennedy, 1,000; Newark, 900; for a total of 2,700. Some estimates of demand indicate that the total figure will be 3,400 by 1975. It is this difference between

TABLE 2.16. PROJECTED PEAK-HOUR DEMAND "MIX" (OPERATIONS)

Type	High estimate	Medium estimate	Low estimate
747	40	36	32
SST	16	14	12
Stretch	25	20	15
4 engine	25	20	15
2-3 engine	40	35	30
Totals	146	125	104

capacity and demand (700 operations) that has created the need for the fourth jet airport to serve the area. Using the 8 to 10 percent factor, this would indicate a peak-hour area demand of around 300 operations.

The nature of this 300 operations per hour demand is an interesting question to pose to the experts when the mix of aircraft and airports for 1975-1980 is discussed.

With major (costly) improvements at Kennedy, such as a third parallel runway configuration (at least one more is physically possible) and improved air traffic control, a peak traffic flow of perhaps 120 operations per hour might be reached. Airport surface control devices to semi-automate the surface routing of large aircraft at complex intersections or gates could do much to maximize capacity at any airport, as could improvements in runway and taxiway design. Chicago, for instance, has expansion plans with widely spaced runways wherein somewhat larger peak-hour figures may be expected. Table 2.17 shows high and low estimates of passenger flow.

Studies by the Port of New York Authority indicate that about 85 percent of New York's passengers are "terminal" passengers, the remainder being "through" passengers. The concentration of business interests in the area and stopovers to see the city are the reasons for the high "terminal" percentage. A city like Chicago may have a more even mix; Miami, on the other hand, may have 95 percent terminal passengers. A high percentage of terminal passengers adds to airport problems, since a passenger leaving the airport proper requires transportation, adding to the total traffic congestion of parking facilities and access roads.

Although employees working at the airport have varying schedules, they too can contribute to traffic flow problems during the peak hours, since some of their commuting schedules coincide with the times the passengers desire to arrive at or depart from the airport. Some 40,000 people are employed at a major airport such as Kennedy. Aircraft crews arriving and departing, maintenance workers, ticket agents, and other employees often have work schedules that coincide with the peaks of

TABLE 2.17. ESTIMATES OF PASSENGER FLOW

High Estimate			(Rounded numbers)	
Type	Movements	Seats per aircraft	Passengers (80%) (thousands)	Passengers (85%) (thousands)
747	40	500*	16.0	17.0
SST	16	300	3.8	4.1
Stretch	25	200	4.0	4.3
4 Engine	25	150	3.0	3.2
2-3 Engine	40	90	2.9	3.0
High Total	146		29.7	31.6 (rounded)
Low Estimate				
Type	Movements	Seats per aircraft	Passengers (80%) (thousands)	Passengers (85%) (thousands)
747	32	500	12.8	13.6
SST	12	300	2.9	3.0
Stretch	15	200	2.4	2.5
4 Engine	15	150	1.8	1.9
2-3 Engine	30	90	2.2	2.3
Low Total	104		22.1	23.3 (rounded)

  * The figure of 500 passengers is used for the 747 because of the history of increases in passenger load that have followed the introduction of every jet in the past. "Stretched" models of the 747 are contemplated in this figure, as well as the pressure for major reductions in fares for 747 service, realized by high-density seating.

the travel day. Hangar crews and other service staffs will also increase in size as the number of passengers and size and number of aircraft increase.

Assuming the figure of 85 percent terminal passengers, the passenger flow demand rate (both to and from the airport) would be about 27,000 per hour with the high estimate and about 18,000 with the low figure. The employee flow (assuming a spread over four to five hours) can add another 8,000, particularly in the earlier evening rush hours when hangar crews, ticket agents, and other employees change shifts. Thus, the possible demand for peak flow, assuming only the current number of employees can create a flow to and from the airport of 35,000 (high estimate) or 25,000 (low estimate) persons per hour.

The possibility of driving the family car to the airport and parking it there will be denied to many of these people in the future. The passenger parking capacity at Kennedy is roughly 6,000 in the central-terminal area and 3,000 in the long-term area. At present these facilities are often near maximum capacity, with certain serious delays occurring occasionally to departing passengers who cannot readily find a parking lot open and then, after finding a lot, must drive through its vast area to find an open slot.

TERMINAL PASSENGERS AND MULTIPLE AIRPORTS

Even if one argues that Kennedy will not handle the loads herein postulated, the concept of the passenger and employee flow rates of from 25,000 to 35,000 per hour in the 1975-1980 period are worthy of consideration. If the saturation of parking, access roads, terminal gates, taxiways, or runways controls airport capacity first, limiting the overall situation, the overflow will move to one of the other two existing airports. However, even here, where the total 1975 aircraft movements will be around 3,400 per day for the area's three airports, it is obvious that the peak-hour figures will be exceeded. A March 1967 study of "Jetports and General Aviation in the New York Metropolitan Area" by the Metropolitan Commuter Transportation Authority suggests that peak hour IFR demand for the New York area will be around 300 operations by 1980. If this is distributed to four major airports, this will still be close to their theoretical capacity.

Thus, the peak passenger hour of say 30,000 for Kennedy may never be realized, but part of it will appear elsewhere in the three (or perhaps four) other major jet airports that will be essential for the area by 1980. This implies that the number of terminal passengers is likely to increase, since the interconnection problem of a "through" passenger may now involve another airport. Thus, the terminal passenger figure might rise to 90 percent (from 85 percent), increasing the total number of passengers that need transport to or from an airport by about another 1500 per hour.

It is interesting that passenger flow is based on the assumption that the aircraft are carrying about half the passengers away from the field. If the weather should delay a morning operation, say, two hours, some 25,000 passengers wishing to depart would accumulate, and some 25,000 arrival passengers would be delayed (hopefully in the air or at other cities). When the weather clears, the total "peaking" might be enormous, since arrivals rather than takeoffs might be permitted to use the runways for the first hour because of diminishing fuel reserves and the fact that many mid-morning flights assume the arrival of another flight to provide equipment. One could envision the first hour (after the fog lifted and the airport became fully operational) witnessing 38,000 passengers attempting to board aircraft and some 25,000 passengers off-loading, creating a total passenger density for about an hour of about 63,000 inside the terminal buildings.

The inability to move passengers one or two at a time into the airport by auto, taxi, or air taxi will become painfully evident toward 1975-1980 as these passenger-flow figures actually develop with the introduction of the jumbo jets, the SST, the fleet expansion of current jet types, and the possible introduction of the "skybus." The cost per seat-mile will be lowered, and the vast, untapped traveling public will want to fly. At least such projections seem to be what justifies the approximately $18 billion that are expected to be expended for new aircraft alone (not facilities) by 1975.

Another Method for Examining Passenger Flow to and from the Airport

To attempt another approach to this problem, let us assume that the total peak-hour area movements in 1980-1985 (IFR) will be around 300 air carrier aircraft. There will be more aircraft flying in VFR and the total area count will be higher, as it would include general aviation. However, by this time it is possible that general aviation will find better services at Teterboro, Republic, Westchester, MacArthur, and several other fields that will cater to their business. Further, priority will be given to the larger aircraft and to those carrying the greatest number of passengers, since they can better afford to pay for the services of a major jet airport (assuming that a cost gradient will have been effected).

Thus, the peak hour might have a mix of airline aircraft on an area basis (serving four jetports) that would be different from that mentioned previously, perhaps 20 percent jumbo jet and SST, 35 percent four-engine jets, and 45 percent two- and three-engine jets. The total area (peak-hour) flow would then be 58,500 seats for the four major jet airports, assuming the 300 aircraft are all air carriers (see Table 2.18). If the load factor in this peak hour is 80 percent, total passenger flow is about 47,000; at 85 percent it is near 50,000.

Various combinations of jumbos, SST's, and other aircraft can be

TABLE 2.18. POTENTIAL AIRCRAFT MIX

	Number	Seats per aircraft	Seats total (thousands)
Jumbo and SST	60	400	24
4 engine	105	200	21
2-3 engine	135	100	13.5
Total	300		58.5

projected. However, it is clear from the two simplified examples that
the airport or airports where large aircraft congregate will be the airport or airports of greatest stress. There would seem to be a tendency
to keep the large aircraft at no more than two airports, even though
one airport would be more desirable if it could handle the load. The
international carriers, customs clearance, the myriad of details needed
for operation of such large equipments as jumbos, SST's, and air-buses
will dictate that they concentrate at, say, two airports rather than being
evenly divided among the four airports.

As the figures show, the two- to three-engine jets do not generate
the large passenger-flows. Consequently, it is likely that the peak-hour
flow of 50,000 passengers will find perhaps 80 percent of the passengers
at two major or "super" airports and the remaining 20 percent at the
other two jet airports. Such an uneven distribution comes close to the
20,000 per hour figure for a single major airport that was arrived at
by other methods.

NEED FOR PASSENGER TRANSPORT TO BUSINESS, RESIDENCE, AND OTHER AIRPORTS

There will be obvious needs for cargo operations and mixed cargo-
passenger flights; yet, in the peak hours we are discussing (8:00-10:00
a.m. and 5:00-7:00 p.m.) the cargo traffic will hopefully be low, as it
normally tends to build at night and peak during the off-hours relative
to passenger flow. This is not only typical of the business today but is
probably the nature of the future cargo business, since shipments often
are prepared during the work day and needed elsewhere the next working day. Thus, even though cargo flights will perhaps add traffic to the
four-airport system in the early morning and late evening hours, they
would not seem to detract from the peak-hour passenger flows during
the peak passenger periods. As noted, it is the peaking that is serious,
since, if the flow is interrupted for any reason, delays become exorbitant
and the accumulation of passengers pyramids.

Approximation of Short-Haul Air Movements

For a first attempt, let us assume that the private auto, bus, and taxi
service that normally conveys airline passengers can be expanded somewhat, but that out of the 50,000 per hour (area) passenger flow (half
inbound, half outbound), 20 percent will be conveyed by short-haul
air vehicles such as the large helicopter and STOL of the 1975-1980 era.
What would it take to handle this amount of traffic?

Since the fourth jet airport of the New York area will require up to 20,000 acres, it is likely to be remotely located relative to the existing three jet airports. Assuming it will be about 50 to 70 miles distant and that urban spread has also taken place, it is likely that several marshalling points such as the 6 to 10 large general aviation airports and perhaps a dozen smaller ones will then operate STOL or helicopter service to the four jetports. This urban complex of marshalling points and the 10 to 20 helicopter gates that may be on Manhattan Island, and perhaps a STOL-port, will create a network of routes and marshalling points. If 20 minutes is the average flight time, and if 10,000 passengers are to be moved in an hour, and assuming two operations per hour per aircraft, 50 (STOL-helicopter) aircraft carrying 100 passengers each would be required. A fleet of 100 aircraft carrying 50 passengers each would also do the job with twice the frequency of service, an important feature for such types of service.

If the total number of passengers to be moved to the four jet airports is increased to 40 percent of the peak hourly flow, this would be 20,000 passengers per hour and would require a fleet of 100 aircraft carrying 100 passengers each in the short-haul (urban, core, and airport) operation. These might be about half large helicopters and half large STOL aircraft, with "interfacing" occurring at the marshalling and transfer points.

The STOL, and the helicopter in particular, can use nonjet airport space (unused runways and taxiways) so that this traffic will not add to the saturation of major airports. Further, the passenger can be served best by delivering him to the gates affording direct access to or from his jet. This type of passenger service makes it possible to reduce the number of passengers in terminal buildings, parking lots, and access roads, saturation of which is now threatening. With IFR capability equal to or better than the jet transports (Cat II), the service could be as reliable as the present auto and bus, which by this time might be quite unreliable owing to traffic congestion along arteries leading to the jetport and at the jetport itself.

Much as the air traffic flow to New York during peak periods is controlled at distances up to 500 or 1,000 miles (in ATC language, "flow-control"), so it could be with the passenger flow. The 20 some marshalling points would be remote from the major jetports. Delays caused by such factors as weather would result in the retention of the passengers at these local marshalling points. When the fog lifted they could then be moved into the jetports. Further, the passenger would find that going to Westchester or Republic field for ticketing, baggage, and customs, and departure from such a point for London or Los Angeles, would be a significant convenience. The family car could be parked at the airport near his residence, or his wife could drive him to the airport (about 20 minutes' driving time in the dispersed urban areas).

Thus, the mass of humanity and autos that may clog the airports sooner than the air traffic could be encouraged to use a new mode of interairport and transairport service.

Cost of Delays to the Traveler

One can assume that the cost of a trip by air is generally much less than the value to be gained from the trip, be it for personal or business reasons. Thus, when we examine losses due to delay or saturation of facilities serving the air traveler we should add to the lost revenues such factors as aggravation, lost business, and personal tragedies. The simple matter of not arriving on time at the airport can become quite serious if only one flight suits the traveler's purpose — a contract signing, funeral, or wedding, or even the beginning of a three-week vacation.

To place a dollar value on this type of loss is difficult, but attempts to do so should be made. It is likely to range from a figure equal to the fare to one, two or three times higher. Certainly the total cost of delays and inability to move the masses of airline travelers to and from the airports should include this public cost in addition to the direct revenue losses of the carriers.

Occasions now arise when a passenger allowing ample time to drive to the airport (say two hours) is confronted with the fact that he cannot dispose of his auto after arriving there. This is a serious dilemma, since loss or damage to the auto if not properly parked can be a serious deterrent to his abandoning it just to make the flight. Occurrences such as this can be costly reminders that other means of transport must be found and employed. With the alternative of going by helicopter-STOL, it seems likely that a few such experiences will convince the traveler of the wisdom of the marshalling point concept.

WORLD EDUCATION TRENDS AND THEIR POTENTIAL IMPACT ON AIR TRAVEL

Education whets curiosity, stimulates imagination, and increases the range of economic opportunity. Educated people ordinarily have both the desire and the means to travel, and their occupations commonly call for a considerable amount of travel by air.

Education affects air travel both directly and indirectly. Direct effect is indicated by the existence of a certain amount of air travel (although a relatively small proportion of all air trips) for the purpose of "going

to and from school." Doubtless reduced rate "youth fares" are tending
to increase the volume of air travel to and from school to some extent.
International educational travel for purposes of study, teaching, and
research may also be expected to exert a greater direct impact on air
transportation in the future than it has in the past. While travel by individual scholars to foreign countries dates back to ancient times, it is
only in recent years — mainly since World War II — that international
educational exchange has become a major feature of international
relations.

INDIRECT IMPACT OF EDUCATION

But neither domestic travel to and from school nor travel in connection with international educational exchange is nearly as significant
at the present time as what might be called the indirect impact of
education on air travel. This is indicated by the fact that professional,
technical, managerial, and administrative people tend to travel by air
more frequently than persons in other occupations. It is also note-
worthy that the proportion of persons with college degrees or with
some college training is significantly higher among air passengers than
among the general population.

The most recent air passenger market surveys conducted by the Aviation Department of the Port of New York Authority, published in
May and June 1965, were based on a sample of passengers on domestic
and overseas flights of scheduled airlines leaving New York's three
major airports between April 1, 1963, and March 29, 1964.

The 1963-1964 domestic survey revealed that almost eight out of ten
passengers had attended college, that 63 percent of all passengers were
in "professional, technical, managerial or official" occupations, and
that 63 percent of all passengers were traveling for business purposes.
The median family income of the 1963-1964 air passengers was $15,000
(as compared to $6,190 for the population as a whole). The survey
report commented that "education is a fairly good indicator of air
travel frequency. The number of college graduates increased as trip
frequency rose, from three out of every ten on one to two trips to seven
out of ten for the most frequent passengers."

The domestic survey found that while 6 percent of all air travelers
were students, only 2 percent represented students going "to or from
school."

The percentage of New York domestic air passengers who were either
college graduates or had some college education was considerably
higher than the U.S. average (per 1962 U.S. census data):

TABLE 2.19. COLLEGE EDUCATION AND AIR TRAVEL

	N.Y. air passengers (1963-1964)	1962 U.S. average
College graduates	55%	9%
Some college	23%	9.1%*

*1 to 3 years college

The 1963-1964 overseas survey did not obtain information with respect to the education of New York air passengers, but found median family income to be $13,300, again more than twice the U.S. median for 1962. The survey revealed that 10 percent of all American resident passengers were students (as compared with only 5 percent in a similar survey conducted in 1956-1957). However, only 4 percent of the American resident passengers (versus 11 percent of the foreign resident passengers) declared the purpose of their trip to be "study or research." (Comparable figures in the domestic survey showed 6 percent students of whom one third were going to or from school.)

The 1963-1964 overseas survey report stressed the fact that overseas air passengers are younger than they used to be. "In 1963, 18 percent of New York's departing overseas passengers were younger than 25, compared with 13 percent in 1956."

The most notable difference between the domestic and overseas markets as shown by the 1963 New York surveys was that only 24 percent of the overseas air passengers were traveling for business purposes (as compared with 63 percent of the domestic passengers). But of the 76 percent of overseas passengers flying for other than business reasons, only 6 percent declared their objective to be education or research.

The trend in youth fare air travel cannot yet be readily determined from available industry-wide data, but a study of the volume of youth fare traffic carried by domestic trunk carriers has been compiled by the Civil Aeronautics Board for the six-month period ending September 30, 1966 (CAB Form 41 and Carriers' Youth Fare Reports). During this period the carriers reported that 1,211,706 "standby" passengers and 181,966 "reserved space" passengers traveled on youth fares, representing 3.6 percent of all passengers handled and contributing approximately $27 million in "standby" and $5 million in "reserved space" revenues. The load factor for the carriers during the period averaged 62.8 percent; the figure would have been only 60.7 percent if youth fare traffic had not been carried. It should also be mentioned that, since there was a major airline strike during the period of the survey, the volume of youth fare travel as well as other air travel was doubtless less than it would otherwise have been.

TRENDS IN U.S. EDUCATION

In view of the direct and indirect impacts of education on air travel, it seems quite likely that current trends in education will exert a positive influence of considerable magnitude on the future volume of air travel. School enrollments, and especially college enrollments, are increasing far more rapidly than population (see Table 2.20).

TABLE 2.20. U.S. POPULATION AND FALL SCHOOL ENROLLMENT
(MILLIONS)

	Population	High school enrollment	College enrollment (degree credit)	Total school enrollment
1930	123	5	1.1	30
1940	133	7	1.5	30
1950	152	6	2.7	31
1960	181	10	3.2	45
1965	191	13	5.5	55
1975*	227	17	9.0	63

* Projections from 1965.
SOURCE: *Statistical Abstract of the United States* (1966) and U.S. Office of Education, *Projections of Education Statistics to 1975-1976* (1966) (OE-10030-66).

Each year since 1951 there has been a rise in the proportion of young people enrolled in college. In 1951 there were 24 college students for each 100 persons 18 to 21 years of age in the population; by 1964 there were 44 college students per 100 persons in the same age group.

If present trends continue, we can expect increases in bachelor degrees and first-professional degrees granted by institutions of higher education from 536,000 in 1965-1966 to 930,000 in 1975-1976.

Air travel will be affected not only by future growth in college enrollments and graduating classes but also by the growth in teaching staffs at all levels of education. The projections in Table 2.21 were published by the U.S. Office of Education.

TABLE 2.21. GROWTH IN TEACHING STAFFS

	Teachers and instructional staff 1965-1966	1975-1976
Elementary and high schools	1.9 million	2.4 million
Higher education (full-time staff)	306,000	454,000

It is worth noting that total expenditures for all levels of education reached a total of more than $45 billion in 1965, as compared to less than $17 billion in 1955 and approximately $4 billion in 1945. Expressed as percent of gross national product, education expenditures were 6.62 percent in 1965, 4.22 percent in 1955, and 1.97 percent in 1945. Projections of such magnitude into the next few decades suggest major changes in the general sophistication and interests of persons entering the travel markets in the future.

INTERNATIONAL EDUCATIONAL EXCHANGE

The exchange of persons between nations for educational purposes has been one of the most significant educational developments during the second half of the twentieth century. It has been estimated that currently about 250,000 students annually are studying at institutions of higher learning in countries other than their own, and this figure does not include the thousands of scholars teaching and engaged in research, or the other thousands traveling abroad on short-term educational and cultural assignments. By virtue of its speed, convenience, and, to an increasing degree, economy, air travel is becoming more and more an agent of international educational exchange, and mutual advantage suggests that the partnership should be encouraged.

The United Nations Educational, Scientific and Cultural Organization (UNESCO) estimates that the world's total enrollment in higher education in 1960 was approximately 12,100,000. More than three million of these students were in the U.S.A. During the period 1955-1959 the average number of students per 100,000 population in different countries ranged widely, as shown for selected countries:

U.S.A.	1,728	Germany	411
U.S.S.R.	1,041	France	409
Netherlands	769	Sweden	384
Japan	687	Switzerland	345
Canada	619	United Kingdom	284
Denmark	474	Mexico	190

Asia has the highest numerical total of students in higher education in the world; Africa has had the highest percentage increase in enrollment during the last decade; Europe has the highest number of institutions of higher education in relation to population. North America is not expanding in higher education as fast as other continents but has a greater percentage of students enrolled than any other continent.

In 20 countries which in 1959 had a total enrollment of over six million students (over half of the then estimated world enrollment), foreign students increased from 84,000 in 1950-1954 to 179,000 in 1960-1962. UNESCO reports that foreign students make up a small but steadily growing group — about 2.8 percent in 1960-1962.

There is considerable variation among the different countries with respect to the ratio of foreign students to total enrollment. In the United States in 1960-1962 it was only 1.5 percent, in France 11 percent, in Switzerland 32 percent, in Austria 25 percent, in Ireland 23 percent, in the United Kingdom 10 percent, and in Germany 7 percent.

In its report, *Open Doors 1966,* issued in September, 1966, the Institute of International Education (809 United Nations Plaza, New York, N.Y. 10017) estimated that more than 114,000 students, teachers, and scholars were involved in educational exchange between the United States and more than 150 other nations during the preceding year. This included approximately 92,000 foreign students, scholars, and teachers in the United States and some 22,000 U.S. nationals in other countries.

The number of foreign students in the United States has grown greatly since World War II, as shown:

1921-22	6,163
1930-31	9,643
1940-41	6,570
1950-51	29,813
1960-61	53,107
1965-66	82,709

While 37 percent were self-supporting in 1965-1966, the majority of foreign students required outside support. Educational institutions contributed to the support of 23 percent, foundations to 12 percent, the United States government to 9 percent, and foreign governments to 7 percent. It is reported that 44 percent of all foreign students were pursuing graduate degrees.

Kenneth Holland, President of the Institute of International Education, believes the potentialities of educational exchange would be greatly enhanced if foreign students (and foreign faculty members) did not cluster at a small number of U.S. institutions:

"If all the benefits of exchange are to be attained, the United States' full capacity for international education must be realized and all effective elements of the American academic world must play their part. It is to be hoped that the great majority of recognized colleges and universities, which now receive only token numbers of foreign students and scholars, will begin to participate more fully in international education."

For the academic year 1965-1966, the University of California had 4535 foreign students, New York University 2599, and Columbia University 2539. Other schools with over 1000 each were Minnesota, Wisconsin, Michigan, Illinois, Pennsylvania, Howard, Harvard, and Cornell.

But if foreign students are unevenly distributed in the United States, U.S. students are even more clustered at a relatively small number of institutions abroad. More than two-thirds of the American students in 1965-1966 were at only 44 institutions, each reporting more than 100 American students. The great majority were in Western Europe, Canada, and Latin America (principally Mexico). Due to reporting difficulties, definitive figures of the total number of Americans studying overseas are not available, but more than 100,000 passports were issued to "students" in 1965.

Agencies Facilitating International Exchange

In the course of this survey only a few of the many private and government agencies involved in international educational exchange could be visited. They were, however, some of the most influential organizations in the field, and all indicated considerable interest in the possibilities of more intimate relations with the air transport industry. Privately sponsored agencies visited included the Institute of International Education and the Council on Student Travel in New York City and the National Education Association in Washington. Public agencies included the U.S. Office of Education in the Department of Health, Education and Welfare, and the U.S. Advisory Commission on International Education and Exchange in the Department of State.

It is clear that there is mutual advantage to be gained by cultivating effective liaison between commercial aviation and public and private agencies which facilitate international exchange. As air transport's capacity increases with the advent of larger aircraft, the advantages of cultivating educational travel — which can be accommodated largely off-peak — will become more evident.

THE IMPACT OF LEISURE TIME AND RECREATION ON THE AIR TRAVEL INDUSTRY

Since 1900 the average work week has steadily declined from approximately 70 hours to the present 41 hours. Although relatively stable for the past several years, this figure is generally expected to decline gradually during the forthcoming decade. As a consequence, leisure and recreation will grow in importance, with significant economic and social ramifications.

THE CHARACTER OF LEISURE TIME

The amount of daily free time available to the average person has increased about 25 percent since the turn of the century. Any further increase during the next decade may well be offset by increased commuting times. If this proves to be the case, by 1980 the average person will have about the same amount of daily free time as today, in spite of the declining work week. Heretofore a considerable portion of this free time has been spent at home, "just relaxing," without specific recreational activities. Changes are occurring in the amount of free time devoted to specific activities in the home, however. It has been estimated that by 1980 approximately 80 percent of the total at-home free time will be occupied by activities such as games or sports, politics, or cultural self-improvement. As the average level of education rises, more of this time will be devoted to expanding intellectual interests. A rising level of educational attainment produces an awareness of cultural opportunities which could create a desire for travel.

The kind of recreation a person wishes accords with the blocks of time at his disposal, between daily leisure and vacation periods (including holidays and weekends). Longer block-time leisure promises to account for much of the future growth of free time, as more and longer vacations and holidays, early retirement, and possibly longer weekends become a reality. Labor unions are pushing for all of these, and the idea of having more Monday holidays, which has been around Congress for many years, is beginning to gain support. Adoption of this plan would lead to many more extended-weekend vacations and would have a considerable impact on travel and recreation patterns. It would also set a further precedent for more frequent leisure periods of similar duration.

An interesting way to view the changes in leisure is to consider its economic and social impact on the basis of national totals. For instance, total vacation leisure time will increase and should represent a greater relative increase than the rise of daily leisure. Total vacation leisure roughly doubled between 1900 and 1950 and should double again by 1975. Total retirement leisure, which increased by 400 percent between 1900 and 1950, is expected to double again during the last half of the century. Figure 2.5 indicates the overall leisure-time trends. Population growth is, of course, an important factor in these projections.

Spending Power and Leisure Time

The population in the United States is expected to reach 250 million by 1980, a 28 percent increase in 15 years. Changes in the age, income, and education of the population should have considerable significance for the travel industry. For instance, by 1980 there should be about 25 million people in the over-65 group, an increase of 30 percent over 1960. This group will have the greatest amount of leisure time. Thirty-six percent of the population will be in the over-35 age group by 1980.

In 1960 this group held 85 percent of the total disposable income, with an increasing discretionary spending power. The profile of income distribution is also changing: in 1960 only 38 percent of families had incomes in excess of $7000 per year in 1965 dollars; by 1975 64 percent of the population should be in this category, providing a spectacular increase in total income and discretionary spending power, particularly at the higher income level (see Figure 2.6).

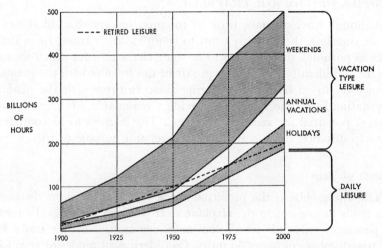

Figure 2.5.   Distribution of leisure time, projections for U.S. population over 14.
SOURCE: Stanford Research Institute.

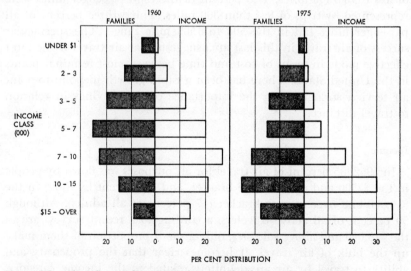

Figure 2.6.   Changing profile of U.S. income distribution, in 1965 dollars.
SOURCE: National Industrial Conference Board.

People in the higher income category of the population normally devote more daily time to their work and therefore place a higher premium on their leisure time. Much of their leisure time will be devoted to changing their environment, to rest and relaxation, and to satisfying cultural aspirations. Consequently, this travel-prone segment of society represents a large air travel market potential.

PROFILE OF THE AIR TRAVELER

Although travelers have little in common (except that, in the case of air travelers, they usually want to complete their travel in as little time as possible), there appear to be some characteristics which we can isolate and identify, giving us a profile of the traveler with the greatest propensity to go by air. Comparing these features with the general population in a time span will provide a reasonable estimate of total market potential for vacation air travel. The features to be compared are trip distance, income, occupation, age, and purpose of trip.

Length of Trip

The automobile is the preferred mode of travel for short distances but tends to lose out to the airplane as trip length increases. In terms of passenger miles, air travel dominates commercial carrier traffic for all trip distances of over 300 miles. Considering all modes of travel in 1960, 89.3 percent of all passenger miles were traveled over distances of less than 1500 miles; 41.8 percent of the total passenger miles were represented by trips of less than 300 miles. Thirty-three percent of all passenger miles fall in the 500 to 1500 mile range. The spectacular success of air travel in this last area suggests that air travel is the most effective mode in terms of cost and time between most terminal points in the United States. There has been a rapid growth in point-to-point air service, strengthening the importance of time savings in relation to travel distance.

Income

In 1962, 85 percent of air travel for all purposes was flown by people in the $7500 and over income bracket, and 60 percent by those in the $10,000 and over income bracket (17 percent of all adults). Although 50 percent of all active travelers, according to a recent survey, are in the $10,000 and above category, only a small proportion of them make up the bulk of air travel. It becomes clear that the propensity and ability to travel by air are definitely related to the income category. In view of the expected change in the profile of income distribution and of anticipated lower fares made possible by high-capacity aircraft, it appears that the greater portion of the population will have the financial ability to be travel-prone. On this basis they will represent a considerably enlarged and promising air travel market. Heretofore, the air mode has only narrowly penetrated this rapidly expanding potential.

Occupation

Given the relationship between income and air travel, a relationship between occupation and air travel can be anticipated. In 1962, 29 percent of all professional and technical workers took at least one air trip. Of the managerial and self-employed, 27 percent took at least one air trip. These two classes represent the majority of air travelers. The professional and managerial groups are also among the most highly educated.

Age Group

Considering income, occupation, and vacation time available, it might be expected that experience as an air traveler would be greatest among the more mature groups in society. The highest experience rate in 1962 was found to be in the 35-44 age group. An interesting question about the future of air travel is whether those experienced fliers in the younger age groups will continue to travel by air as they grow older. An analysis of the data reveals that in 1955 9 percent of the 45-54 age group took an air trip, compared with 6 percent of those in the 55-64 age group. In 1962, when the former group reached the 55-64 age level, flying experience in the older age group was up from 6 to 9 percent. Similarly in the over-65 age group, the experience factor rose from 3 percent to 5 percent between 1955 and 1962. It appears that experienced air travelers retain their propensity to travel by air as they grow older. A Port of New York Authority survey made in 1963 indicated that a substantial percentage of air travelers were under 35. Additionally, the airline campaign to promote air travel among teenagers through special low standby "youth fares" is preconditioning this generation with favorable attitudes toward air transportation. Consequently, we can assume that people in these age groups will continue to be predisposed to air travel as they grow older.

Purpose of Trip

An analysis of the travel market must distinguish between business and nonbusiness travel. Generally, business travel makes up approximately 30 percent of all trips taken by all modes of travel. Nonbusiness trips, including those taken for personal affairs, visiting friends and relatives, and vacations make up the other 70 percent. The motives for nonbusiness travel are complex and varied; other than for simple pleasure, they appear to be related to social prestige.

On the basis of several studies, it appears that business air travel has accounted for about 60 percent of air revenue passenger-miles. Personal travel, including vacations, accounts for only 40 percent of air passenger-miles. We can assume that the air mode should be able to attract a proportionate share of the total travel market, and a considerable increase in nonbusiness air travel should therefore be possible, particularly in view of the growing interest of the air carriers in promoting such travel.

The amount of business travel reflects the level of business activity and is related to the gross national product. A convenient way to forecast business travel by air has been to consider such travel as a function of GNP growth. A straight-line projection of historical data points of business air travel suggests that business travel by air would amount to 60 billion revenue passenger-miles by 1980. This trend would coincide with a not unreasonable GNP growth rate of approximately 5.5 percent in current dollars. If we assume that air transportation will become more desirable and efficient with additional point-to-point air service and new aircraft design, we can forecast that a greater proportion of business travel will be by air. An estimate of possible business air travel by 1980 would amount to about 80 billion revenue passenger-miles.

The most recent forecast of probable and possible air traffic trends by The Boeing Company indicates that business air travel would be 30 percent and nonbusiness air travel 70 percent of total air travel — values more in line with the current breakdown for all modes (see Figure 2.7).

The expected spectacular growth in nonbusiness air travel is supported by our assessment of changing vacations, the predicted changes in the general population, and our characterization of the air traveler.

Further study of travelers is necessary in any systematic analysis of air transportation marketing. Research on the nonair traveler and the infrequent air traveler was recently undertaken by the Behavior Science Corporation (BASICO) of Panorama City, California (a subsidiary of Planning Research Corporation). Their study, entitled *The Development of New Markets for Air Travel*, was completed in early 1968. Also, results of a research project entitled "The Profile of the Pacific Traveler" became available in the fall of 1967. This

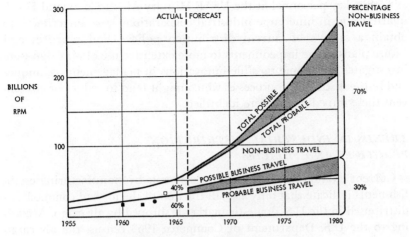

Figure 2.7. **Projections of business and nonbusiness travel on U.S. domestic airlines.**
SOURCE: The Boeing Company.

study was conducted by Travel Research International for the use of Pacific Area Travel Association.

TRENDS IN BUSINESS AND MILITARY DISTRIBUTION POLICIES AND PRACTICES AND THEIR LIKELY EFFECTS ON POST-1975 DEMAND FOR COMMERCIAL AIR CARGO TRANSPORTATION

The effective demand for air cargo transportation has expanded by a factor of two during the five years 1961-1966; however, in 1966 only about 0.1 percent of the U.S. domestic intercity freight demand was satisfied by air. Recent forecasts of the growth in the air cargo market made by ICAO, the CAB, and others indicate that over the next 15 years the effective demand for air cargo service may increase by an order of magnitude. If such rapid growth is to be achieved, potential shippers will need to be made aware of the utility of air transportation in satisfying their total distribution requirements and the price of air cargo service vis-à-vis competing surface transportation will need to be reduced sharply.

The present study attempts to determine how air cargo service is being utilized today and to identify likely trends in its utilization in the next two decades. Within the limitations of the time and resources

available, key personnel at the USAF Military Airlift Command Headquarters and in nine large industrial corporations were interviewed to
obtain a sample of current distribution policies and practices and
future plans. Some impediments to more extensive use of air cargo were
investigated, and some possible innovations in management techniques
and in the distribution processes which might tend to reduce or circum-
vent these impediments were identified.

TRENDS IN INDUSTRIAL DISTRIBUTION
PRACTICES AND POLICIES

Current data on intercity freight shipments by manufacturing establishments indicate that only a small fraction of the myriad commodities
distributed in the U.S. domestic market is shipped by air cargo. According to the U.S. Department of Commerce 1963 census, the air cargo
demand was concentrated in the following commodity groups (listed
in descending order of ton-mile volume):

1. Communications products and parts (SIC Group 366)
2. Precision instruments (photo equipment, watches, clocks, etc.)
   (SIC Group 38)
3. Transportation equipment parts, except motor vehicles (SIC
   Group 37)
4. Clothing and related products (SIC Group 23)
5. Industrial machinery, except electrical (SIC Group 359)
6. Electrical products and supplies (SIC Group 36)
7. Metal cans and products (SIC Group 34)
8. Rubber and plastic products (SIC Group 37)

Of the 1.77 trillion ton-miles of the U.S. intercity freight transportation demand in 1966, the percentage distribution by transport mode
was as follows:

**TABLE 2.22. DISTRIBUTION OF FREIGHT TRANSPORTATION
DEMAND FOR 1966**

Transport mode	Percent of U.S. domestic intercity freight demand
Rail	42.9%
Truck	22.4
Oil pipeline	18.8
Lakes, rivers, and canals	15.8
Air cargo	0.1
	100.0%

Although there is obviously room for a sizable expansion in air cargo
demand, it is not likely that air cargo will ever account for a large

percentage share of the total freight transportation demand as measured in tons or ton-miles, since the commodities that account for most of the total demand are of such low value per pound that the advantage of high-speed transportation in terms of the total cost of distribution is trivial. For example, when considered on a weight basis, about half of all intercity freight shipped consists of products of mines, which have an average wholesale value at destination of a half cent per pound. Products of agriculture account for more than 10 percent of total freight by weight, with an average value of about 5 cents per pound. Products of forests, which account for about 5 percent by weight of the total, have an average value per pound of less than 5 cents. Nevertheless, the U.S. demand for freight transportation is so vast that only a fractional increase in penetration by air could result in a significant expansion of present air cargo traffic.

Survey of Air Cargo Acceptability

To obtain a current insight into the attitudes, policies, and plans of U.S. industry regarding factors affecting the selection of cargo transportation mode, personal interviews were held with a sample of corporate executives responsible for distribution in large corporations. These corporations are in the following SIC categories:

- Commercial air cargo carrier (SIC Group 4511)
- Communications and electronic equipment (SIC Group 36)
- Chemicals, plastics, and synthetics (SIC Group 28)
- Foods (SIC Groups 202, 203, 204, 205)
- Soap and toilet articles (SIC Group 284)
- Tobacco (SIC Group 21)
- Drugs and medicines (SIC Group 283)
- Building and construction materials (SIC Groups 24 and 28)

The 1966 net sales of these corporations varied from $0.5 billion to $4 billion. The particular corporations selected for the survey were chosen so as to provide a fairly broad industrial coverage and a depth of expertise in industrial distribution practices. The highlights of the results obtained from the survey are presented here.

1. *A major obstacle to more extensive use of air cargo transportation is the high cost of the service*

An analysis of transportation statistics for 1966 shows that although the air cargo mode satisfied about 0.1 percent of the total demand for freight transportation, it accounted for more than 1.5 percent of the total freight revenues. A case illustrating this disparity between weight shipped and freight revenues is that of a drug company with annual sales in excess of $100 million per year. In 1966 air cargo shipments accounted for about 1.7 percent of its total freight shipments by weight from plants to distribution points, but air cargo transportation costs accounted for 20 percent of the firm's total transportation budget. The commodity shipped was a very high-value-per-pound ethical drug, and air cargo was chosen as the transportation mode solely because of the highly time-dependent efficacy of the particular drug. Another firm, a large chemical corporation, reported that it finds that the cost for shipping by air cargo is about 15 times greater than by truck. Accordingly, the air cargo mode is selected only in unusual circumstances.

2. *The total distribution cost concept is not widely accepted*

Although a few of the corporations surveyed indicated that there was top management agreement with the concept of total distribution cost, most indicated that they are just beginning to "scratch the surface" in implementation of this concept. In private industry the generally accepted elements of distribution — packaging, materials handling, storage or warehousing, inventory, order processing, transportation, insurance, etc. — are divided among several managers with widely varying levels of authority and responsibility. Even among large shippers, who supposedly are sophisticated in management techniques, the costs of direct transportation are of primary concern in selecting the transportation mode. On the other hand, some evidence of broader cost consideration was noted. As a case in point, a building and construction materials manufacturer made an unsophisticated total distribution cost analysis of one of his more than 2000 products, which suggested that several changes in the company's distribution system should be made. These changes were made and resulted in savings of more than $300,000. This case is being used as a "lever" to obtain acceptance by the company's top management of the total distribution management concept. All of the corporations surveyed emphasized that the acceptance of this concept (if it is accepted at all) will be a slow, evolutionary process.

3. *Commercial air cargo transportation is not used routinely*

A recent survey conducted by *Air Cargo* magazine revealed that among approximately 1000 large shippers (most of whom had annual transportation charges in excess of $100,000), 93.8 percent had used air cargo transportation to some extent during 1966. Nevertheless, air cargo is almost never considered as a routine method of transportation. In most cases air cargo rates are considered to be prohibitively high and are not routinely cycled into corporation freight-rate analyses.

4. *Computer-aided analysis of distribution costs is not utilized*

In many cases the inventory accounting is still done manually. Even in the largest corporations, computer-aided cost accounting and control of the elements of distribution, such as inventory control and order processing, are relatively new. Computer aids are a necessity in producing useful real-time control information on total distribution costs for the complex multiplant/warehouse system typical of most large corporations. In many cases it may be appropriate to develop a mathematical model and use computer simulation to achieve optimum cost management results. As the use of computers and automatic data-processing equipment for distribution cost control becomes more prevalent, the acceptance and implementation of the concept of total distribution cost management may also become more widespread.

5. *One factor contributing to the high cost of air cargo service is the small size of shipment*

The great majority of today's air freight shipments weigh less than 500 pounds, and the average air express shipment weighs less than 50 pounds. The current and projected "saturated" status of the U.S. mail, and the relatively high cost and poor service offered by truckers and railroads for small shipments have apparently contributed to the recent increase in the use of air cargo. The necessity for increased speed in delivery may have been an incidental factor. A point to be considered is that there are significant elements of the total cost of providing air cargo service which vary with the number of shipments (billing, manifesting, pickup and delivery).

6. *Recognition of the many advantages that containerization offers to shippers and carriers has been relatively slow*

The standard 8 ft × 8 ft × 10 ft (and up to 40 ft on the long dimension) intermodal containers currently utilized by land and sea surface carriers weigh approximately 3.5 lb per cu ft of space available for stowage. Since a cargo density of between 10 and 15 lb per cu ft is required to load current and projected all-cargo aircraft to the "full and down" condition, such containers would represent between 20 percent and 30 percent of the total aircraft payload. By 1970 it is expected that structural improvements will reduce the weight of these containers to about 2 lb per cu ft of available stowage volume, but this will still represent 10 percent to 15 percent of the total payload. In addition to such tare weight considerations, the investment in containers, their inventory control and their "back haul" requirements present obstacles to wide-scale use. The total systems approach to distribution management must be utilized to determine whether or not containerization will be advantageous to the shipper. A shipper who worries primarily about the costs of direct transportation and not the overall cost of his physical distribution process may reject the concept of containerization. Analysis shows, however, several significant advantages for containerization, for both shipper and carrier. The shipper saves in

- Preparation and packaging
- Net weight of shipments
- Decreased losses from damage and pilferage
- Time of en route handling

The carrier saves in

- Decreased handling at the terminal
- Decreased airplane ground time for loading
- Reduced claim costs

An analysis of the benefits of containerization was made by the Lockheed-Georgia Company. This study compared the loading of a Lockheed L-300 Air Freighter (a proposed commercial version of the USAF C-141) under the opposing conditions of palletized and containerized cargo. The following is a summary of the results:

TABLE 2.23. L-300 CONTAINERIZATION STUDY

	Containers	Pallets
Volume of payload packaged shipment (cu ft)	7,600	8,800
Tare weight of containers/pallets (lb)	19,200	3,200
Net payload (lb)	102,600*	120,000
Terminal labor ($/ton)	1.60	12.40

* Volume-limited to 13.5 lb/cu ft

The useful volume of the L-300 for containerized shipment is 7600 cu ft, while that for the palletized shipment is 15 percent greater, or 8800 cu ft. The tare weight of the containers is 19,200 pounds, or six times the 3200-pound tare weight of the pallets. But the terminal labor for the containerized shipment of $1.60 per ton is 13 percent of the $12.40 per ton estimated for the palletized shipment. There is at present no consensus among shippers and airlines regarding the future use of containers in air cargo shipments. A careful systems analysis study of this subject is indicated.

Review of Survey Findings

The preceding review of commercial distribution policies and practices points up several potential impediments to a rapidly expanding demand for air cargo transportation. One impediment is the relatively high cost of air cargo service and the nonacceptance and/or implementation of the total-distribution-cost concept on the part of commercial shippers. It was found that the corporations surveyed varied considerably in their ability to grasp and control the many decisions that influence the total distribution problem. Most have extensive warehouse holdings and numerous distribution centers, and maintain large inventories. Although one soap and toilet article manufacturer ships over 95 percent of its freight by truck and one food processor strives to utilize rail transport exclusively, the rest of the corporations surveyed utilized the "transportation" concept, devoting a great deal of effort to the minimization of total *transportation* costs. In most cases the freight rates were negotiated by corporate headquarters staff members to lend the weight of the entire corporation to the negotiations, and transportation and warehousing decisions were made exclusively by the corporate headquarters. From the results of this brief survey, it appeared that in most cases the corporations were not employing the total-distribution-cost concept. The survey results indicated that the data needed to implement the total-distribution-cost concept were not readily available to management. In the cases of several firms surveyed, the terms "transportation costs" and "total distribution costs" seemed to be viewed as synonymous. The corporations surveyed evidenced a determination to upgrade the sophistication of their distribution management practices, but indications were that this would take a long time.

This survey tends to corroborate the findings of a recent study by a large management consulting firm of the distribution management in 26 large and profitable companies representing a wide range of industries, including chemicals, petroleum, food processing, building materials, and metals fabrication. The consulting firm rated each company with respect to four basic yardsticks of distribution management.

1. Generation and use of meaningful and timely control information
2. Personnel competence
3. Awareness by top management of economics of distribution
4. Grasp of overall distribution problem

The results indicated that only five of the 26 companies received a grade of "good," most were "average," while six were rated as "poor." It is significant that the five companies rated "good" had the highest return-on-investment performance.

TRENDS IN MILITARY DISTRIBUTION
PRACTICES AND POLICIES

In general the distribution practices and policies of the Department of Defense are not directly pertinent or applicable to the commercial air cargo market. However, the Department of Defense purchase of air cargo transportation from commercial air carriers is substantial. The resulting interaction between the air carriers and the Military Airlift Command is serving to acquaint the airlines with the technical and administrative innovations being developed by the Military Airlift Command. Since some of these innovations are potentially applicable to commercial air cargo operations, they will be discussed briefly here.

Military Transportation Management

Management of the Department of Defense's long-haul transportation operations is largely concentrated in the Military Airlift Command (MAC) and the Military Sea Transport Service (MSTS). The operations of both MAC and MSTS are financed under the Industrial Fund concept. Under this concept of operation, the agencies of the Department of Defense that use the service are charged directly. The MAC and MSTS operating budgets and schedules reflect the current pattern of user demand, and the flexibility and efficiency of the Department of Defense transportation services are enhanced. The users of the MAC and MSTS services — the Army, Navy, and Air Force agencies — must plan, program, and budget for their airlift and sealift requirements in essentially the same way that they would if they used commercial services. MSTS and MAC must so manage and control their operations that they provide the service demanded by their "customers" at "tariff" rates which relate to the cost of providing the service. To maintain the integrity of the Industrial Fund, tariff schedules are periodically updated and are published in appropriate U.S. Government Regulations. The users of the services are billed directly at tariff rates.

Commercial Augmentation

Approximately 63 percent of MAC's expenses in fiscal year 1966 were attributable to "commercial augmentation," or the purchase of airlift services from commercial carriers. In fiscal year 1966 MAC's expenditures for commercial augmentation amounted to $394.2 million, and in fiscal year 1967 the estimated expenditures for commercial augmentation were $500 million. Of MAC's total fiscal year 1966 demand, roughly 90 percent of the passenger and 30 percent of the cargo demand were satisfied by commercial carriers.

During the first half of fiscal year 1967, the airlines carried 957,000 military passengers and 77,000 tons of priority cargo and mail under MAC contracts valued at $350 million. The USAF estimates that in its worldwide operations, scheduled commercial airline services accounted for 71 percent of the passengers and 67 percent of the cargo moved during the first half of fiscal 1967.

With the burgeoning airlift requirements for service to the Vietnam area, the airlines have increased their MAC charter services substantially. Fiscal 1968 MAC contracts for commercial augmentation are expected to exceed $600 million.

The FY 1961–FY 1966 trend in expenditures for MAC's commercial augmentation is shown in Table 2.24.

TABLE 2.24. COMMERCIAL AUGMENTATION PROCURED BY THE MILITARY AIRLIFT COMMAND (MAC)

Fiscal year	Contracts for commercial augmentation (millions)
1961	$113.0
1962	184.8
1963	211.9
1964	192.5
1965	231.3
1966	394.2

SOURCE: MAC, "Airlift Service Management Report" (July 1965–June 1966), p. 14.

The majority of the commercial augmentation missions are flown in aircraft allocated to the Civil Reserve Air Fleet (CRAF). The CRAF, established in 1952, consists of specifically identified civil aircraft which become available to the Department of Defense for augmentation airlift during emergencies. The CRAF will operate under MAC operational control during a national emergency. As of June 30, 1967, the CRAF included 376 passenger and cargo aircraft owned by 23 U.S. airlines.

Apart from the significant and important economic benefits to commercial air carriers of this commercial augmentation and its impact on the equipment inventory of the commercial carriers, the carriers involved in CRAF operations are exposed to and will likely utilize the innovations being developed by MAC in the areas of computerized scheduling, fleet command and control, materials handling, and containerization.

Commodity/Transport Mode Pairing

An extensive priority system for cargo movement is now being utilized by the Department of Defense. The designation of shipment for air cargo or surface carrier movement is governed by explicit criteria for both CONUS-outgoing and CONUS-incoming movement (continental U.S.). "Back haul" or retrograde air cargo is historically only about 35 percent by weight of outgoing, primarily because of this Department of Defense priority system and rate structure. With the present priority system, this imbalance between incoming and outgoing air cargo will probably increase, especially in view of the programmed increase in airlift capability in the 1970's. Since MAC must recoup all operating costs regardless of the inbound/outbound cargo balance, the customers normally must pay for low volume return flights on a pro-rated basis. A major effort is under way by USAF to make more items eligible for "back haul" air transportation to CONUS, and cut rates for such retrograde service are being considered. Progress is being made in this effort and the USAF estimates that by the mid-1970's about 90 percent of Air Force Logistics Command (AFLC) items will be eligible for air cargo shipment.

Supply Pipeline/Warehousing Policies

A significant recent development in the Department of Defense warehousing policy is the decision by OSD and the military services to phase out their overseas storage depots. Thus, in a few years all Department of Defense supply and distribution depots will be located in CONUS and the needs of deployed forces will be met by MAC and MSTS. This major change in Department of Defense logistics support policy was significantly influenced by the availability of the C-141 and C-5A for high-speed, long-range logistics support operations. As this policy is implemented and results are obtained, commercial transportation users may emulate OSD's use of the total-distribution-cost concept.

Another innovation in supply pipeline policy is the multiple-destination-port concept. Under this concept USAF will have 10 main aerial ports of embarkation (APOE's) located in the continental United States, and all or almost all will be multidirectional regarding destination on the worldwide MAC channel routes. Cargo will originate from east and west coast stations alike to the Pacific areas as well as for European areas. This concept presages a new era in logistics airlift and in utilization and management of future airlift resources.

Other Military Innovations Likely to Affect Future Commercial Operations

1. MAC plans to exercise command and control of its entire fleet of aircraft from one central location at its headquarters at Scott Air Force Base. Computer-aided scheduling and control of aircraft will be provided, and it is planned that schedules will be published one year in advance. Each aircraft will be scheduled one month in advance. Ad-

vanced communications equipment and techniques will permit en route control of aircraft for contingency diversions. The traditional USAF concept of wing and squadron commanders may be discarded. MAC plans to employ isochronal maintenance of its entire fleet; that is each aircraft will be scheduled for routine maintenance inspections and repair on a chronological basis rather than on the basis of accumulated flight hours. The Aircraft Commander may be the commanding officer of the aircraft crew, and strict crew integrity will be maintained.

2. The USAF's 463L Materials Handling System exploits five separate but interdependent families of equipment. This system provides the capability to unload and load a large cargo aircraft within the time required to accomplish "turnaround service" for the aircraft. It is designed to operate efficiently in routine peacetime applications into and out of major terminals as well as under emergency conditions in an "austere environment" without prepositioned ground support equipment. The 463L system is compatible with surface modes of transportation, as well as with various types of side- and end-loading aircraft.

3. Cargo unitization 1975. Under this title MAC is studying the flow of military cargo from vendor to depot to surface carrier to user. The intent is to reduce or eliminate additional packaging, "break-bulk" operations, handling, and documentation by intermediate links in the logistics chain. The use of pallets or containerization is being carefully studied. The military plans to assist in the development of lightweight intermodal containers as part of this new approach to military logistics. The eventual implementation of this study is likely to have a direct impact on the attitude of commercial shippers toward the total-distribution-cost concept.

SOME OTHER FACTORS THAT WILL AFFECT THE DEMAND AND SUPPLY OF COMMERCIAL AIR CARGO TRANSPORTATION

Competitive Actions by Surface Transportation Modes

The surface transportation modes are likely to increase their use of modern management methods and to be more aggressive and open-minded in applying advanced technology to their operations. In an era of rising labor rates the surface carriers may be expected to exploit their advantage in terms of the amount of freight handled per employee. The railroads can substantially improve their dock-to-dock speed by introducing airline-type scheduling and command and control techniques. The truckers can be expected to further exploit the use of "double" and "triple-bottoms" and intermodal containers with "easy-quick" attachments in order to reduce their costs. The emerging federal highway network should improve the speed performance of intercity truck operations.

Surface ship operators can also be expected to move in the direction of higher speed, lower-port-time ships of the LASH type.

Advanced Aircraft Capabilities and Performance

Counteracting such improved potentials on the part of surface transportation are the impressive potentials of many new all-cargo type aircraft. Significant improvements in payload, speed, productivity, first cost per unit of productivity, unit cost and loadability will result from the use of such advanced aircraft, now under development.

Airports and Air Traffic Control

In 1965 the total delay time from congestion at 292 airports with FAA air traffic control towers was more than 333,000 hours, costing about $64 million, of which $41 million was borne by the commercial air carriers. The average cost per minute of delay was $3.17. This problem is now receiving serious attention by the AOCI, AIA, Airframe Manufacturing, ATA, and FAA.

The FAA recognizes that the terminal area problems must be approached on a total systems basis. It is investigating and developing a number of innovations, including computer-aided simulation of new facilities prior to their installation. High-density TRACON is an example. To the degree that these airport and air traffic control congestion problems are alleviated, the speed, performance, and unit costs of air cargo operations will be improved.

Airline Attitudes Toward Investment in All-Cargo Aircraft

During the next 15 years the free world airlines are expected to make major investments in SST's, "jumbo" subsonic passenger transports, and associated ground handling equipment and maintenance hangars. The fiscal problems of raising the necessary capital and the operational problems of introducing these new aircraft into the airline fleets are likely to influence airline management attitudes toward the procurement of new all-cargo aircraft. The airlines may invest in cargo aircraft only if the return on investment is essentially equal to that of similar new passenger aircraft.

The profit required in order to yield this return on investment may serve to inhibit substantial reductions in the price asked for the air cargo service. The results of the brief survey conducted for this study suggest that the effective demand for air cargo transportation is very sensitive to the price of service. It is recommended that this price be carefully analyzed to determine its potential impact on the growth of air cargo transportation.

WAYS TO PROMOTE DEMAND FOR AIR CARGO

Although a number of current forecasts show a tenfold increase in the demand for air cargo transportation during the next 15 years, an examination of the accuracy of forecasts made during the past 15 years shows that the forecasters' batting averages have not been high. An order of magnitude increase in the demand for air cargo transportation probably will not evolve without positive action on the part of the interested parties. The following steps hold promise of yielding positive results.

Reduce the Price of the Air Cargo Service

The results of this survey indicate that the dominant factor restricting the growth of air cargo demand is the relatively high price of the service. It is suggested that the airlines, aircraft manufacturers, and other interested parties undertake a systems analysis of ways and means of reducing the cost of air cargo service. Points made in the following paragraphs bear more or less direct relation to cost, and suggest specific ways in which it can be reduced.

Provide Encouragement and Assistance to Potential Shippers in Organizing for Total-Distribution-Cost Management

Except for very high value commodities, it is unlikely that the total transportation costs by air cargo will closely approach those for surface transportation in the foreseeable future; it is more realistic to expect that innovations and improvements in air cargo performance will be countered by performance, marketing, and pricing strategy on the part of the surface modes. The marketing of air cargo service is primarily a commercial airline responsibility, but the airframe manufacturers may be of assistance. The airlines, which will benefit directly from expanded air cargo operations, should be encouraged to consider the development of a new facet of their service — the systems analysis and management of distribution for shippers. Manufacturers and wholesale/retail distributors whose gross annual sales are less than $100 million (medium-sized shippers) and new businesses may provide a large potential for air cargo service. The airlines should sell them the total-distribution-cost concept before the "traffic manager" and/or "transportation" concept takes hold and their distribution systems become inflexibly tied to surface transportation. Such firms should be encouraged to use computer-aids to provide distribution cost control information.

Ensure Cross-Seeding and Wide Communication of Innovations

Some technical innovations under development by the military, particularly in the areas of materials handling, computer-aided accounting and inventory control, and aircraft scheduling may serve to reduce the cost of providing commercial air cargo service; these should be considered by the airlines operators.

Reduce Paperwork Required for Commerce

Paperwork is a significant element of transportation cost. One large distributor — a corporation which utilizes the total-distribution-cost concept — today is shipping more than twice the weight and four times the number of pieces of freight that it did 20 years ago. Twenty percent fewer people are needed for the shipping today, but the number of people required to handle the paperwork has increased by more than 80 percent during the 20-year period. Particularly in international commerce large numbers of employees are required to fill out, file, check, stamp, and otherwise process the 810 different categories of forms covering imports and exports to and from the U.S.A. It was reported that the U.S. has prescribed 43 mandatory forms for exports and 80 for imports. It may be possible to eliminate export declarations by using bills of lading to provide the same information. Emphasis should be placed on streamlining the control functions and separating them from the statistical functions so that the latter do not impede shipment.

Some corporations are already trying to reduce the administrative details of distribution. Their receptivity toward the total-distribution-cost concept should be enhanced.

Standardize Shipping Containers

There are now over 500 containers of different sizes, shapes, and materials which are called "standard" containers. It is suggested that some one family of containers — adaptable to movement by air, truck, rail, and ship—be established as standard by both the United States and foreign shippers and carriers. The Society of Automotive Engineers is now attempting to develop specifications for such standard containers.

Encourage a Concerted Effort by Shippers, Airport Operators, Air Carriers, Airframe Manufacturers, the U.S. Government, and City Planners to Develop Suitable Facilities and Equipment

Airport improvements, access highway modifications, and equipment and real estate acquisition are problem areas which can require long lead times prior to accomplishment, and the lead times may vary with each geographical location and community. The systems approach must be utilized in advanced planning if the projected air cargo traffic growth is to develop.

GOVERNMENTAL REGULATORY AND PROMOTIONAL POLICIES

This subsection gives an overview of interactions between various levels of U.S., foreign, and international governmental organizations and components of the air transportation system. Each major air transportation system component is discussed, significant trends in governmental regulatory and promotional policy affecting each major component are identified, and the probable impacts of the trends are analyzed.

GOVERNMENTAL STRUCTURE FOR REGULATION AND PROMOTION OF CIVIL AIR TRANSPORTATION

Table 2.25 identifies the domestic and foreign governmental agencies that affect air transportation from either the regulatory or promotional standpoint. The interactions between these governmental organizations and the development and operation of components of the air transportation system are described. Although the matrix attempts to show important interrelationships, it is not all-inclusive. Because the several aspects of federal, state, local, and foreign governmental functions interact with and overlap each other, many governmental organizations exercise authority over the same air transport function. The impacts of interactions among several regulatory or promotional authorities respecting the same air transport function are often multiplicative rather than additive.

TABLE 2.25. GOVERNMENTAL SYSTEM FOR REGULATION AND PROMOTION OF CIVIL AIR TRANSPORTATION

Airport Systems

Governmental Level and Organization	Location — Selection and Use	Development — Planning, Financing, Technical Aid
UNITED STATES, FEDERAL LEVEL		
The Legislative Branch	←	
General Accounting Office	Prevents diversion of federally allocated airport lands to non-airport purposes through audit and review authority	Assists in legislative control over receipt, disbursement, and application of public funds; acts as congressional watchdog
The Judicial Branch		
	←	
Independent agencies		
Civil Aeronautics Board	Designates or approves airports to serve defined city or county areas	Authorizes routes, thereby affecting planning requirements; has favored regional airports and, more recently, use of satellite airports to relieve congestion at regional airports
Equal Employment Opportunity Commission		Secures nondiscrimination in employment
Export-Import Bank of Washington		Assists foreign purchase of U.S. airport equipment
Federal Communications Commission		
General Services Administration	Handles disposition of surplus federal airports	
Interstate Commerce Commission		
National Aeronautics and Space Administration		
National Labor Relations Board		
National Mediation Board		
Securities and Exchange Commission		Enforces registration, disclosure and other investor protection measures on financing involving public security issues
The Executive Branch *The Executive Office*	←	
Bureau of the Budget	←	

Airport Systems

Administration	Rates and Charges	Regulation and Protection (including zoning)	Ownership and Operation
The Congress affects almost all aspects of civil aviation through its legislative powers to define governmental development of regulatory authority, to approve treaties, to grant or deny appropriations that fix expenditure levels, and to investigate performance of, and needed changes in, legislation and international agreements.			
Reviews legislative and executive acts — to assure consistency with Constitution; aviation legislation — to assure consistency with overall legislative framework; and independent agency and executive acts — to assure consistency with fiscal and legislative authority and intent.			
	Has opposed direct passenger head tax for airport financing but has not opposed increased charges to air carriers		
			Secures nondiscrimination in employment
		Controls erection of structures for communications	
			Regulates procurement for federal airports and disposal of surplus federal airports
			Administers federal regulations of fair labor practices and of employees' rights to union representation, conducts elections to certify bargaining agents

Directly, through the Executive Office and the Bureau of the Budget, and indirectly, through the executive departments, the President exercises overall budgetary, financial, and policy responsibility for federal expenditures and promotional and regulatory activities of the executive departments and agencies concerned with air transportation.

Influence of President is felt even by independent agencies, such as CAB, through budgetary and appointive power.

Airport Systems

Governmental Level and Organization	Location — Selection and Use	Development — Planning, Financing, Technical Aid,
National Aeronautics and Space Council	←	
Office of Science and Technology	←	
Department of State		Through the Agency for International Development (AID), finances planning studies of airport requirements in underdeveloped countries
The Treasury Department		
Department of Defense	Military airports; military preemption of airspace and sites limit choice of sites for civil airports	Military, joint use, and some civil airports abroad
Department of Justice		Advises airport planners of department's space needs at airports
Post Office Department		Advises planning officials on space requirements; may finance construction of airport mail-handling facilities, or rent same; is researching ways to improve handling and processing systems, which could produce increased usage of air mail and be applicable for air cargo
Department of the Interior	Locates airports within or serving national parks, monuments, or recreation areas	Plans and acts as local sponsor under the Federal-Aid Airport Program for airports within or serving national parks, monuments, or recreation areas
Department of Agriculture	Locates airports within or serving national forests	Plans and provides local sponsors' funds under the Federal Aid Airport Program for airports in or serving national forests

Airport Systems

Administration	Rates and Charges	Regulation and Protection (including zoning)	Ownership and Operation
Advises and assists the President in developing basic aeronautical plans, policies, and programs and in assigning responsibilities among executive agencies for specific programs, such as the development of the supersonic air transport.			
Coordinates general scientific and technological programs involving combined government and private R&D efforts; responds to research assignments not under the auspices of any other specific section of Executive Branch.			
	Works through ICAO to achieve reasonable charges at international airports		
Conducts customs operations at airports of entry	Bureau of Customs has had rent-free space at airports, thus putting cost on other users; issue is now joined; Treasury has favored airport user charges but not a special fund		
Military airports	Civil use of military airports	Deals with local civil authorities on zoning, noncompatible use of surrounding land, and some aspects of hours and conditions of use (not always successful)	Military airports and some civil airports abroad
Immigration and Naturalization Service (INS) offices function at airports of entry; may also act to force nondiscrimination in operating procedures and regulations	INS airport offices have had rent-free space at airports; this is now at issue	Concerned with protection of airports and airport users under federal statutes — bombs, false bomb scares, interstate or international commerce, criminal acts generally	
	Pays airport for space used		May own mail facilities; normally operates airport mail processing facility
May directly (or through concessionaire) administer, own, operate, protect, and regulate the operation of, and charges at, airports in or serving national parks, monuments, and recreational areas			
Directly (or through contractor) administers, owns, operates, protects, and regulates the operation and use of, and charges at, airports in national forests	Has had rent-free inspection and quarantine space at airports of entry; this is now at issue	Concerned with plant and animal quarantine functions at airports of entry	

Airport Systems

Governmental Level and Organization	Location — Selection and Use	Development — Planning, Financing, Technical Aid
Department of Commerce	Provides data essential to airport planning through the Bureau of the Census and other statistical programs, the Coast and Geodetic Survey, and the Weather Bureau; through Economic Development Administration finances studies of airport development requirements and finances development of airports, facilities, and airport industrial parks in underdeveloped parts of the United States	
Department of Labor	Statistical data developed by the Department of Labor constitute important inputs in forecasting the demand for air services and the future locus of the need for airport services in major metropolitan areas	
Department of Health, Education, and Welfare		
Department of Housing and Urban Development		Provides funds through regional planning authorities for planning of public works, including airports
Department of Transportation Note: This new department includes the FAA; the safety functions of the CAB; the St. Lawrence Seaway; the Coast Guard; the functions of the former office of the Undersecretary of Commerce for Transportation; the former Bureau of Public Roads; and new functions, especially in safety, under the National Transportation Safety Board. It doesn't include the Maritime Board, inland waterways, the Maritime Administration, the ICC, or the CAB (except its safety functions)	Through FAA has right of review over all airports, including military, developed with federal funds and of notification and protest, if necessary, on location of airports built with private or local funds	Finances planning of individual airports but not airport systems (see HUD), through FAA, and finances development of selected airport facilities, including landing areas, on a matching-funds basis; criteria for aid are vague; also through FAA provides technical aids to airport planning (such as techniques for capacity analysis, methodologies for evaluation of airport facilities); works through ICAO on standards for international airports; gives technical assistance to foreign countries on airport planning.

INTERSTATE REGIONAL LEVEL

← ───

| STATE LEVEL Note: States differ in what they do in aviation and how they are organized to perform such functions; hence, no breakdown by state agency is feasible. It should not be assumed, however, that all states do the things described or do all of them the same way, but they could and may do so | By state for state airports; also, some states restrict the location of private airports where such would interfere with public airports | Most states provide some financial aid to airports; state participation in airport planning is increasing, and with it financial aid; some states give planning and technical aid to airport development; also seek to secure greater federal aid |

Airport Systems

Administration	Rates and Charges	Regulation and Protection (including zoning)	Ownership and Operation
	Has rent-free space in airports of entry; this is now at issue	Conducts quarantine functions at airports of entry to protect against import of communicable diseases; also administers interstate quarantine regulations	
		Gives financial aid to urban planning, including research on improved land use and zoning	
FAA has favorably considered setting up a separate corporation to administer the Washington, D.C., airports	FAA predecessor organizations have considered a federal airport user charge to recover grants-in aid; no definitive action ever taken, but Boyd, Secretary of DOT, has favored a passenger head tax to finance airports and airways (airport part could be held for local use, however)	While there has been much discussion on the need for federal action to protect airport departure and arrival paths, including those of military airports, from conflicting land use and to protect communities from adverse airport activities, no action has been forthcoming	Owns and operates some airports including Washington National and Dulles International (both serving Washington, D.C.); has no plans for a national airport system

The tendency of urban development, aviation, and airport service areas to overrun and ignore political boundaries has led to the need for, and creation of, regional authorities, particularly in the field of transportation. These authorities transcend municipal and county boundaries, and sometimes state borders, in such organizations as the Port of New York Authority. Since interstate organizations are few and, in general, function like intrastate regional authorities (except in jurisdiction and source of power), regional bodies are treated below, after states.

States have power to set up special administrative units to plan and operate airports serving large metropolitan complexes; may set up interstate authorities by compact with other states	Not normally a state concern except where states operate airports; with increased state financial aid, may seek fees to recover some of such aid	Normally limited to enabling statutes but some states have developed, or proposed, zoning ordinances to protect airports and other land users from airport use abuses	State systems are rare but emergency fields are provided by some; also some airports provided to give access to recreation areas; recognition of airports as recreation areas is growing

Airport Systems

Governmental Level and Organization	Location — Selection and Use	Development — Planning, Financing, Technical Aid
REGIONAL LEVEL	Authorities or districts determine locations for new airports	Regional authorities plan, finance, and develop airport systems to serve their designated areas, conduct or commission technical studies, and develop planning techniques and measures of capacity and adequacy of airport services; some have taxing authority or power to issue bonds, or both
LOCAL LEVEL	←	Revenue bonds are increasing in popularity as means of financing; concessions revenues, especially car rental and parking, are major revenue sources
INTERNATIONAL LEVEL	←	
Note: Includes foreign governments and international organizations, such as the United Nations or its constituent organization, the International Civil Aviation Organization (ICAO)		There is some international financial assistance through World Bank, etc., for airport planning and development

Airport Access Systems

Governmental Level and Organization	Planning	Financing	Ownership and Operation
UNITED STATES, FEDERAL LEVEL			
The Legislative Branch	←		
General Accounting Office		Congressional watchdog	
The Judicial Branch	←		

Airport Systems

Administration	Rates and Charges	Regulation and Protection (including zoning)	Ownership and Operation
Form of administration is defined by enabling statute or regulatory powers defined by state law, by local joint-powers agreement, or by inter-state compact	Fares, rates, and charges for region's airports subject to overall limitations of enabling law or agreement	Some authorities may be given zoning protection or protection against conflicting land use; most must seek such protection from surrounding municipalities — and are subject to adverse zoning, assessment, or land use decisions and restriction on operations	Normally own the airports they operate but may lease, or purchase and lease back, private airports threatened with takeover for real etate developments

Local governments — county and municipal — locate, plan, finance (at least in part), administer, own, operate, regulate, and protect and determine rates and charges for most public-use airports in the United States.

		No single local administration controls approach and departure paths for most airports; even where adequate zoning and land use regulations are secured, local pressures soon vitiate them through variances	

In most foreign countries the national government locates, plans, finances, owns, operates, protects, and regulates the use of, and the fares and charges for, international-use airports. ICAO and IATA (International Air Transport Association — airline group) have developed airport planning standards. ICAO evaluates international-use airports on basis of adequacy in meeting its standards.

	ICAO seeks uniform basis for charges		

Airspace

	Air Navigation Aids and Systems		
Usage — Rules and Procedures	Planning	Financing	Ownership and Operation

The Congress affects almost all aspects of civil aviation through its legislative powers to define governmental development of regulatory authority, to approve treaties, to grant or deny appropriations that fix expenditure levels, and to investigate performance of, and needed changes in, legislation and international agreements.

Congressional watchdog

Reviews legislative and executive acts — to assure consistency with Constitution; aviation legislation — to assure consistency with overall legislative framework; and independent agency and executive acts — to assure consistency with fiscal and legislative authority and intent.

Airport Access Systems

Governmental Level and Organization	Planning	Financing	Ownership and Operation
Independent agencies			
Civil Aeronautics Board	Authorizes routes, thereby affecting access requirements; participates with ICC in establishing air cargo pickup and delivery zones		
Equal Employment Opportunity Commission			Secures nondiscrimination in employment
Export-Import Bank of Washington		Assists foreign purchase of U.S. equipment	
Federal Communications Commission			
General Services Administration	Controls federal motor pool, including use for airport access		
Interstate Commerce Commission	Participates with CAB in establishing air cargo pickup and delivery zones		Has opposed intermodal ownership or control
National Aeronautics and Space Administration			
National Labor Relations Board			Concerned with fair labor practices, union representation, and elections to choose bargaining agents
National Mediation Board			
Securities and Exchange Commission		Is concerned if public security issues are subject to SEC registration and disclosure requirements	
The Executive Branch			
The Executive Office ⎱ Bureau of the Budget ⎰	Directly, through the Executive Office and the Bureau of the Budget, and indirectly, through the executive departments, the President exercises overall budgetary, financial, and policy responsibility for federal expenditures and promotional and regulatory activities of the executive departments and agencies concerned with air transportation. Influence of President is felt even by independent agencies, such as CAB, through budgetary and appointive power.		
National Aeronautics and Space Council	Advises and assists the President in developing basic aeronautical plans, policies, and programs and in assigning responsibilities among executive agencies for specific programs, such as the development of the supersonic air transport.		
Office of Science and Technology	Coordinates general scientific and technological programs involving combined government and private R&D efforts; responds to research assignments not under the auspices of any other specific section of Executive Branch.		

	Airspace		
	Air Navigation Aids and Systems		
Usage — Rules and Procedures	Planning	Financing	Ownership and Operation
		Has not opposed airways user charges but has urged equitable distribution of charges among military, general aviation, and air carriers; chairman recently questioned need to pass user charges on to customers	
			Secures nondiscrimination in employment
		Assists foreign purchase of U.S. equipment	
Licenses air and ground radio communication systems: allocates frequencies			
		Regulates procurement for federal airways and disposal of surplus equipment	
Preempts airspace usage and rocket launch areas (subject to DOT-FAA review)	Conducts research on guidance, control, and communications systems		Launches satellites for navigation, communication, guidance, and control (especially international operations)
			NLRB labor standards and elected representation procedures may apply to federal government
		Favors airway user charges ⟶	

Airport Access Systems

Government Level and Organization	Planning	Financing	Ownership and Operation
Department of State			
The Treasury Department			
Department of Defense	Generally must work through federal and local highway offices; defense needs constitute a major criterion of route selection; also, military reservations may be barrier to development of effective civil access systems	May wholly or partially finance special accessories or other facilities	
Department of Justice			
Post Office Department	Normally provides, owns, and operates its own airport access vehicles; might use efficient mass rapid transit system, including airport access; where airport air mail facility is equipped to receive and dispatch mail independent of city postal systems, may use contract truckers or bus companies for access		
Department of the Interior	Provides access to its own airports within its controlled areas directly (as roads) or through concessionaire; outside controlled areas, works through federal, state, and local highway officials		
Department of Agriculture	Provides access to its own airports within national forests; otherwise, works through federal, state, or local highway departments		
Department of Commerce			
Department of Labor			
Department of Health, Education, and Welfare			
Department of Housing and Urban Development	Can finance planning studies for airport access systems and make demonstration grants to test new systems	Makes grants to aid development of mass transit systems, including airport access systems	
Department of Transportation Note: This new department includes the FAA; the safety functions of the CAB; the St. Law-	DOT has no specific authority over airport access systems, compared to HUD's well-financed and well-entrenched position. On mass rapid transit systems, HUD grants funds for demonstration and regional airport planning studies. DOT controls highway funds through federal highway program. (This situation creates a potential interagency conflict that may be difficult to resolve — and the resolution is very important to air transportation.)		

rence Seaway; the Coast Guard; the functions of the former office of the Undersecretary of Commerce or Transportation; the former Bureau of Public Roads; and new functions especially in safety, under the National Transportation Safety Board. It doesn't include the Maritime Board, inland waterways, the Maritime Administration, the ICC, or the CAB (except its safety functions)

Airspace

Usage — Rules and Procedures	Air Navigation Aids and Systems		
	Planning	Financing	Ownership and Operation
	Works to achieve international agreements on airspace and air traffic control standards and on principles for establishing user charges; through AID provides technical and financial aid to develop ATC systems in underdeveloped countries		
		Favors airways user charges but not separate fund	
Military preemption of airspace limits civil operations	The federal airways are a joint civil-military system and justified as such in seeking appropriations; FAA does not operate control towers at military fields but military or FAA towers sometimes control both civil and military traffic out of adjacent airports; in time of war, FAA airways-ATC system operates as a part of DOD; military R&D has made major contributions to air traffic control and navigation systems (radar, transponders)		
Provides enforcement when needed			
	Depends on FAA system and controls; may provide some landing aids; supplies local funds for federal-aid programs, such as lighting		
	Depends on FAA system and controls; may provide some landing aids; supplies local funds for federal-aid programs, such as lighting		
FAA has primary responsibility for safe and efficient use of airspace; establishes rules and conditions for its use, including instrumentation requirements, noise, and social acceptability	Plans, finances, owns, and operates the federal airways system, a joint use civil-military system for air navigation and en route and terminal air traffic control; gives financial aid for landing, lighting, and other facilities; operates control towers; cooperates with ICAO and foreign governments in developing compatible international ATC systems. Gives technical assistance and some aid to countries — especially underdeveloped — in improving their national facilities and capabilities. FAA and predecessor organizations have long advocated airways user charges		

Airport Access Systems

Governmental Level and Organization	Planning	Financing	Ownership and Operation
INTERSTATE REGIONAL LEVEL	The tendency of urban development, aviation, and airport service areas to overrun and ignore political boundaries has led to the need for, and creation of, regional authorities, particularly in the field of transportation. These		
STATE LEVEL Note: States differ in what they do in aviation and how they are organized to perform such functions; hence, no breakdown by state agency is feasible. It should not be assumed, however, that all states do the things described or do all of them the same way, but they could and may do so	State participation in airport access is usually limited to the provision of roads and highways, and, in some cases, access is recognized as a need in creating rapid transit districts; increasing importance of access problems together with growing state interest in airport and aviation development should bring more direct state action in this area; some are already seeking to influence federal aid and activities		
REGIONAL LEVEL	Regional transit districts now recognize airport access as a responsibility but regional airport districts rarely do so; Port of New York Authority is researching airport access systems; airport representatives now usually included in highway and regional planning councils	Financial help in the United States will probably be limited to planning, with financing left to mass rapid transit districts or highway bureaus	The state highway or regional rapid transit district, not the airport district, usually owns systems
LOCAL LEVEL	While rarely in the province of airport officials, is often under some supervision; airport representation is now often included in highway and mass rapid transit planning bodies. In the past, highway development has often hampered or prevented airport development.	May finance access and local aviation origin/destination studies	
INTERNATIONAL LEVEL Note: Includes foreign governments and international organizations, such as the United Nations or its constituent organization, the International Civil Aviation Organization (ICAO)	While normally not the province of airport administrations, European, Japanese, and some other foreign governments are probably ahead of the United States in their recognition of, and attempts to solve, airport access as part of general urban planning problem		

Airspace

Usage — Rules and Procedures	Air Navigation Aids and Systems		
	Planning	Financing	Ownership and Operation

authorities transcend municipal and county boundaries, and sometimes state borders, in such organizations as the Port of New York Authority. Since interstate organizations are few and, in general, function like intrastate regional authorities (except in jurisdiction and degree of power), regional bodies are treated below, after states.

Usage — Rules and Procedures	Planning	Financing	Ownership and Operation
Limited to nuisance regulations	While states do not invade the federal air traffic control area, some do seek to upgrade facilities for navigation, particularly landing aids, often with state-provided or -financed equipment; states seek to secure increased federal aid, including towers		
Except for nuisance and hazard control, little action or authority	Provides supplementary assistance, particularly for landing aids; provides local share for lighting and similar aids		
		Provides funds for federal assistance programs for lighting and landing aids; sometimes supplements federally assisted programs, especially for landing aids	
National airspace is a national concern; many major countries do not allow freedom of air transit	Eurocontrol is a jointly owned and financed organization to provide European air traffic control		

International organizations such as ICAO seek to promote free international air movement, to facilitate such movement, and to develop common air traffic control and navigation aids. ICAO sponsors ocean station programs, internationally financed, for search and rescue and weather data; ICAO seeks standardized basis for airways user charges, fosters a system involving satellites for communication and air traffic control to be directly financed by governments based on usage and benefits, leaving it to individual governments as to how they will recover costs for military, commercial, and private use.

Air Safety Systems

Governmental Level and Organization	Weather, Terrain, and Hazard Information		Air Accident Cause — Identification and Prevention
	Data Collection, Analysis, and Presentation	Briefing and En Route Intelligence	
UNITED STATES, FEDERAL LEVEL			
The Legislative Branch	←		
General Accounting Office			
The Judicial Branch	Reviews legislative and executive acts — to assure consistency with Constitution; aviation legislation — to assure consistency with overall legislative framework; and independent agency and executive acts — to assure consistency with fiscal and legislative authority and intent.		
Independent Agencies Civil Aeronautics Board			
Equal Employment Opportunity Commission			
Export-Import Bank of Washington			
Federal Communications Commission		Licenses air and ground radio communication systems; allocates frequencies	
General Services Administration			
Interstate Commerce Commission			
National Aeronautics and Space Administration	Launches weather satellites	Launches communications satellites that transmit weather data	Conducts biomedical and biophysical flight-oriented research
National Labor Relations Board			
National Mediation Board			
Securities and Exchange Commission			
The Executive Branch The Executive Office	Directly, through the Executive Office and the Bureau of the Budget, and indirectly, through the executive departments, the President exercises overall budgetary, financial, and policy responsibility for federal expenditures and promotional and regulatory activities of the executive departments and agencies concerned with air transportation.		
Bureau of the Budget	Influence of President is felt even by independent agencies, such as CAB, through budgetary and appointive power.		

Airmen, Mechanics, and Related Personnel

Air Safety — Regulation and Enforcement	Performance Requirements and Licensing	Training	
		Provision	Standards and Licensing

The Congress affects almost all aspects of civil aviation through its legislative powers to define governmental development of regulatory authority, to approve treaties, to grant or deny appropriations that fix expenditure levels, and to investigate performance of, and needed changes in, legislation and international agreements.

| | | Secures nondiscrimination in employment | |

| Has established safety standards for government-purchased autos; could do same for aircraft and use of foreign or domestic air carriers | | | |

| | | | Conducts biomedical and biophysical flight-oriented research |

Air Safety Systems

Governmental Level and Organization	Weather, Terrain, and Hazard Information		Air Accident Cause — Identification and Prevention
	Data Collection, Analysis and Presentation	Briefing and En Route Intelligence	
National Aeronautics and Space Council	Advises and assists the President in developing basic aeronautical plans, policies, and programs and in assigning responsibilities among executive agencies for specific programs, such as the development of the supersonic air transport.		
Office of Science and Technology	Coordinates general scientific and technological programs involving combined government and private R&D efforts; responds to research assignments not under the auspices of any other specific section of Executive Branch.		
Department of State	Facilitates cooperative international weather data collection and information systems		Arranges for U.S. participation in investigations of foreign air accidents, particularly where U.S. citizens or equipment are involved
The Treasury Department			
Department of Defense	Collects and analyzes some weather data made available for civil use	Uses weather data from civil sources in military briefings and en route information	Has own regulations and own accident investigation board, but in civil airspace, military aircraft and airmen are subject to civil rules and control
Department of Justice			
Post Office Department	Concerned with protection and recovery of mail in event of aircraft accident		
Department of the Interior			
Department of Agriculture			
Department of Commerce	Collects, analyzes, and disseminates data on weather; forecasts changes and hazardous conditions in all parts of the United States	Participates in FAA pilot-to-weatherman, direct-communication program on en route weather information	
Department of Labor			
Department of Health, Education, and Welfare			
Department of Housing and Urban Development			

Airmen, Mechanics, and Related Personnel

Air Safety — Regulation and Enforcement	Performance Requirements and Licensing	Training	
		Provision	Standards and Licensing
			→
			→
	Arranges and finances training of foreign personnel in air transport and ATC operations		
	Favors fees for tests and licensing		
	Conducts own training and qualifications programs; often source of civil pilots after their military service		
Provides enforcement when needed (passengers in dangerous condition, interference with pilot, dangerous shipments)			
		Analyzes need for particular labor skills; has some special training and vocational programs	

Air Safety Systems

Governmental Level and Organization	Weather, Terrain, and Hazard Information		Air Accident Cause — Identification and Prevention
	Data Collection, Analysis and Presentation	Briefing and En Route Intelligence	
Department of Transportation Note: This new department includes the FAA; the safety functions of the CAB; the St. Lawrence Seaway; the Coast Guard, the functions of the former office of the Undersecretary of Commerce or Transportation; the former Bureau of Public Roads; and new functions especially in safety, under the National Transportation Safety Board. It doesn't include the Maritime Board, inland waterways, the Maritime Administration, the ICC, or the CAB (except its safety functions)	FAA collects some weather data, so does the Coast Guard. FAA also performs some weather analysis, supplementary to that done by Weather Bureau, applicable to aviation	FAA provides both preflight briefing and en route intelligence regarding weather or hazards ahead; is practicing direct pilot-to-weatherman communication; also remote weather information through flight information desks at unmanned stations	Now responsibility of National Transportation Safety Board (of DOT) with help from FAA. U.S. assists in foreign air accident investigation, particularly where U.S. nationals or aircraft are involved. NTSB, while within DOT, is independent of secretary of DOT in policy areas
INTERSTATE REGIONAL LEVEL	The tendency of urban development, aviation, and airport service areas to overrun and ignore political boundaries has led to the need for, and creation of, regional authorities, particularly in the field of transportation. These		
STATE LEVEL Note: States differ in what they do in aviation and how they are organized to perform such functions; hence, no breakdown by state agency is feasible. It should not be assumed, however, that all states do the things described or do all of them the same way, but they could and may do so	Weather data collection is not generally a state function but some states are providing assistance to brief private flyers at general aviation airports without towers		States usually assist federal investigation
REGIONAL LEVEL	Rarely a regional activity	At nontower airports may provide briefing service	Assists federal officials
LOCAL LEVEL		At nontower airports may supply local weather briefing	Aids federal officials
INTERNATIONAL LEVEL Note: Includes foreign governments and international organizations, such as the United Nations or its constituent organization, the International Civil Aviation Organization (ICAO)	International exchange of weather data; international system based on ocean stations, but satellites are under consideration. ICAO-endorsed programs would provide worldwide weather and hazard data collection, projection, and communication	ICAO seeks compatible international air navigation systems and procedures as major safety measure While there is no universal international acceptance of safety standards, there is substantial international cooperation in air accident investigation and identification of probable cause	

Airmen, Mechanics, and Related Personnel

Air Safety — Regulation and Enforcement	Performance Requirements and Licensing	Training	
		Provision	Standards and Licensing
FAA issues and administers regulations; NTSB conducts hearings and investigations to identify probable cause of accidents and means of prevention, including revision of regulations	FAA establishes standards, gives tests, and issues licenses for airmen and mechanics; has proposed fees for licensing	Trains controllers and safety inspectors; trains, and provides technical assistance in training of foreign aviation technicians	FAA establishes standards for training establishments and licenses those approved to train airmen and mechanics

authorities transcend municipal and county boundaries, and sometimes state borders, in such organizations as the Port of New York Authority. Since interstate organizations are few and, in general, function like intrastate regional authorities (except in jurisdiction and degree of power), regional bodies are treated below, after states.

Nuisance and hazard instructions	States rarely in this area	Aviation skills are part of state-sponsored training and educational programs in some states	
		May provide training for mechanics and persons with similar skills; pilot training usually a private enterprise	
		May include training for some aviation skills in vocational education programs	
		ICAO aids national training programs and testing standards; seeks compatible international system	

While there are differing national standards, there are no true international tests or standards of competences for airmen and persons with supporting skills.

Aircraft

Governmental Level and Organization	Research and Development	Performance Standards and Licensing	Use of Airports and Airways
UNITED STATES, FEDERAL LEVEL *The Legislative Branch*	The Congress affects almost all aspects of civil aviation through its legislative powers to define governmental development of regulatory authority, to approve treaties, to grant or deny appropriations that fix expenditure levels, and to investigate performance of, and needed changes in, legislation and international agreements.		
General Accounting Office	Congressional watchdog on propriety of expenditures for aircraft research and development		
The Judicial Branch	Reviews legislative and executive acts — to assure consistency with Constitution; aviation legislation — to assure consistency with overall legislative framework; and independent agency and executive acts — to assure consistency with fiscal and legislative authority and intent.		
Independent agencies Civil Aeronautics Board		The Board has demonstrated its power to affect the choice of aircraft of subsidized air carriers. It has no direct authority over choice of aircraft for trunk carriers. In the case of air taxi operations, their exemption is conditioned on limiting operations to aircraft under 12,500 lb gross takeoff weight, but recently some exceptions have been made.	Authorizes the flight of foreign civil aircraft within U.S. navigable airspace for purposes other than public air transportation
Equal Employment Opportunity Commission	Is concerned with nondiscrimination in manufacturing employment		
Export-Import Bank of Washington	Facilitates foreign purchases of U.S. equipment by loans		
Federal Communications Commission			
General Services Administration	Regulates procurement of aircraft for federal government use		
Interstate Commerce Commission			
National Aeronautics Space Administration	Research and development on aeronautical structures, power plants, fuels, guidance and control systems communications, and advanced aircraft (including super- and hypersonic)		
National Labor Relations Board		Jurisdiction over manufacturers' and suppliers' employees	

Noncommercial Civil Air Transportation

Performance Standards	Permits and Licensing	Use of Airports and Airways
		→
		→

CAB has no jurisdiction over private flyers, including executive or other corporate flyers, provided they do not offer public air transportation. Contract flying, publicly held out as such, probably requires CAB approval, as does air taxi service. Without a public holding out to offer such service, CAB does not have jurisdiction—ICC and CAB have some general review rights over ownership and operation of private airlines by railroads or other surface carriers

Can facilitate foreign purchase of private aircraft also

Regulates railroad ownership of private air systems

Aircraft

Governmental Level and Organization	Research and Development	Performance Standards and Licensing	Use of Airports and Airways
National Mediation Board			
Securities and Exchange Commission	Financing through security markets subject to disclosure requirements; transactions by insiders regulated		
The Executive Branch			
The Executive Office The Bureau of the Budget			
National Aeronautics and Space Council	Defines plans, policies, and programs; assigns responsibilities among executive agencies		
Office of Science and Technology	Coordinates and evaluates the several governmental and private efforts in aeronautical R&D (among others) and picks up spot assignments not fitting anywhere else		
Executive Departments Department of State	Facilitates exchange of technical data and cooperation on joint R&D efforts or foreign licensing to produce U.S.-designed equipment		
The Treasury Department Bureau of the Customs Bureau of Internal Revenue	The depreciation policies of the department, within limits fixed by the Congress, affect the number of aircraft purchased		
Department of Defense	In effect, defense R&D on aircraft and propulsion systems has, in past, subsidized the development of most civil aircraft (not for SST but probably for V/STOL aircraft)	Recent military cargo aircraft, such as the C-141 and C5A, have ostensibly been designed to meet civil standards also, but so far none has had wide acceptance because of military design features	Military aircraft using civil airports and airways are subject to civil terminal and air traffic control; all military aircraft will be transponder-equipped, for example
Department of Justice	Security protection and clearance for classified R&D information for researchers with need to know; antitrust statutes apply to manufacturers and suppliers	Enforces when necessary	

Noncommercial Civil Air Transportation

Performance Standards	Permits and Licensing	Use of Airports and Airways
		Facilitates private aircraft operations to and from foreign countries
		Volume of personal travel may be adversely affected by Bureau of Internal Revenue's accountability requirements
Enforces federal regulations when necessary	INS functions at airports of entry	

Governmental Level and Organization	Research and Development	Aircraft Performance Standards and Licensing	Use of Airports and Airways
Post Office Department			
Department of the Interior			Can establish standards for use of its airports
Department of Agriculture			Can establish standards for use of its airports
Department of Commerce	Through sponsored scientific and technical research and dissemination of U.S. and foreign information, contributes to airport research and development	Controls export of aircraft and related equipment; protects developments through patent office	
Department of Labor			
Department of Health, Education, and Welfare			
Department of Housing and Urban Development			
Department of Transportation	DOT can sponsor research in aircraft and systems. FAA has sponsored SST development and kindred studies on V/STOL and short-haul aircraft	Through FAA establishes performance standards for U.S. and foreign aircraft to be operated in the United States; issues prototype and type production certificates for new aircraft	FAA authorizes the use of particular aircraft types over particular airways and at particular airports, specifying conditions and equipment; establishes standards for takeoff and landing at particular airports
INTERSTATE REGIONAL LEVEL	The tendency of urban development, aviation, and airport service areas to overrun and ignore political boundaries has led to the need for, and creation of, regional authorities, particularly in the field of transportation. These authorities transcend municipal and county boundaries, and sometimes state borders, in such organizations as the Port of New York Authority. Since interstate organizations are few and, in general, function like intrastate regional authorities (except in jurisdiction and degree of power), regional bodies are treated below, after states.		
STATE LEVEL			States may seek to ban excessively noisy or dirty aircraft from some airports and divert pleasure flying and training from congested airports and areas
REGIONAL LEVEL	Not normally a regional function		May limit use of airport and terminal airspace for particular purposes at particular hours or subject to particular operating conditions

Noncommercial Civil Air Transportation

Performance Standards	Permits and Licensing	Use of Airports and Airways
		Controls use of airports in national parks, monuments, and recreation areas
	Quarantine inspection functions at airports of entry to prevent import of communicable diseases	
		Aids in airport and airport access planning and development
Establishes and implements performance standards for noncommercial civil aviation operations	Grants noncommercial operating authority through licensing of aircraft and airmen	Authorizes use of particular airports and air routes by noncommercial as well as commercial operators
		May assign or seek, through fees, to divert noncommercial flying to low-activity airports

Aircraft

Governmental Level and Organization	Research and Development	Performance Standards and Licensing	Use of Airports and Airways
LOCAL LEVEL			Local ordinances may restrict use of some airports or access corridors by socially unacceptable aircraft, or may restrict use to particular hours
INTERNATIONAL LEVEL Foreign governments and international organizations, such as the United Nations or ICAO	Individual countries support own R&D, some by international arrangements (as Franco-British for SST Concorde and U.S.-funded European research), but little truly international R&D, despite efforts of technical officers of IATA, ICAO	ICAO, with some support from IATA, has attempted to promote uniform standards; major impetus comes from major markets like United States, which sets own standards	Policies based on international, often bilateral, agreements respecting airports and terminal airspace; international air usage is matter of ICAO negotiation plus an individual country's rules

Commercial Air Transportation

Governmental Level and Organization	Routes and Points Served	Agreements and Cooperative Working Arrangements	Interlocking Relationships, Mergers, and Acquisitions
UNITED STATES, FEDERAL LEVEL *The Legislative Branch*	←		
General Accounting Office			
The Judicial Branch			
Independent agencies Civil Aeronautics Board	The Board grants domestic route authorizations, subject only to judicial review. International routes are subject to presidential approval or veto, their implementations subject to bilateral agreements. Foreign air permits are granted by the CAB within the framework of bilateral treaties — subject to presidential approval. CAB assists State Department in negotiation of agreements with foreign governments on routes and services. Freight forwarders, air taxi operators, and related services are authorized by exemption from certification obligations, conditionally.	Board reviews contracts, or agreements among U.S. carriers, between U.S. and foreign carriers, and between carriers and noncarriers, such as manufacturers or financial companies, where the agreement may carry effective control over major part of carrier's investment.	In the interests of maintaining competition, the CAB regulates mergers, acquisitions of control, and interlock relationships involving air carriers. Cooperative working arrangements or competitive practices that might restrict competition are reviewed from this viewpoint. Controls IATA (International Air Transport Association) agreements on international tariffs through ability to disapprove agreements involving U.S. flag carriers — not by direct authority, although legislation to give CAB such rights has often been proposed.

Noncommercial Civil Air Transportation

Performance Standards	Permits and Licensing	Use of Airports and Airways
		May assign, or seek to divert through fees, noncommercial flying to low-activity airports

European and other foreign countries tend to restrict personal flying, especially sports flying (but not corporate executive flying), much more than does the United States. Progress in facilitation of noncommercial operations is encouraging, but use of private aircraft still constrained, particularly limited as to use of major airports during peak periods.

Commercial Air Transportation

Labor Conditions and Relations	Use of Airports and Airways	Tariffs and Tariff Agreements	Schedules, Capacity, and Service Adequacy

The Congress affects almost all aspects of civil aviation through its legislative powers to define governmental development of regulatory authority, to approve treaties, to grant or deny appropriations that fix expenditure levels, and to investigate performance of, and needed changes in, legislation and international agreements.

		Congressional watchdog on propriety of expenditures for transportation procurement & subsidy	

Reviews legislative and executive acts — to assure consistency with Constitution; aviation legislation — to assure consistency with overall legislative framework; and independent agency and executive acts — to assure consistency with fiscal and legislative authority and intent.

| The CAB normally incorporates labor-protective provisions in orders approving mergers or acquisitions of control over substantial parts of assets or route transfers. It has no authority over wage rates or labor contracts as such; authority over hours and conditions of work from safety standpoint was transferred to the National Transportation Safety Board. | The Board has established its legal right to designate the airport for service to a particular point or points in route authorizations, to deny use of an airport, or to change the airport used. Is now considering action in several cases through designation of airports, limitations on specific airports used (especially encouragement of use of satellite airports), to alleviate airport congestion. | CAB has jurisdiction over tariff rates and fares charged for U.S. air transportation, but tariffs for foreign carriage are reached through control over agreements or unfair trade practices. It fixes air mail rates and authorizes and pays subsidy under its mail rate authority. | While the CAB has no direct control over schedules or capacity offered, it is responsible for assuring that carriers adequately discharge their certificate obligations, and can remove service or certificates for inadequacy. Normally it adds other carriers. Local service certificates contain a commitment to offer such service, and the subsidization of such carriers gives the CAB added force. |

Commercial Air Transportation

Governmental Level and Organization	Routes and Points Served	Agreements and Cooperative Working Arrangements	Interlocking Relationships, Mergers, and Acquisitions
Equal Employment Opportunity Commission			
Export-Import Bank of Washington			
Federal Communications Commission			
General Services Administration	May intervene where government need for specific service exists		
Interstate Commerce Commission	Delineates ground/air cargo pickup and delivery areas — air-truck joint service	Air-truck agreements must be approved by ICC	ICC with CAB limits prevents transmodal transportation systems intermodal ownership control
National Aeronautics Space Administration			
National Labor Relations Board			
National Mediation Board			
Securities and Exchange Commission		Public financing; transactions by insiders subject to SEC regulations on disclosure; protection of investors	Public disclosure rul registration requirem on new companies, a securities transaction insiders

Commercial Air Transportation

Labor Conditions and Relations	Use of Airports and Airways	Tariffs and Tariff Agreements	Schedules, Capacity, and Service Adequacy
Nondiscrimination in hiring, wages, training, testing, promotion, retention — respecting sex as well as race or region; investigates discrimination charges, attempts conciliation; may use the courts directly or, if discrimination pattern is found, through attorney general; initiates action programs; works with state and local governments			
			Through facilitation of purchase of U.S. aircraft by foreign companies, enables these foreign air carriers to offer equipment competitive with U.S. air carriers.
	Licenses aviation ground and air communication systems		
		Regulates the procurement of transportation by federal agencies	
...ts to assure fair employment standards, ...hts to collective bargaining, election of bargaining agent			
...diates or arbitrates disputes between airlines and employees over wages, working conditions, and union recognition; handles jurisdictional disputes among unions; seeks fair redress of grievances without interrupting interstate commerce			

Commercial Air Transportation

Governmental Level and Organization	Routes and Points Served	Agreements and Cooperative Working Arrangements	Interlocking Relationships, Mergers, and Acquisitions
The Executive Branch			
The Executive Office *The Bureau of the Budget*	The President, in exercising review authority respecting foreign air routes of U.S. flag carriers and foreign air permits to foreign flag carriers, has in the past relied on the Departments of Commerce for economic issues; will probably now rely on the Department of Transportation for policy as well as economic issues.		
National Aeronautics and Space Council			
Office of Science and Technology			
Executive Departments *Department of State*	Through the Deputy Assistant Secretary for Transportation and Telecommunications, develops policy recommendations and approves policy programs concerning air transportation; negotiates foreign air transport rights and agreements		
The Treasury Department *Bureau of the Customs* *Bureau of Internal Revenue*	Through accountability requirements for executive travel in business aircraft, Bureau of Internal Revenue has caused reclassification of some travel from business to pleasure		
Department of Defense	May participate in CAB route, rate, or other proceedings to urge defense needs in support of, or against, proposed actions		
Department of Justice	INS functions at airports of entry; overtime required is at carrier expense; issue is now joined. Seeks to prevent illegal entry into the United States.		Second-guesses CAB on whether agreements, merg or trade practices will restrain trade or constitu unfair competition; intervenes in CAB proceed where appropriate; takes court action against C and, where Presidential approval has been requi has blocked CAB action.

Commercial Air Transportation

Labor Conditions and Relations	Use of Airports and Airways	Tariffs and Tariff Agreements	Schedules, Capacity, and Service Adequacy
	Issues passports and visas for travel to and from the United States; negotiates air access landing and traffic rights with foreign countries	The Department's Bureau of Education and Cultural Affairs promotes educational and cultural exchange with foreign countries (especially of students), giving rise to the demand for special fares	
	Limited number of points with customs facilities limits points of entry to United States; Customs requires overtime payments by air carriers as price for adapting to carrier's operating requirements on arrivals and departures		Primary responsibility for currency stabilization led to reduction in duty-free imports of U.S. tourists and push against foreign travel by U.S. nationals; also, Internal Revenue depreciation policies affect aircraft purchases, and thus available capacity
		CAB establishes — in cooperation with the military and air carriers — special tariffs for military carriage	DOD contracts with aircraft operators for passenger and cargo transport in United States and abroad; some supplemental carriers depend entirely on this business
ids in enforcement of deral statutes, as eded and to prevent terference with interate commerce and stal service		Carrier conferences on rates and tariffs conducted in accordance with procedures approved by Department of Justice. Usual that they only meet when government representatives are present. If any tariff or agreement is considered improper, Department of Justice reserves right to act.	

Commercial Air Transportation

Governmental Level and Organization	Routes and Points Served	Agreements and Cooperative Working Arrangements	Interlocking Relationships, Mergers, and Acquisitions
Post Office Department	In addition to its concern with scheduled air carrier service (extensions of which it supports in CAB hearings, where appropriate), Post Office seeks increased freedom to designate star routes for air taxi — air mail service to reach points not served by scheduled air carriers or being abandoned by surface transit; especially seeks overnight air mail service.		
Department of the Interior	Seeks, through participation in appropriate CAB proceedings, adequate service to national parks, etc.; also arranges service to Pacific trust territories	In addition to contracting for service to trust territories, contracts for forest protection, seeding, fire-fighting (for national parks and similar areas), and for airlift (for mineral and topographical surveys)	
Department of Agriculture	Seeks through participation in appropriate CAB proceedings to secure adequate service to national forests; responsible for plant and animal quarantine functions at airports of entry to protect United States from import of plant or animal disease; also assures humane treatment of animals moving in interstate commerce by air	Contracts for aerial spraying, seeding, and fire-fighting for national forests	
Department of Commerce	Through U.S. travel service stimulates foreign travel to the United States; conversely, its analyses of adverse U.S. balance of payments have led to appeals to U.S. citizens to curtail foreign travel and to reduction in duty-free allowance to U.S. travelers		

Commercial Air Transportation

Labor Conditions and Relations	Use of Airports and Airways	Tariffs and Tariff Agreements	Schedules, Capacity, and Service Adequacy
	Concerns itself with airports designated to serve particular points and has power to force into hearing any change in designation it finds would adversely affect air mail service	Participates in air mail rate proceedings (fixed by CAB but paid by post office) to seek lower rates; has often second-guessed CAB on mail routes and sought reversal through court action	Seeks, through formal action and informal pressure, increases in, and schedules timed more conveniently to, mail service needs; favors plan to move all mail by air that could be so expedited
	Controls use of airports in national parks, monuments, and recreation areas		
	Controls use of airports in national forests		

Commercial Air Transportation

Governmental Level and Organization	Routes and Points Served	Agreements and Cooperative Working Arrangements	Interlocking Relationships, Mergers, and Acquisitions
Department of Labor			
Department of Health, Education, and Welfare	Quarantine inspection functions at airports of entry to prevent import of communicable diseases; overtime at carrier expense		
Department of Housing and Urban Development			
Department of Transportation	FAA participates in CAB route proceedings to advise on condition of airports at points considered for service; has pushed concentration of service through regional airports. DOT has declared its intention of participating in major CAB rate and route proceedings in policy issues		
INTERSTATE REGIONAL LEVEL			
STATE LEVEL	Some states intervene directly in CAB route proceedings. Others assist local governments in seeking retention, or enlargement, of service rights. Some states authorize intrastate operators, such as PSA and Air California. Alaska recently denied CAB jurisdiction over intrastate operations.		
REGIONAL LEVEL	Regional agencies participate in CAB proceedings to protect or augment routes; have recently sought authority to secure service through multiple airports (satellites serving the same area)	Will object, through legal action, if considered to be adverse	Will object if consider to be adverse

Commercial Air Transportation

Labor Conditions and Relations	Use of Airports and Airways	Tariffs and Tariff Agreements	Schedules, Capacity, and Service Adequacy
Establishes limitations on hours of work and minimum wages; facilitates employment of minorities and women; operates U.S. employment service; promotes effective management-labor relations		Analyzes effect of air tariffs and increased use of air transportation on wholesale prices and the cost of living	
	Aids in airport and airport access planning and development		
	Certifies as safe or unsafe for use, by specific aircraft types and routes used, airports designated for service to particular points by CAB or air carriers		
Most states have labor laws that parallel or supplement federal statutes applicable to air carriers	Directly or through local nuisance statutes, states sometimes limit air carrier operations over particular areas or at particular times	States have asserted jurisdiction over tariffs for intrastate operations	
	May seek to specialize particular airports for particular service to conserve airspace and airport capacity (this among air carrier destinations as well as between commercial and pleasure flying)	Will intervene where regional interests are believed to be affected	Seek to increase service and capacity offered; will initiate CAB adequacy-of-service investigation or informal action where case is believed to be strong

Commercial Air Transportation

Governmental Level and Organization	Routes and Points Served	Agreements and Cooperative Working Arrangements	Interlocking Relationships, Mergers, and Acquisitions
LOCAL LEVEL	Local agencies participate in CAB or state route authorization proceedings to retain or augment certified air service	Will object through legal action if considered to be adverse	Will object if considered to be adverse
INTERNATIONAL LEVEL Foreign governments and international organizations, such as the United Nations or ICAO	Policies based in bilateral negotiations and treaties that provide basis for exchanges of air rights; growing protectionist attitude toward national carriers precludes general international agreement on air rights	Accomplished by direct carrier-to-carrier negotiations usually, but subject to national government review	Trend toward supranational carriers of SAS type

SOURCE: Stanford Research Institute

SOCIOECONOMIC ASPECTS OF TRENDS IN GOVERNMENTAL POLICIES RESPECTING THE AIR TRANSPORTATION SYSTEM

Satisfactory air transportation, whether commercial or noncommercial, domestic or international, depends on adequate performance of, and interaction among, numerous component subsystems. Some of these are: airport systems, airport access systems, airspace utilization systems, air safety systems, airmen and mechanics, aircraft systems, and noncommercial and commercial air transportation.

Governmental action or failure to act respecting one subsystem affects others, usually with multiplicative effects. We will discuss here the socioeconomic aspects of specific trends in governmental regulation and promotional policies as they relate to each major subsystem of the air transportation system, noting overlaps and interactions where appropriate.

Airport Systems

1. *Planning regional airports and channeling federal funds for airport system planning through regional planning groups.*

Integration of airport planning into regional planning may be a mixed blessing. While it will lead to recognition of air transport and airport access problems as part of the total planning responsibility of

Commercial Air Transportation

Labor Conditions and Relations	Use of Airports and Airways	Tariffs and Tariff Agreements	Schedules, Capacity, and Service Adequacy
May have local labor ordinances applicable to air transportation	May restrict socially unacceptable aircraft or operations	Will intervene when regional interests are believed to be affected	Seek to increase service and capacity offered; will initiate CAB adequacy-of-service investigation or informal action where case is believed to be strong
National regulations apply; some limited international conventions based largely on safety concepts	National determinations are controlling	Normally a matter for negotiations among air carriers but some countries have injected the fare issue into bilateral negotiation	Some countries seek agreement or impose schedule limitations in some markets (including outright ban), others through control of freedom rights, pooling, and other devices to control level of service offered in particular markets

urban areas, aviation interests will have to compete with other metropolitan and regional interests for funds. Economically viable airports may be expected to depend on their own resources more than they have in the past, or even to contribute to development of other airports in the same regional system. Airport planners will be compelled to consider the impact of their operations on the community to an even greater extent than formerly.

2. *Dispersal of commercial air transportation services by setting up satellite airports throughout major metropolitan areas.*

3. *Relegation of pleasure flying and less essential general aviation to more remote airports or those with low commercial activity.*

4. *Formation of regional governmental authorities such as airport districts.*

Trends 2 and 3 should result in increased protection of airport systems by focussing regional attention on increased need for airport access. As airport and air transport operations become integrated into the total community they will have greater acceptance and more solid community support. The Civil Aeronautics Board is giving impetus to the trend toward dispersal by adding points in major areas through "hyphenated" authorizations, such as San Francisco-Oakland-San Jose. Airport districts (trend 4) will be able to bargain more effectively with air carriers and may even impose charges on general aviation. They can also help develop compatible land uses.

5. *Airport control of approach and departure space as a condition for governmental assistance in airport landing aids and lighting.*

Requirements for control over approach and departure paths may increase airport land ownership or cause pressure for intermunicipal cooperation leading to regional zoning and other protective policies. Certainly there will be need for closer integration of airspace and airport planning.

6. *Clearly defined terminal airspace and access corridors in and out of all major metropolitan areas, and positive control of all aircraft in such designated zones and corridors.*

One effect of controlled airspace may be to limit the use of smaller airports unless the aircraft using them are transponder-equipped and both airports and aircraft are otherwise properly instrumented to receive and respond to centralized control. This limitation will bring added pressure to develop regional airport systems that include general aviation airports as well as commercial ones.

7. *Reduction in federal aid to airports, partly offset by state financial aid for airport developments.*

8. *State planning and technical assistance to develop regional airport organizations.*

9. *Effort by federal government to coordinate federal and state programs.*

These obverse trends in federal and state participation in airport financing will give added impetus to the creation of special airport districts. These state-created districts would provide a broader tax base than do municipal airports. As the tax base more closely conforms to the area served, there will be broader local participation in airport and aviation development and planning.

Airport Access Systems

1. *Recognition that adequacy of airport access systems is a major constraint on an effective air transportation system.*

2. *Recognition that airport access is a necessary responsibility of those charged with developing mass rapid-transit systems to serve urban complexes.*

Although, as a percentage of total volume, air transportation rapid-transit requirements are quite small, aviation officials may be able to demonstrate how the provision of adequate airport access benefits a community in terms of its overall economic and social needs. The need for socioeconomic justification of aviation in this context is somewhat new to airport authorities and air carriers, but they must realize its value if air transportation is to retain an important place in the total transport system and not have its usefulness destroyed by increasing ground access time.

A professional approach to the airport access problem as a part of the total urban problem of moving people and goods may eliminate some of the proposed fads and gimmicks. Since the Department of Housing and Urban Development is a major source of funds for mass rapid-transit planning and demonstration projects, improved airport access systems will also develop within the framework of regional planning systems. The emerging role of the Department of Transportation, with its jurisdiction over interurban rail and highway systems as well as over the Federal Aviation Agency, is also an element to be reckoned with in this development. And the division of responsibility over mass rapid transit between HUD and DOT has yet to be resolved.

In many major urban complexes the satellite airport system probably will help solve the airport access problem and, in turn, will get help from surface transport planning groups. In efforts to reduce parking and terminal congestion at airports, the problem of handling the loads of the big airports may also be broken down into multiple centers. This concept can be integrated with the concept of a regional-satellite airport system.

If the airport is to perform effectively its primary function of transfer between ground and air, preflight and postflight operations such as ticketing and processing of cargo will also need to be done elsewhere. Such functions may be relegated to check-in points at urban nodes that may also act as mass rapid transit hubs and V/STOL (Vertical or Short Takeoff and Landing) ports.

Airspace Utilization Systems: International

Because trends in international government airspace utilization and control policy are different from those within the United States, each category must be considered separately.

1. *Development of common standards and a common system for airspace control and air navigation aids.*

2. *Adequate facilities and equipment for transocean as well as transnational operations.*

3. *Major assistance in control and use of over-ocean airspace.*

The socioeconomic benefits to be had from these trends are clear; they will result in safer, more efficient air transport operations internationally. However, the problem remains of who owns and who pays for facilities used in international air travel. A dual system of user charges probably will result. Charges for terminal air traffic control and air navigation services will normally be part of airport usage charges, whereas charges for in-transit usage will be a separate user charge. The failure of the Canadian effort to effectively implement a system of transit charges may lead ultimately to intergovernmental financial support for in-transit facilities. Costs can be allocated on a basis similar to that governing the present ocean-station program, leaving to each country its own method for securing reimbursement for use by its national aircraft, air carriers, and private operators. It is probable that, if such a system were adopted, the United States would impose general user charges on all civil users for an allocated civil share of these costs, scaled in some way to the level of use and the benefits received.

The development of satellite communications systems will contribute to the control of over-ocean airspace. Possibly an international organization empowered to control air transportation and airspace usage over international waters will result (like Eurocontrol).

Airspace Utilization Systems: Domestic

1. *Requirements for additional extensive and expensive instrumentation and automation of aircraft and ground systems.*

The major effects of these requirements will be increased air safety and more economical and efficient use of aircraft and landing areas. The efficiency and reliability of the air transport system will be improved, particularly under bad weather conditions. However, extensive instrumentation will be required on private planes that must operate in controlled airspace, as it is now on air carriers and other commercial transports. Such instrumentation will add to the costs of air transport and other air operations and to the training and capability requirements of pilots and crews. The costs of such systems will be recovered in part through user charges.

If the systems are efficient and are operable within a reasonable time after the investment of air carriers and private flyers, the economic benefits may equal or exceed the costs. The social benefits in terms of lives saved will be substantial and will take on particular importance with the increase in aircraft capacity. There is also a growing need to assert positive control over private aircraft in commercial air transport lanes, and to separate aircraft and operators having different performance capability and characteristics.

Air Safety Systems: International

1. *Upgrading air safety systems and regulations of most countries over the next decade.*

2. *Added pressure for upgrading the international convention on passenger liability.*

3. *More financial and technical assistance for improvement of international and foreign air safety.*

In future bilateral negotiations, particularly with small, new nations or those seeking multiple U.S. service designations, the United States may insist on adherence to minimum safety standards and provision of minimum standards of internal air traffic and air navigation aids as a condition of access to the lucrative North Atlantic traffic. Additionally, the United States may prohibit the operation of American carriers in countries, airports, or airlanes that are considered unsafe.

Air Safety Systems: Domestic

1. *Adapt techniques and facilities used in developing air transportation safety to upgrade surface transportation safety.*

2. *Conversely, to pool information from air and ground safety sources to develop regulations and procedures for safer air transport.*

These trends will benefit air transportation by increasing the economy and efficiency of its operations. By decreasing the fear of air travel, they will broaden the market. How rapidly these benefits are accrued will depend on the technical and financial efforts put behind the work of the National Transportation Safety Board and cooperating federal, state, and local agencies.

Airmen and Mechanics

1. *Stricter performance requirements and licensing standards for airmen, mechanics, and persons with related skills.*

As a result of technical requirements of new aircraft and instrumentation, and of air traffic control and air navigation, it becomes more and more difficult to train personnel adequately. However, we have increasing knowledge of the causes of accidents and techniques to prevent them.

2. *Pilots, mechanics, and other personnel to be rated or licensed according to the complexity of the job.*

3. *A corresponding requirement for the training of government personnel, such as controllers, and for upgrading training facilities, both air carrier-operated and private.*

These trends will lead to increased professionalization of the air transport system working force, both governmental and private, which will in turn increase salary levels and attract persons to these activities. On the economic side, increased capability and safety should partly or wholly offset the increased cost. From the point of view of social benefits, increased safety and efficiency of air transportation technical personnel and physical systems will enhance the value of air transportation to the community at large. Government, management, and unions will be challenged to work out these new technical standards on a constructive basis without substantial labor disputes or interruption of performance. Also, government, industry, and labor alike will be called upon to develop training programs and other means to ensure the provision of the large numbers of mechanics, airmen, and others required to serve future traffic.

Aircraft Systems

1. *Federal government to assume a major role in the design and development of new types of aircraft.*

The most immediate effect of this trend will reflect the European experience, namely a substantial reduction in the number of manufacturers and the concentration of production in a limited number of companies. This impact has already been felt to some degree as a result of the increasing costs of airframe design and development. The federal government may attempt to balance this monopolistic trend by deliberately spreading contracts and subcontracts among companies to artificially maintain competition.

The federal government has already participated in the development of the supersonic air transport. However necessary and desirable this may have been, it has engendered a trend toward quasi-socialization of the air transport industry. Control over the objectives and direction of production is increasingly vested in a government bureaucracy, rather than resulting from economic forces — the competitive relationship between aircraft manufacturers and between air carriers. It is too early to tell how widespread the effects will be, but the air transport industry and the government must both recognize it as a trend which if continued will alter the balance of competitive forces within the air transport industry.

2. *Requirements for social acceptability of new aircraft in respect to noise, pollution, and other hazards.*

3. *Requirements for compatibility with existing airport and air traffic control and air navigation systems.*

This may be implemented by requiring a prototype and by licensing production of new aircraft.

4. *Extension of standards to airports and air corridors.*

These trends could materially affect the size of markets for particular aircraft by limiting their usefulness. Design, testing, and manufacturing procedures and costs will be affected. This, in turn, will lead airframe manufacturers to design aircraft that are socially acceptable and compatible with air traffic control and airport systems. This may possibly open up airport and airways system design to airframe companies, which would then be likely to support regional planning and more general public financing of airports and airways.

Extension of standards to airports and air corridors means that some aircraft, because of noise, air pollution, or incompatibility with control systems, may be restricted to a limited number of airports and air corridors.

Noncommercial Air Transportation

1. *Noncommercial transport performance standards and the right to use airports and airways to be subject to international and domestic federal, state, and local action.*

Such action will affect airport systems, air space control, air safety, aircraft, and requirements for airmen and similar technical personnel.

2. *The use of certain airspace or airports to be limited to aircraft and pilots with specified operating capabilities.*

Airspace and airport separation of aircraft and pilots having different performance and operating capabilities will further limit individual scope and may require of a pilot substantial time and money for additional qualification. Unjust discrimination against private flyers will tend to disappear as more precise knowledge is obtained of the causes and prevention of air accidents. In an era of increasing congestion and scarcity of usable airspace and airports, increased restrictions upon the few will generally mean increased advantages to the many. Those whose benefits from the use of private air transportation will justify the expense of meeting these requirements will find safer and more economical use of airspace and more sophisticated airport and air navigation systems.

Commercial Air Transportation: International

1. *Air safety standards in the international field to be upgraded.*

2. *Increase in present number of pooling arrangements, or numerous supranational carriers along the lines of SAS.*

   The trend is for foreign governments to turn to international carriers backed by intergovernmental combines in seeking joint treaty rights with the United States, in order to reinforce their drive to secure multiple points for service to the United States. This may easily give rise to the treatment of service between their urban centers as internal or cabotage traffic, from which the U.S. carriers might be barred. A restrictive policy in air rights would undoubtedly extend to rate and capacity restrictions, which would circumscribe the present healthy growth of international air transportation.

Commercial Air Transportation: Domestic

   As a result of regulatory policies, the U.S. air transport industry has become a complex of various types of carriers — domestic and international trunk carriers, local service, and third level carriers such as air taxis, all-cargo craft, supplemental carriers, and helicopters. Whether or not this structure can, or even should, survive the combined impact of technological change, massive traffic growth, and trends in governmental policies is doubtful. The trends are listed here.

1. *Elimination of subsidy for the local service carriers.*

2. *Mergers of local service carriers affected by new aircraft such as the 737 and the DC-9.*

3. *Authorizations substantially changing the concept of local service.*
   Here we should mention cross-authorizations among local service

carriers, extending them into each other's territory, diluting the regional service concept that led to their original creation.

4. *More competitive authorizations to local service carriers to duplicate trunk lines — usually on a nonsubsidized basis — in major traffic markets.*

5. *Trunk authorizations for multiple points of service to metropolitan areas.*

This increases the presence of trunk carriers in airports previously served exclusively by local service carriers.

6. *Blurring of the distinction between domestic and international carriers, and overlapping authorities of domestic and international all-cargo carriers.*

Governmental trends in U.S. regulatory and development policies affecting commercial air transportation will affect the present structure of the industry, including the types and scope of different classes of carriers, the corporate structure, and the competitive balance.

It seems inevitable, in the face of governmental trends and economic and technological pressures, that the present division of the air transport industry into classes will disappear and give way to fewer, larger, though perhaps more generally competitive organizations. For example, as the helicopter carriers were moved off subsidy, they became, in effect, subsidiaries of trunk lines — now seeking to create their own joint terminal carrier in the Washington area. What effect this change in industry structure will have on individual carriers or classes of carriers, on the economic health of the industry, and on the adequacy of air service is not clear at this time.

The executive branch, through the newly formed Department of Transportation, now has a vehicle to determine and implement policy through route proceedings, rate cases, and executive action. The policies it follows and succeeds in implementing will be a major determinant in shaping the future structure of air transportation and its corporate components. How the industry acts and what Congress proposes will also help to determine the socioeconomic character of the air transport industry a decade from now. We will need all our collective wisdom to produce a healthy solution that will apply capabilities of advanced technology to the enormously expanded future requirements for air passenger and cargo movements. Furthermore, the financial and operating conditions must be at least tolerable, if not fully acceptable, to our urban society at large, and to nonaviation users of land adjacent to the airports.

AIR TRANSPORTATION FISCAL POLICY

The purpose of this section is to examine the need for a federal fiscal policy affecting air transportation, and to propose a systematic approach to determining what that policy should be. Several points should be emphasized initially:

1. The interface between the government and the transportation industry is so fragmented that total systems direction is difficult to implement.
2. Current government techniques can be improved through fiscal coordination.
3. The total transportation system, including the public and industry, can benefit from a well directed federal fiscal policy.
4. The evolution of the transportation system involves both growth and change. The elements of change will contribute most to betterment, and it is here, through its influence on system changes that the federal government has its greatest opportunity to contribute.
5. One of the goals for fiscal policy should be the development of a system that will remain flexible and in balance under extraordinary and unforeseen circumstances, as well as during periods of normal growth and change.
6. In establishing federal fiscal transportation policy, U.S. and foreign international economic policy pertaining to transportation should be taken into consideration.

FISCAL POLICY DETERMINATION

Ideally, financial management encompasses planning, organization, and control functions at the highest management level in the system. The means by which finances are managed are probably the most powerful determinant in the evolution of the air transportation system, and a significant factor in this process is the role of the government.

A systems approach would require the following steps:

• Those segments of private industry and government which are best able to provide the various elements of a total system should be identified.
• Federal policy objectives should be defined, both qualitatively and quantitatively, concerning the requirements of the public in the operation of a total transportation system.
• Procedures and techniques through which the federal government

and industry can cooperate in achieving these objectives should be determined.

The planning, organization, and control functions of financial management are currently performed by various offices cognizant of the several transportation modes, the Congress, and the local communities. No overall fiscal policy germane to the several modes has been defined for their joint development. Also lacking is a clear fiscal policy regarding the balance between transportation system support by the community as a whole (the taxpayer) and by the user (the passenger).

Transportation is a national asset. If the system must be supported solely by the traveler, then we must be content with the system that is economically viable under this constraint. If, on the other hand, the system is to provide more general benefits (e.g., to communities unable to provide adequate economic support for the services) or if more extensive transportation is needed for the defense structure, support from the taxpaying community must continue. Congress must determine the extent to which federal resources are to be channeled into the overall transportation system for these purposes.

SUGGESTED OBJECTIVES OF THE FISCAL POLICY

The technology of air transportation has made great advances. If we are to take advantage of what it can do, we should set out a fiscal policy that gives guidance in accord with an overall perspective. It should have these aims:

1. Identify the relationships between private industry and the air transportation system.
2. Define those policy objectives which best serve the interests of the public.
3. Direct the expenditure of federal resources in a manner which facilitates progress toward goals common to industry and government.
4. Provide for air transportation growth.
5. Provide for new types of service, routing, and distribution.
6. Develop plans for eliminating safety hazards, saturation points, noise, and bottlenecks.
7. Provide better interfaces between air, ground, and sea transportation.
8. Maintain competition between air, rail, highway, and sea transportation, leaving the choice to the public.
9. Encourage development of the total transportation system (for example, by federal financing of experiments in new services).

At present these objectives are being pursued by various uncoordinated agencies throughout the entire governmental structure. A systems approach could be helpful, both now and in the future.

Air Transportation System Evolution

The establishment of a systems-oriented fiscal policy is anything but simple and requires immediate attention. A 1967 symposium on "Aviation and the Transportation System," sponsored by the Connecticut General Life Insurance Company, provided a synopsis of the shortcomings of today's system. President Johnson stated the theme, "We must know — and we must have the courage to let our people know — that our system is no longer adequate." Both growth and modification are mandatory in order to meet the challenge of providing an adequate system.

Perhaps the two most apparent shortcomings in the field of transportation are the growing inability of the current air transportation system and the automobile to expand service in proportion to the demand of our population centers. Within the major hubs these shortcomings manifest themselves in the form of congestion, delay, and noise. The crisis in transportation involves the entire population, not merely the air traveler.

AIR TRANSPORTATION SYSTEM BENEFIT FROM GOVERNMENT

It is in the area of change that the government can offer the greatest benefit to the air transportation system. The overriding guideline is the public interest, and the federal government is the only participant in the system having this motivation as well as a total system perspective. The total perspective should assure that the solutions advocated will be general in nature, rather than expeditious with regard to some small portion of the problem.

Figure 2.8 indicates the dollar flow within the domestic air transportation system. Arrows joining the boxes identify the flow of net dollars or benefits among the participants of the system. The federal government has a dollar arrow to nearly all of the participants. If regulatory activities were included, additional arrows would be directed from the federal government to every other box. Before a systematic fiscal approach can be implemented, it will be necessary to understand these relationships thoroughly. Unfortunately, quantitative data are not generally available at present.

A relative balance among the participants represented by the boxes

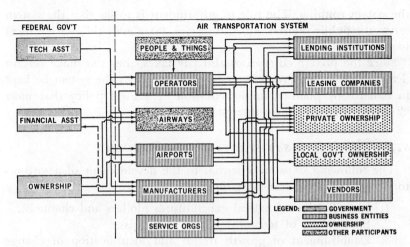

Figure 2.8.   Net dollar flow in domestic air transportation.

must be maintained to avoid such undesirable situations as the bottle-necks at some airports, limitations in capability of manufacturers to produce new equipment, problems of dollar sources to finance the industry, and difficulties in supplying such items as parts and fuel.

If the system is to function, federal fiscal policy must have the flexi-bility to maintain this balance even during a war or recession.

Each participant in the system carries some responsibility for other participants. These relationships are shown graphically in Figure 2.9. The ultimate beneficiaries, the "people and things" using the air trans-portation system, are also the prime source of the revenue that keeps

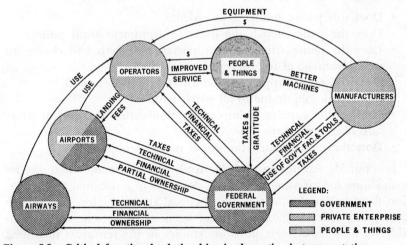

Figure 2.9.   Critical functional relationships in domestic air transportation.

the system running. The role of government is to see that the system serves the public interest. For this service, taxes are paid and the fiscal loop is closed.

Since the private enterprises also pay taxes, they too make certain demands on the government. It is mandatory that the system be kept in balance by planned implementation of a fiscal policy that most effectively serves all these interests.

STEPS TOWARD A SATISFACTORY FISCAL POLICY

The following steps are essential to the development of a satisfactory fiscal policy for transportation.

1. Identification of federal expenditures (dollars and channels).
2. Exploration of technical system alternatives.
3. Establishment of growth trends and identification of change characteristics desired.
4. Establishment of effectiveness criteria.
5. Establishment of cost criteria (budgets).
6. Evaluation of cost/effectiveness.
7. Selection of solution possibilities within budget and effectiveness bounds.
8. Definition of national transportation development policy, dollars and channels, and implementation responsibility.
9. Monitoring of public acceptance of innovations.
10. Development of promising solutions.

In the development of fiscal policy, it may be helpful to ask the following questions, to which "yes" answers are desired:

- Does this policy follow a precedent?
- Does the policy match the overall government fiscal policy?
- Does the policy stimulate transportation growth and change to take advantage of technological capability?
- Does the policy apply to all forms of transportation?
- Is the policy equitable to all participants?
- Is the policy capable of implementation within the present structure of government?
- Does the policy match the stated national objectives?

It is outside the province of this study to recommend where the responsibility for carrying out the development of a national transportation fiscal policy should rest. As discussed in connection with Table 2.25, many federal, state, and local agencies at present are responsible for and are actively pursuing studies in the ten areas identified above. In view of the complexity of the problem and the large numbers of agencies already involved, it would be difficult to propose a neat organizational arrangement which would insure the development of a fiscal policy adequate to meet the national demands of an evolving transportation system. Instead, it must suffice merely to point out that greater attention must be given to examination of the problem on a basis which encompasses all transport modes and takes adequate account of the whole spectrum of interfaces between transportation and other social needs and desires. It is hoped that some appropriate group will pick up this challenge and begin to develop the needed unifying policy.

INTERMODAL COMPETITIVE TRANSPORTATION: HIGH-SPEED COMMON CARRIERS

The most significant development in the field of surface transportation for passengers during the forthcoming two decades seems likely to be the inauguration of high-speed intercity common carriers. Much of this activity will have its greatest impact in the period beyond 1980. However, the initial phases of the development of these systems which will occur between 1968 and 1980 may well reduce the rate of traffic and operational growth of domestic United States air carriers, particularly those with short-haul routes operating in highly congested areas. In turn, they may also reduce the rate of growth in airport and airway traffic during this period.

For these reasons it is important to understand clearly the purposes and expected accomplishments of these programs.

BACKGROUND AND OBJECTIVES

The most complex U.S. transportation problems are typified by the Northeast megalopolis, generally referred to as the Northeast Corridor, encompassing an area extending from Portland, Maine, to Richmond, Virginia. This region, the most heavily urbanized large-scale complex of its type in the world, contains 40 million inhabitants, or approximately 20 percent of our national population, living on only 1.4 percent of the country's land area.

Predicated upon research initiated by President Kennedy, President Johnson, in his 1965 State of the Union Message, called for $20 million to improve transportation systems in this corridor. In final form, a bill was passed calling for $90 million over a three-year period, $18.5 million of which was appropriated for fiscal year 1966.

This improvement is the responsibility of the Department of Transportation. The specific direction of the effort is delegated within that

Department to the Office of High Speed Ground Transportation (OHSGT). This program has three objectives:

1. To effect major improvements in the level of service of conventional rail systems in the Northeast Corridor.
2. To achieve a fundamental advance in the technology of high-speed ground transportation applicable to a number of United States regions.
3. To lay the foundation for the development of "totally new techniques and systems of ground transportation" capable of speeds in the 200 to 500 mph range.

RAIL DEMONSTRATION PROGRAMS

In an effort to fulfill the first of the three objectives, $18 million will be spent on what is referred to as the "Rail Demonstration Programs." This project will attempt to measure public response to improved rail transportation systems. One part of the project will be the expenditure of $6 million on the test track and vehicles to be used in the development of more advanced railroad technology. The remaining $12 million principally will be devoted to three demonstration programs: New York–Washington, Boston–New York, and Washington-Jacksonville. If successful, these will have a significant effect on the traffic and operations of air carriers serving the East Coast of the United States. They may also have a significant effect upon airport and air traffic control planning for all airports in the Northeast Corridor (defined for this purpose to include passenger traffic to and from Portland, Boston, Providence, Hartford, New Haven, New York, Philadelphia, Trenton, Baltimore, Washington, and Richmond). For example, in 1965 a relatively large proportion of total domestic air traffic to and from Boston, New York, and Washington originated or terminated within the Northeast Corridor, as shown in Table 2.26.

TABLE 2.26. AIR TRAFFIC IN THE NORTHEAST CORRIDOR

City	Percent of total domestic air traffic in and out of this city which originated or terminated its journey within the northeast corridor
Boston	56
New York	25
Washington	40

The New York–Washington Demonstration Program

During fiscal year 1966 the Department of Transportation entered into an agreement with the Pennsylvania Railroad under which the railroad would offer substantially improved service between New York City and Washington to start in 1968 and to run for a period not to exceed two years. The service to be provided is specified in a detailed operating contract covering four separate service phases over the two-year test period.

A fleet of 50 new electrically propelled, mutiple-unit passenger cars will be acquired by the Pennsylvania Railroad for the demonstration service. The railroad will upgrade its roadbed, structures, and catenary to permit speeds of 100–110 mph on most of the route and will also improve stations, particularly by the construction of high-level platforms.

Frequency of service between New York and Washington (226 miles) and between New York and Philadelphia (90 miles) will be increased about 45 percent. The demonstration trains will run between Washington and New York in less than three hours, with at least four intermediate stops. This will be at least 35 minutes better than the fastest existing schedule and 50 minutes better than the average train on the route.

A different combination of service elements will be offered in each of the phases. The contract calls for several experiments, such as varying types of meal service, luggage handling, use of coach attendants, fixed or reversible seating, determination of intermediate station stops, and provision of suburban stations with ample parking. Other experiments such as fare levels, on-board sound and/or visual entertainment, improved methods of ticketing passengers and processing seat reservations will also be utilized. Additionally, the contract provides for the training of public-contact personnel for improved performance.

Negotiations are also being conducted with the American Telephone and Telegraph Company to provide commercial telephone service for use by passengers on demonstration trains. For the first time, passengers on moving trains will be able to receive, as well as initiate, calls over the standard commercial network.

The Government's contribution to this demonstration will be $9.6 million, which may be reduced by arrangements to share equally with the Pennsylvania Railroad in increases in revenues produced by the improved service. The complete expenditures of the railroad on this project cannot be accurately stated at this time, though the railroad has stated that it has committed at least $45 million to this program. The contract for the demonstration establishes the lower limit of the railroad's commitment in terms of minimum service, equipment and roadway standards which it must provide, without specifying costs.

With the frequency of trains, improved passenger comfort, and substantially increased merchandising, this program has the potential to significantly affect the New York–Washington air travel market in the near future. If successful in its initial stages, the true effect of the program upon air transportation may not be felt until additional train capacity is provided through follow-on orders for additional railroad cars.

The Boston–New York Demonstration Program

Demonstrations planned for the Boston–New York "Shore Line" of the New Haven Railroad will provide a test of public reaction to improved service provided by two three-car gas turbine trainsets to be leased from United Aircraft Corporate Systems Center for a two-year period, starting in late 1967 or early 1968. This equipment will operate in regular passenger service between Boston and New York City with four intermediate stops at elapsed times no greater than three hours and fifteen minutes.

The trainsets embody a number of significant innovations — including direct propulsion by lightweight free gas turbine engines developed originally for aircraft, extreme light weight of body and undercarriage, and a new form of suspension described as "pendulous." The suspension, combined with a lowered center of gravity and guided axles, is expected, according to the manufacturer, to enable the equipment to round curves at speeds up to 30 percent faster than is possible with conventional equipment.

Early plans for the demonstration north of New York contemplated operation between Providence and Boston, since this was the only segment of the New Haven Railroad line capable of high-speed operations. In April 1966, however, the Connecticut Transportation Authority offered to make available the sum of $500,000 if the Department of Commerce would operate a passenger demonstration from Boston through to New York. Inasmuch as this promised to offer a more meaningful demonstration, the Department agreed to operate this service for one year, contingent on the ability of the United Aircraft trainsets to operate between Boston and New York at an elapsed time no greater than three hours and fifteen minutes, with at least four intermediate stops (contrasted with the previous schedule of four hours and fifteen minutes). It was understood also that the Department would expend up to $500,000 in Connecticut to make road and structure improvements necessary for the faster runs. The federal government will initiate schedules and pay for the cost of necessary maintenance work on road and structures between Providence and Boston.

Since the New Haven Railroad, prior to the New York Central and

Pennsylvania merger, was unable to participate financially in the demonstration, the Department of Commerce tentatively agreed to compensate it for appropriate incremental expenses of operating the experimental trainsets on schedules the Department will prescribe. Under these conditions, the government would be entitled to additional revenues attributable to demonstration runs.

The Department will negotiate an operating contract with the railroad specifying the schedule standards of on-time performance, cleanliness, inspections, and other elements required for a valid test of public reaction, and will carry out experiments similar to those on the Washington–New York demonstration.

Initially, this program may not significantly affect the Boston–New York air travel market, since the experiment will be much smaller than New York–Washington. However, if successful, this program could well lay the foundation for a substantial expansion of this service during 1969 or 1970.

The Washington-Jacksonville "Auto-Ferry"

The Department of Transportation has proposed the construction of a car-carrying passenger train. However, as a result of recent congressional hearings on the Department of Transportation budget, this program may be either postponed or abandoned. This train, which would be operated by the Seaboard Coast Line Railroad, would be utilized between Washington and Jacksonville, Florida. Though fares for this service have not been fully determined, general agreement has been reached that a prospective passenger would pay approximately $100 for himself and his automobile for a one-way journey. This is approximately $75 more than the one-way rail coach fare. However, the driver would be able to bring along a "reasonable number of passengers" free of charge.

Each railroad car would be bilevel for quick loading and would contain broad windows to afford good sightseeing. Each train would carry 85 automobiles on 10 railroad cars. At either end of the train there would be two service cars, each of which would contain a dining room, television, movie theatre, and nursery. This program, if successful, could significantly affect air travel between the East Coast and Florida. Its true impact upon the air travel market would not be limited to those travelers who originate their journey in Washington and terminate it in Jacksonville. Rather, this program has the potential to affect the entire East Coast–Florida air travel market, since passengers originating their journeys in cities north of Washington or terminating their journeys south of Jacksonville may choose to travel by "auto-ferry" on what has historically been considered to be the "boring" portion of a typical East Coast–Florida trip.

Assuming one round trip per day between Washington and Jacksonville, the initial phases of the program may not have a significant effect upon air travel, since its capacity would be limited to approximately 5 percent of the present air travel market. However, if successful, the purchase of additional trains with larger capacity might indeed have a very significant effect upon air travel.

ESTIMATED SCHEDULE FOR DEVELOPMENT OF A HIGH-SPEED GROUND SYSTEM

The Office of High Speed Ground Transportation does not have a timetable for construction of a high-speed ground transportation system. However, they have — reasoning by analogy with major aerospace projects — volunteered that perhaps 15 years might be required to realize an operating system of this type, which includes research, development, design, and construction.

Such a period of time might be broken into a timetable, as in Table 2.27.

TABLE 2.27.   TIMETABLE FOR DEVELOPMENT OF A HIGH-SPEED GROUND SYSTEM

1966-1969	Completion of Rail Demonstration Program: establishment of test track; completion of technology development projects on various system elements such as propulsion, suspension, control, power, guidance, and life support; completion of system engineering studies on a spectrum of system types and selection of most promising alternatives for presentation to government decision-makers; development of cost effectiveness methodology for weighing alternatives.
1969-1970	Depth studies and design of complete systems for analysis, costing, and comparison; prototype testings; government decision on type of system or systems for corridor operation; completion of studies of financing and administration.
1970-1978	Design and construction
1978-1980	Operational shakedown
1980	Operation of full-scale system

GEOGRAPHIC IMPLEMENTATION OF HIGH-SPEED GROUND SYSTEMS

High-speed intercity common carrier ground transportation systems can be economically justified only in the United States corridors where distances and densities of passenger movements make ground systems attractive and partly self-supporting. The justification for such systems can be determined only by complex analyses of capital and operating costs, interest rates and depreciation periods, fares, subsidies, and other factors, including assumptions as to future demand, induced demand, and modal split of traffic.

There are only a few major U.S. corridors. However, these megalopolitan regions contain approximately 50 percent of the population. They are listed in Table 2.28.

TABLE 2.28. MAJOR UNITED STATES MEGALOPOLITAN CORRIDORS

Corridor	Area	Percent of United States population	Approx-imate mileage
Northeast	Portland, Maine to Richmond, Va.	20.0	500
Great Lakes	Star-shaped, centered on the western end of Lake Erie as follows: Bay City, Mich., to Detroit Muskegon, Mich., to Detroit Cincinnati to Detroit Philadelphia to Toledo Albany, N.Y., to Toledo	10.0	1,500
California	San Francisco to San Diego	8.0	600
Chicago	Milwaukee, Chicago, Peoria, Ill., to St. Louis	4.5	300
Texas	Dallas to Port Arthur	2.5	600
Florida	Jacksonville to Miami	1.7	400
Northwest	Seattle to Eugene, Oreg.	1.3	300
Missouri River	Kansas City, Mo., to Sioux Falls, S.D.	1.2	300
Piedmont	Atlanta to Durham, N.C.	1.2	400

The three largest of these corridors — those of the Northeast, Chicago, and California — appear to have the greatest potential for actual high-speed ground transportation systems in the next two decades. Since the Northeast Corridor provided the impetus for the program, and since the largest population would be served per mile of construction, it must be regarded as the most likely site for the first installation, perhaps by 1980. The California and Chicago Corridors can be regarded as probable sites for such systems in the decade following the construction of the system in the Northeast Corridor.

IMPACT UPON AIR TRANSPORTATION

From Table 2.28 it can be noted that the approximate length of a typical "corridor" ranges from 300 to 600 miles. It is therefore appropriate to examine the volume of air traffic presently generated in these mileage ranges in order to gain a perspective of the impact of high-speed ground transportation upon air travel.

Table 2.29 indicates several significant characteristics of present day air travel when evaluated by length of passenger journey:

- In 1965, 25 percent of all domestic passenger miles were generated in markets of 600 miles or less. However, 58 percent of domestic passengers were generated in these same markets.
- The percentage of all domestic passengers generated in markets of 600 miles or less did not change significantly from 1960 to 1965, i.e., 60 percent in 1960 and 58 percent in 1965.
- Over three-quarters of the absolute growth in domestic industry passenger miles between all U.S. cities from 1960 to 1965 was generated in markets of more than 600 miles. However, passenger miles in markets of less than 600 miles still grew by 68 percent during the same period.

TABLE 2.29. COMPARISON OF DOMESTIC AIR TRAFFIC GROWTH BY LENGTH OF PASSENGER JOURNEY 1960 VS. 1965

Length of passenger journey (miles)	1960		1965	
	Passengers (thousands)	Passenger miles (millions)	Passengers (thousands)	Passenger miles (millions)
1–99	1,013	78	1,231	97
Percent of total	2.6%	0.3%	1.9%	0.2%
100–199	5,487	874	8,561	1,369
Percent of total	14.1%	3.3%	13.1%	2.9%
200–299	6,474	1,585	10,427	2,538
Percent of total	16.7%	6.0%	15.8%	5.4%
300–399	4,655	1,608	8,036	2,785
Percent of total	11.9%	6.1%	12.3%	6.0%
400–499	3,223	1,435	5,555	2,472
Percent of total	8.3%	5.4%	8.5%	5.4%
500–599	2,209	1,228	3,868	2,149
Percent of total	5.7%	4.6%	5.9%	4.6%
600 and above	15,807	19,695	27,901	35,174
Percent of total	40.7%	74.3%	42.5%	75.5%
TOTAL	38,868	26,503	65,583	46,584
Percent increase	—	—	68.7%	75.8%

SOURCE: Civil Aeronautics Board: "Airline Traffic Surveys" (1960 and 1965).

From this table one can assume that about half of all domestic airline passengers in the 1975–1980 period will travel in markets of 600 miles or less. However, the substantial volume of passenger mile growth will occur in markets of more than 600 miles.

The impact of high-speed ground transportation upon air travel may be of an entirely different magnitude than its impact on aircraft operations.

- It may reduce the rate of overall passenger-mile air travel growth, but since as much as 90 percent of this growth in the 1975–1980 period may be in markets of 600 miles or more, this impact may not be of substantial proportions.
- Its most critical effect will probably be to reduce the rate of passenger growth on an airport-by-airport basis in the general geographic area of those corridors identified in Table 2.28.

Assuming that the Northeast, California, and Chicago Corridors are those most likely to receive initial high-speed ground transportation systems, it is pertinent to examine the impact of such systems upon air traffic in the cities of these corridors.

Tables 2.30 through 2.32 evaluate air traffic generated during 1965 within each of these corridors. In developing this information, it was necessary to assume which cities might be included as part of an intracorridor high-speed transportation system. They are indicated on each table.

The purpose of these tables is to determine the percentage of intra-corridor air traffic presently generated by each city which might be included as part of a high-speed ground transportation system. The results of this analysis at least give an *indication* of those cities (and

TABLE 2.30. NORTHEAST CORRIDOR

City assumed to be incorporated into high-speed ground transport system (1)	Total 1965 air passengers to/from all U.S. cities (2) (thousands)	Intracorridor 1965 air passenger travel	
		total (3) (thousands)	percent of column 2 (4)
Portland, Maine	124	88	71%
Boston, Mass.	4,628	2,581	56
Providence, R.I.	444	247	56
Hartford, Conn.	859	308	36
New Haven, Conn.	11	8	73
New York, N.Y.	16,316	4,004	25
Trenton, N.J.	4	1	25
Philadelphia, Pa.	3,117	619	20
Wilmington, Del.	18	5	28
Baltimore, Md.	1,351	292	22
Washington, D.C.	5,373	2,124	40
Richmond, Va.	390	144	37
TOTAL	32,635	10,421	32%

SOURCE: Civil Aeronautics Board: "Airline Traffic Survey" (1965).

TABLE 2.31. CALIFORNIA CORRIDOR*

City assumed to be incorporated into high-speed ground transport system (1)	Total 1965 air passengers to/from all U.S. cities (thousands) (2)	Intracorridor 1965 air passenger travel	
		total (thousands) (3)	percent of column 2 (4)
Sacramento	538	300	56%
San Francisco/Oakland	5,717	1,735	30
Fresno	193	121	63
Bakersfield	79	42	53
Los Angeles/Burbank	7,853	2,026	26
San Diego	1,031	296	29
TOTAL	15,411	4,520	29%

*NOTE: The above data do not include traffic of Pacific Southwest Airways and are therefore understated.
SOURCE: Civil Aeronautics Board: "Airline Traffic Survey" (1965).

TABLE 2.32. CHICAGO CORRIDOR

City assumed to be incorporated into high-speed ground transport system (1)	Total 1965 air passengers to/from all U.S. cities (thousands) (2)	Intracorridor 1965 air passenger travel	
		total (thousands) (3)	percent of column 2 (4)
Milwaukee, Wis.	881	81	9%
Chicago	9,071	423	5
Peoria, Ill.	164	62	38
Springfield, Ill.	106	46	43
St. Louis	2,179	322	15
TOTAL	12,400	934	8%

SOURCE: Civil Aeronautics Board: "Airline Traffic Survey" (1965).

airports) whose air traffic may be most significantly affected by high-speed ground transportation. A much more sophisticated analysis of future demand patterns must be completed for each city before valid conclusions can be drawn.

Within the framework of the above qualifications, certain significant information may be derived from these tables:

- The percentage of intracorridor air travel within each corridor varies widely from city to city within the corridor, i.e., 56 percent of all Boston air travel is within the Northeast Corridor, whereas only 20 percent of all Philadelphia air travel is within the corridor.
- The percentage of intracorridor air travel varies widely between the Chicago Corridor and the Northeast and California Corridors.
- The absolute volume of intracorridor air travel varies widely between the three corridors.

• Fifty percent or more of all air travel at several major cities, since it remains within the corridor, is highly vulnerable to the future competition of a high-speed ground transportation system. For example, the following are some of these cities:

City	Intracorridor air travel as percent of air travel between the city and all other domestic cities (%)
Portland, Maine	71
Fresno, Calif.	63
Boston, Mass.	56
Providence, R.I.	56
Sacramento, Calif.	56

PROBABLE COSTS OF HIGH-SPEED GROUND SYSTEMS

The technology is not sufficiently advanced to permit definitive cost estimates for high-speed common carrier ground transportation systems. A range of $3 million to $6 million per route mile appears probable. On this basis, the cost of high-speed common carrier ground transportation systems for the major corridors would fall into the range of $2 to $4 billion each.

The cost breakdown by category of expenditure is approximately as follows:

	Percent of total
Track and structures	73
Electrical and control	8
Vehicles	6
Stations and parking	5
Right-of-way acquisition	5
Utility relocation	2
Yards and shops	1

INTERMODAL COMPETITIVE TRANSPORTATION: HIGHWAYS

THE INTERSTATE HIGHWAY PROGRAM

The Interstate Highway Program, initiated in 1956, authorized the completion of 41,000 miles of new roads by 1972. Approximately half of this mileage has now been completed.

The original estimate of expenditures required for this program was $27 billion, with 90 percent of its costs financed by the federal government and 10 percent by state governments. It is now estimated that these costs will approximate $50 billion prior to completion in 1972 or 1973.

New highways which have been completed under this program undoubtedly have reduced the demand for air travel, particularly in short-haul markets. However, the greatest impact upon air travel is yet to come. In several significant areas, critical portions of major routes are yet to be completed. When these gaps are closed, bus and oil companies, as well as automobile manufacturers, will be in a position to more extensively merchandise the increased advantages of highway travel.

For example, by 1972 the highway gap will be closed on the following major air routes:

1. Northeastern cities–Florida
2. Midwest cities–Florida
3. Great Lakes cities–Florida
4. Northwest cities–Southwest

It is significant to note that the U.S. Bureau of Public Roads has recently undertaken a four-year study of the network of roads and highways. To be completed in 1968, the study will allow four more years for the formulation and initiation of a follow-on program to succeed the Interstate Highway Program when it is completed in 1972.

An initial proposal suggests an addition of 10,000 more miles to take care of "requirements stemming from the continuing upsurge in numbers of automobiles." Assuming that the recommendations of this study are limited to an additional 10,000 miles of highway, and that the cost of construction will approximate the $1.2 million per mile now estimated for the present program, the construction of this newly recommended mileage will require an additional public expenditure of approximately $12 billion.

Referring to information contained in the previous section concerning high-speed common carrier ground transportation systems, it is estimated that the construction cost of such a system for one of the major corridors will range between $2 and $4 billion dollars. Recognizing that national resources which may be made available for the improvement of transportation systems are not unlimited, it should be anticipated that a significant debate upon the cost/benefit of alternative transportation systems will take place between 1968 and 1970. For example, if the capital to be expended for improvement of national transportation systems was limited to $12 billion, which expenditure would produce the greatest public benefit — a further expansion of the Interstate Highway Program by 10,000 miles or the construction of three or four high-speed common carrier ground transportation systems?

It is significant to note that at present the air transportation industry does not have a well-thought-out constructive position on this subject. It is particularly important to short- and medium-haul air carriers that the necessary analysis be completed and that an integrated aviation industry position be developed no later than 1968.

The "ABC" Program

This program covers primary, secondary, and urban-extension roads. It represents approximately 10 percent of the purchase by state and local governments of all goods and services related to highways. Unlike the Interstate Highway Program, it is financed almost equally by federal and state governments.

Since July 1956, over 170,000 miles have been completed in this program at an approximate cost of $12.3 billion. Recommendations have been made for work through fiscal year 1973 and extension beyond that year is virtually assured.

To this date, there has been no integrated industry-wide program developed by the aviation community (commercial carriers as well as general aviation) to present its needs for improved surface transportation facilities to state and local governments.

The Appalachia Program

The Appalachia Program has allocated a minimum of $1.2 billion for road development over a six-year period. It will add 2,350 miles of highways plus an additional 1,000 miles of access roads, and may be the forerunner of new regional highway programs in other parts of the country. Such programs may have a particular impact upon short-haul air transportation, leading to the consolidation of airports presently located within approximately 100 miles of each other.

CHANGES IN AUTOMOBILE TECHNOLOGY

Safety Requirements

There is growing national concern over automobile safety, as evidenced by congressional hearings and subsequent legislation. It is difficult to define the impact of these changing requirements upon air transportation. However, it is reasonable to assume that the incorporation of additional safety devices will increase the purchase price of vehicles to some degree. In addition, greater emphasis upon research to improve automobile safety technology is to be expected. How these and other changes may affect air travel is yet to be determined.

Electric Automobiles

Motivated by increasing attention to the problems of air pollution, the principal technological change in automobile development within the coming decade will in all probability be the electric car. If successful, its coming will have a profound effect upon not only the automotive industry itself but also the oil, steel, chemical, and electrical industries.

The automotive industry tends to maximize the difficulties and time required to develop a viable electric car, while the electric industry and battery makers tend to minimize the problems. Yet nearly everybody agrees that present technology could produce a small, short-range battery car of reasonably good performance by 1975. It would fall, however, into the second-car category, which is only 25 percent of the total car market, and of that segment of the market electric automobiles might be expected to take only 5 to 10 percent. For long "over-the-road" driving, the conventional gasoline engine would retain the bulk of the market.

It does not, therefore, appear that the development of the electric car will have a seriously adverse effect upon air travel within the next decade. However, technological changes in this area should be closely monitored to determine their application toward the development of electric "over-the-road" automobiles.

INTRAURBAN TRANSPORTATION DEVELOPMENTS

The population of the United States is expected to increase from approximately 200 million in 1967 to 300 million by the year 2000. By 1970, three-fourths of this population will be concentrated in urban areas. By the 1980's there will be approximately 140 million people living in about 40 urban complexes which will spread over less than 2 percent of the land area of the United States. By the year 2000, four-fifths of the population will be concentrated in these urban areas.

In conjunction with this massive population growth and its substantial concentration in urban areas, the number of automobile registrations is expected to grow at approximately double the rate of population growth. By 1980 there will be almost one car for every two people in the nation — an increase in car registrations of approximately 50 percent over 1965.

This large number of automobiles will not be satisfactorily accommodated on the highway systems of the 1980's, particularly in urban areas. Consequently, the economic and social vitality of urban areas will greatly depend upon the development of effective mass transit systems. Such systems will not be satisfactory unless they are successful in attracting significant numbers of passengers away from the automobile.

For example, without the development of an effective mass transit system, the peak traffic volume on a highway leading into Manhattan during New York City's 1967 transit strike will be normal by 1976 — a situation which might completely choke the growth of air travel's most important city.

The transportation industry must define its needs for the development of interfacing urban mass transit systems. Industry-wide coordinated effort will be necessary to integrate the air transport systems of the future with the urban mass transit systems.

DEVELOPMENT OF MARITIME TRANSPORTATION

The principal maritime technological development prior to 1975 may be the inauguration of significant volumes of service with air-cushion vehicles.

The present state of technological art involves the use of air-cushion vehicles with the following characteristics:

- Small passenger capacity (10 to 20 passengers).
- Short-range operation (on the order of 50 miles).
- Effective operating speeds of approximately 30 mph.
- Estimated operating costs which are too high to produce a reasonable rate of return at passenger-generating fares.

Several significant advances in technology may occur within the next 10 years to raise capacity to 50–75 passengers, operating range to approximately 200 miles, and speeds to 50–75 mph. Operating costs presumably will produce an adequate return on investment at reasonable fare levels.

After 1980 it may be technologically feasible to develop and operate air-cushion vehicles with large payload capacities at speeds in excess of 100 mph with reasonable operating costs. If so, these developments could affect air travel in the following ways:

- Air-cushion vehicle service may be inaugurated between Florida and points in the Bahamas, between the Hawaiian Islands, and between New York or Boston and Nantucket/Martha's Vineyard.
- Similar services may be inaugurated between the United States and Bermuda or Puerto Rico by 1980.
- After 1980 the inauguration of air-cushion vehicle service between the United States and Europe may be feasible. The desired design

characteristics of vehicles of this type presently considered by
maritime engineers involve a vehicle with the capacity to transport 100 automobiles and passengers from New York to Southampton in 24 hours at a fare of $100 each way.

INTERMODAL COMPETITIVE CARGO
TRANSPORTATION TRENDS

Air transportation competes primarily with motor carrier and sec-
ondarily with rail for overland shipment of commodities, and with
ships for overwater shipment. In 1964 air carriers accounted for .10
percent (1.5 billion ton-miles) of the total domestic intercity freight
traffic, motor carriers for 22.5 percent (347 billion ton-miles), and rail
for 44 percent (680 billion ton-miles). The residual 33 percent (516
billion ton-miles) represents movements by inland waterways and pipelines. It is assumed that air will not in the immediate future compete
with these modes. In 1964 air accounted for .07 percent (.25 million
tons) of a total of about 370 million tons of commodities moved into
and out of U.S. seaports.

The magnitude of these disparities makes it hard to predict that
fraction of future air-freight traffic which will derive from attracting
commodities away from competitive modes of transport. This difficulty
is somewhat substantiated by Figure 2.10, which shows the variation
of exponential growth rate of domestic air-freight traffic from 1950 to
1965 compared with the growth of the gross national product (in constant dollars).

It is the purpose of this section to examine some of the socioeconomic

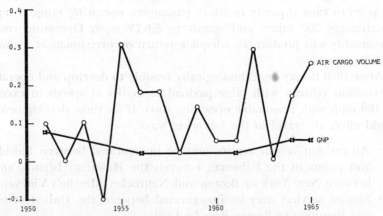

Figure 2.10. **Annual compound growth rates of air cargo volume and Gross
National Product.**
SOURCE: North American Rockwell.

factors which might most significantly contribute to gross modal shifts
in freight transportation and, where possible, to identify those critical
factors which, by virtue of their leverage, merit further and more detailed consideration.

DOMESTIC FREIGHT TRAFFIC

Figure 2.11 presents the gross correlation between total volume of
intercity freight traffic and disposable personal income from 1945
through 1964 and indicates that domestic freight volume, *in toto,* is
fairly strongly related to, and thus will change with, this determinant.
Our principal interest, however, centers on establishing a basis for
estimating how the division of this volume among the competing
transportation modes will change with time and what factors will
predominate in causing this change.

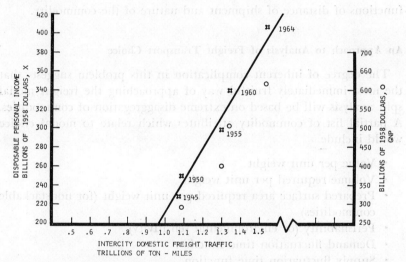

**Figure 2.11. Correlation of intercity cargo traffic with disposable personal income
and Gross National Product.**
SOURCE: North American Rockwell.

It might be pointed out here that past study of the modal split between motor carrier and rail transportation of freight in terms of
simple economic models has been disappointing and is not likely to
provide an adequate basis for accurate projection. The failure of these
attempts can be related to the following:

1. The paucity of the data base with respect to commodity flow
   and the consequent degree of geographical and categorical
   aggregation enforced on the models,

2. The failure of the postulated model structures to provide a sufficient representation of the actual economics of modal choice
(as affected by the nature of the commodity, the industry producing and distributing it, and the geographical and temporal
characteristics of the demand).

The rectification of these shortcomings is no trivial task. The simplest
expression for total cost of maintaining a particular commodity in a
marketplace will include, in addition to direct costs of shipment, terms
relating to

The cost of maintaining inventory levels
The cost of maintaining goods in transit
The cost of preparation for shipment
The cost of spoilage

All these elements are sensitive to modal choice in different degrees as
functions of distance of shipment and nature of the commodity.

An Approach to Analysis of Freight Transport Choice

The degree of inherent complication in this problem suggests that
the most immediately fruitful way of approaching the freight modal
split analysis will be based on extreme disaggregation of commodities.
A partial list of commodity attributes which relate to modal choice
would include

- Value per unit weight
- Volume required per unit weight
- Prepared surface area required per unit weight (for nonstackable
  commodities)
- Perishability (or environmental sensitivity)
- Demand fluctuation time function
- Supply fluctuation time function
- Diversity of type
- Geographical distribution (production-consumption) network

Therefore the disaggregation must be to a level where alternatively
a single commodity attribute can be identified as dominant with respect to modal choice, or in the marginal cases where more than one
significant attribute can be recognized and evaluated.

In the aggregative view, the most apparent socioeconomic phenomena which might be expected to stimulate changes in the commodity
modal split pattern are

1. The rather rapid decentralization which appears to be at work

in most metropolitan areas (or expressed differently, the rapid proliferation of peripheral urban places with between 50,000 and 250,000 population).
2. The related dispersal of primary (i.e., "exporting") industry and retail outlets.
3. The trend toward more value added per unit cost of input factors in industrial production.

The specific implications of these phenomena can be seen grossly to be

1. Dispersal of both production and consumption nodes in a dynamic growth pattern with increased average surface-traffic density and longer average intra-area trip lengths.
2. Increased sensitivity of product cost (through inventory levels required at both producer and consumer level) to transportation time. (Reaction time plus transit and handling time.)
3. Decreased sensitivity of product cost to the transportation component.

These effects will tend individually and jointly to decide against motor carrier and rail commodity transport in favor of air, increasingly as metropolitan dimensions increase and as the cost of providing adequate surface transportation increases (with the increased average value and extent of land traversed).

However, since passenger travel is also sensitive to the metropolitan decentralization process (by virtue of the decreased utility of the personal automobile), perhaps the most dramatic impact of demographic change on air freight traffic will derive from the expansion of the short-segment-length air collection-distribution system which is presently oriented primarily to passenger traffic, but which could provide a collection-distribution system for commodities. Such a system would be characterized by minimal modal interface complication, minimal multiple-handling cost, and minimal door-to-door delay. The total implications of this possibility on the overall modal split are difficult to quantify, but it may easily be seen that the effects will be far-reaching and regenerative as the working and consuming public develops increased independence of surface travel.

Summary of Sensitive Areas in Assessment

The areas which appear most significant to the assessment of how commodity traffic will be distributed between air and its competitive modes include

1. *Domestic intercity commodity flow.* Analysis should be made on a sufficiently disaggregative level to permit estimation of
    a. The traffic volume which is most economically transportable by air, insensitive to expected levels of economic and demographic change.
    b. The traffic volume which is marginally economic for air or motor carrier transport depending on the economic and demographic environment.
    c. The traffic volume which is most economically transportable by motor carrier or motor carrier/rail, insensitive to expected levels of economic and demographic change.
2. *Metropolitan growth patterns.* These should be modeled to show relations of metropolitan growth to per capita productivity, frequency distribution of discretionary income, and population composition and growth. The model should be formulated with particular regard to providing good estimates of metropolitan dimensions, land value patterns and distribution of production-consumption nodes (or density).
3. *A model of air, motor vehicle, and rail transportation* should be superposed on the metropolitan growth model to examine and evaluate modal split patterns and their implications of communal demand for transportation and community growth. Such a model would clarify the local and national economics of carrier operations.

It is not anticipated that technological innovations will have a profound effect on the character or cost of either rail or motor carrier transport except as the motor carriers, complementing air transport, may also make use of automated cargo-handling and containerization to minimize handling time and match large plane productivity.

INTERCONTINENTAL FREIGHT TRAFFIC

At present and for the predictable future, surface-displacement ships (as opposed to air-cushion ships) offer the only competition to air-cargo movements on intercontinental routes. In contrast with the domestic movement of cargo by transportation modes which are competitive with air, the movement of cargo by ship is characterized by long in-transit time, because of the longer average distances travelled, the schedule frequency, and the time to on-and-off load. These factors, together with the low rate associated with most classes of ocean shipment, make the division of commodity traffic between air and ship much more distinct and less susceptible to socioeconomic change. As a consequence, it may be expected that the total modal shift from ship

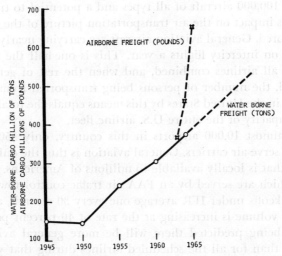

Figure 2.12. Comparative trends of waterborne and airborne cargo traffic, 1945–1965.
SOURCE: North American Rockwell.

to air will be relatively rapid and relatively simple to identify and estimate, since the gains if existent will not be marginal. Figure 2.12 shows comparative trends of waterborne and airborne traffic from 1945 through 1965.

The most significant changes in ship transportation of commodities might be expected to stem from the improvement in speed and reduction of cost which can result from improved power plants including nuclear power, the reduction in operating cost with automation of crew functions, and the reduction in cost and delay of on-and-off loading by automation of cargo handling. It is not likely, however, that these changes will sufficiently close the gap between ship and air transport to have a profound effect on the air/ship modal split.

The only foreseeable exception to this dictum might stem from the development and proliferation of high-speed (100 mph) air cushion (or captured air bubble) ocean-going craft operating at substantially lower costs per ton-mile than aircraft. However, such an event is completely speculative at this time, and there has been no convincing rationale which demonstrates the lower cost per ton-mile of this type vessel.

GENERAL AVIATION TRENDS AND POTENTIALS

It is claimed that general aviation is in its third period of explosive growth since its inception. Certainly with a current active inventory of close to 100,000 aircraft of all types and a potential to triple in size by 1985, its impact on the air transportation picture of the future cannot be ignored. General aviation aircraft are carrying nearly 40 million passengers on intercity flights a year. This is one-half the total being carried by all airlines combined, and when the rest of general flying is included, the number of persons being transported from one point to another in the United States by this means equals the total passenger-carrying capacity of the entire U.S. airline fleet.

Of the almost 10,000 airports in this country, only 550 or so are licensed to serve air carriers. General aviation is thus the only air transportation that is locally available to millions of Americans. At the 300 airports which are served by an FAA air traffic control tower, general aviation takeoffs under IFR average one every 30 seconds, around the clock. The volume is increasing at the rate of 40 percent per year. By 1970 it is being predicted there will be more general aviation IFR departures than for all the scheduled airlines during that year. Thus, the impact of general aviation on the air traffic control facilities of airports also serving scheduled airlines is now considerable and, within a relatively short period of time, will be overwhelming.

SOME SOCIOECONOMIC FACTORS INFLUENCING THE GROWTH OF GENERAL AVIATION

The current growth of general aviation is to a considerable extent due to the fact that the light aircraft is no longer merely a pleasure vehicle but has proved to be of definite economic value in both transportation and industrial applications (aerial spraying, movement of goods to inaccessible areas, property surveillance, and mapping, for example). An expression of this basic change in the role of the light aircraft has been the dramatic shift in the pattern of the types of aircraft flown by the various user groups. In the early postwar years, most aircraft in use were small, slow, fabric-covered, one- to three-seat versions. Subsequently, the demand for these aircraft declined sharply and the manufacturers turned to the production of larger, more sophisticated models. Between 1954 and 1964 only 14,000 one- to three-place aircraft were produced for both domestic and export markets, as compared to 50,000 larger-capacity aircraft. General aviation aircraft have thus become larger, faster, and far more dependable than they were.

Two opposing factors have contributed to the growth of general aviation as a means of transportation. First, airline equipment is getting larger and faster, making possible longer route lengths between stops and tending away from stops at low-service points. Opposing this

TRENDS IN THE NATIONAL ECONOMY

The population of the United States, which reached 200 million in 1967, continues to grow at a rate which could add another 100 million people by the end of the century. However, the slowing down of growth rates from 1.7 percent for 1950–1959 to 1.4 percent for 1960–1966 and to only 1.1 percent for 1965–1966 suggests that the population growth factor will require close watching if realistic forecasts are to be made.

Actually, the people who will participate in the labor force in the late seventies and early eighties are already in the present population. Hence, declining population growth rates during the period we are considering may actually have a positive rather than a negative effect on air transport demand if they mean that real income grows at a faster rate than the growth of population. The declining population growth will also produce some shortage in skilled personnel, thus requiring that salaries and income adjust to talent shortages. The need for stretching professional and executive talent should also tend to generate more frequent air trips.

The total U.S. labor force is predicted to increase from 78 million in 1966 to 86 million in 1970, 94 million in 1975 and 101 million in 1980. More women are joining the labor force than in the past. Among young married couples there is an increasing tendency for both husbands and wives to work, which should permit their family incomes to average considerably higher than in the past. Unemployment in 1966 was at the lowest rate since 1953 (less than 4 percent of the civilian labor force), and there appears to be no solid reason for anticipating less than the relatively full employment conditions that have prevailed in recent years.

With the labor force increasing at a rate which permits total productive man-hours to grow at a rate of $1\frac{1}{2}$ percent per year, and with labor productivity in the economy growing at a rate of about $2\frac{1}{2}$ percent per year, the potential output or gross national product of the country advances at a rate of about 4 percent per year. This rate is substantially greater than the average long-term growth rate of less than 3 percent from 1900 to 1963 and exceeds the postwar average growth of 3.4 percent per year from 1947 to 1963.

Real disposable income per capita, which is considered to be the best single measure of consumer welfare, rose 24 percent during the six years preceding 1966, matching the net increase during the previous 13 years. In spite of a 3 percent (rather than the usual 1 percent) increase in the Consumer Price Index from 1965 to 1966, real disposable income per capita increased by $3\frac{1}{2}$ percent.

While continuing high levels of business activity and industrial production may be expected to increase the demands for business travel and freight transport, including air cargo, it appears that real income of the average consumer is the most significant factor to watch in the projection of total air transport demand into the late seventies and beyond. From 1950 to 1966 the individual consumer gained nearly 40 percent in spending and saving power and increased his annual expenditures for durable goods 60 percent, for nondurable goods 26 percent, and for various services (including transportation) 50 percent.

The sixfold increase in consumer expenditures for recreation alone since 1940 and the 140 percent increase since 1950 are indicative of the growing availability and use of disposable income beyond the amounts needed for food, clothing and shelter. Unquestionably, the American public year by year is gaining considerably in its ability to purchase air carrier services and enjoy the products of general aviation. But purchasing power can be used for many alternative purposes and will be spent for air transportation only if the capacity of the air transport system and the quality of the services it provides are maintained at the levels which will assure consumer satisfaction.

PROJECTIONS OF AIR TRANSPORT DEMAND

Faced, as it is, by such constraints as the acceptable level of the quality of service and sheer physical limitations of system capacity, future air traffic is obviously difficult to forecast, even if it is agreed that population and purchasing power are likely to continue to increase.

It is necessary, nevertheless, to continually assess the future demands that, if not constrained, will be imposed upon the system. Just as many economists and planners are continually attempting to forecast future growth in the national economy, other specialists are closely following trends in air transport demand and making predictions of future demand levels.

Recent forecasts by airlines, aircraft manufacturers, and government agencies (both national and international) were examined in detail. While it was possible to obtain numerous forecasts and projections, no agreement exists with respect to any specific formula or equation which could be relied upon to provide accurate data on the levels of demand 10 or more years in the future. Most of the forecasters do not explain their methodology, and some are hesitant to be publicly identified with their projections.

Notwithstanding differences in methodology, and hence in the range of the forecasts for specific years, all projections point in the direction of a continuation of recent growth rates ranging from 10 to 15 percent annually for domestic airline passenger traffic and even higher for the passenger traffic of U.S. international air carriers and air cargo movement by all types of carriers.

The Federal Aviation Agency (whose forecasts for 1970, 1975, and 1980 were found to be well in the range of those recently made by a number of U.S. airlines and aircraft manufacturers) anticipates the total passenger enplanements of domestic carriers to increase from 85 million in 1965 to 258 million in 1975 and 435.5 million in 1980. During the same period, the number of passengers enplaned by U.S. international carriers is expected to grow from 10 million in 1965 to 29 million in 1975 and 47 million in 1980. With many U.S. airports already taxed to capacity during peak periods, it is obvious that the threefold increases in demand expected by 1975 and fivefold increases expected by 1980 cannot possibly be accommodated without major increases in airport capacity as well as improvements in airport access and air traffic control.

The inadequacies are especially evident in the case of the 22 communities identified as "large air transportation hubs" which in 1965 collectively accounted for 68 percent of all domestic passengers enplaned and 79 percent of all domestic cargo carried by U.S. scheduled airlines. The first ten of these hubs generated over half of all the passenger trips, and the largest three — New York (including Newark), Chicago and Los Angeles — accounted for more than one-fourth of the total.

AIRPORTS AND PATTERNS OF URBAN GROWTH

Airports cannot be considered simply as appendages to cities, nor are they passive components in the pattern of urban growth. The airport has taken over many of the functions and qualities, good and bad, of the central railroad terminal. Like the railroad terminal in earlier days, the airport today generates activities and linkages and pulls the city in its direction.

Airports, however, are not the predominant influence in the growth pattern of the city. To understand their particular influence we must look generally at the forces that direct the rate and kind of changes that are occurring. In brief, these forces are causing the metropolis to stream toward its periphery. The immediate consequence of this is that airports will nearly always be located within the urban boundary, and their users will travel to them from all parts of the metropolis.

The development of airports within the urban fabric raises three kinds of problems. The first two are particularly pressing. The third has appeared thus far only in a few cities but will be more common in the future.

1. How to Plan Compatible Use of Adjacent Land

Airports, in common with all other transportation complexes, generally are not good neighbors. The noise they generate can be decreased by technological means, but not enough to be satisfactory. Their environs, therefore, will be suitable to special uses only. Such constraints are not likely to be enforceable except by governmental agencies. For that reason alone, airports must necessarily be planned in concert with public bodies.

2. How to Plan Convenient Access

The airport is a special node in the urban transportation system, and an especially important one. The access problem will not be solved simply by providing good linkages to the central business district. That is only one of the sources and sinks of air travelers. In the aggregate, the others are larger and they are dispersed over the metropolis.

3. How to Plan a Multiairport System

Even under the best of circumstances the airport is limited in the space available to it for expansion simply because the city also is growing toward and around it. Multiple airports per metropolis are in the offing. To work as a system, they will require efficient linkages. It will be cheaper and far more reasonable to make these links part also of the urban transportation system.

The weight of these three kinds of problems strongly recommends foresight in airport planning on the order of decades, plus the cooperation of many public agencies.

EDUCATION, RECREATION, AND USE OF LEISURE TIME

While a certain amount of air travel is occasioned directly for purposes of domestic and international study, teaching, and research, the indirect impact of trends in education may be expected to be far more significant. This is indicated by the greater propensity of well-educated professional, technical, managerial, and administrative people to travel by air than persons in other occupations. It also shows up in the high ratio of persons with college degrees or with some college training among air passengers. Since education widens the horizon for the individual and increases his range of economic opportunity, current and projected trends of high school and college enrollment (far exceeding population growth rates) may be expected to exert a considerable positive impact on air travel, both domestic and international.

The exchange of persons between nations for educational purposes has been one of the most significant educational developments during the second half of the twentieth century. Air travel, by its speed and convenience as well as its increasing economy, is becoming more and more an agent of international educational exchange, and mutual advantages suggest that the partnership should be encouraged. As air transport's capacity increases with the advent of larger aircraft, the advantages of cultivating off-peak educational travel will become more evident.

Within our evolving social environment, leisure and recreation are increasingly assuming a role of vital importance. As has been indicated, the growing rate of productivity and of personal incomes has greatly stimulated expenditures in the recreation category.

It is becoming well established that additional leisure will take the form of more vacations two, three, or four days in length, and also, more than one longer vacation per year. This trend will have a substantial impact on patterns of travel, recreation facilities, and travel-associated industries. Resort and hotel facilities and other attractions will shape the amount of expenditures and the extent of participation in this kind of air travel.

The nonbusiness portion of air travel (about one-third of domestic and three-fourths of overseas passengers) will be greatly influenced by intangible factors. Favorable attitudes toward vacation travel will develop through daily leisure conditioning and education. Heretofore the air mode has not been very successful in capturing a large share of the domestic nonbusiness travel market. It is clear, nevertheless, that the potential for nonbusiness air travel exceeds the business air travel potential by a large margin.

The extent to which the air mode is capable of penetrating the nonbusiness travel potential is circumscribed by psychological restraints and sharp competition for discretionary income expenditures. Sophisticated marketing techniques can do much to overcome the psychological barrier and attract large numbers of passengers. In short, the nonbusiness air travel market has all the trappings for an exciting and growing operation: insatiable demand for more vacations, and the discretionary money and leisure time to make them possible. Realization of this potential will require energetic promotion on the part of the air carriers.

DISTRIBUTION POLICIES AND THE DEMAND
FOR AIR CARGO SERVICES

The effective demand for air cargo transportation has expanded by a factor of two during the past five years, but in 1966 only about .1 percent of the U.S. domestic freight demand was satisfied by air. Recent forecasts predict that over the next 15 years the demand for air cargo service may increase by an order of magnitude.

Current data on intercity freight shipments by manufacturing establishments reveal that only a very small fraction of the myriad commodities distributed in the U.S. domestic market is shipped by air cargo. Although there is obviously room for great expansion in air cargo demand, it is unlikely that air cargo will ever account for a large percentage of the total freight transportation demand measured in tons or ton-miles. The reason is that the commodities that account for most of the demand are of such low value per pound that the advantage of high-speed transportation in terms of total distribution cost is trivial. Nevertheless, the U.S. demand for freight transport is so great (with ton-miles per capita doubling from 1940 to 1966) that a relatively small increase in the proportion sent by air could result in a significant expansion of air cargo traffic.

The "total distribution cost" concept, although important, should not be overstressed. Other factors, more oriented to marketing and sales than to costs, are important determinants of the use of air freight. In many situations, for instance, the avoidance of perishability losses or losses due to obsolescence is more important than savings in warehousing and storage costs.

These are some of the obstacles to be overcome if air cargo demand is to grow:

- The high cost of the air cargo service.
- Lack of wide acceptance of the "total distribution cost" concept involving tradeoffs between transportation costs and savings in other physical distribution costs.
- Failure of management to consider, routinely, the use of air cargo transportation.
- Lack of computer-aided analysis of distribution costs.
- The prevalence of high-cost small shipments. The great majority of air freight shipments average 500 pounds or less and air express averages less than 50 pounds per shipment.

- Relatively slow-growing recognition and acceptance of the many advantages that containerization offers to shippers and carriers.
- Failure of shippers to understand air logistics as a means of increasing sales and profits by enlarging market areas and increasing the length of time perishable or obsolescence-prone products can be on the market.

Military Airlift Command Innovations

In general, the distribution practices and policies of the Department of Defense are not directly pertinent or applicable to the commercial air cargo market. However, military purchases of air cargo services from the commercial carriers are quite substantial. As a result, the commercial carriers are becoming acquainted with technical and administrative innovations being developed by the Military Airlift Command.

A significant recent development is the decision to phase out overseas storage depots. This major change in logistic support policy was influenced by the availability of large aircraft such as the C-141 and the C-5A for high-speed, long-range logistic support operations.

Another innovation in supply pipeline policy is the Multiple Destination Port Concept. Under this concept ten multidirectional aerial ports of embarkation will permit cargo to originate from East or West Coast stations alike for shipment to either the Pacific or European areas.

Another MAC innovation is the plan to exercise command and control of its entire fleet of aircraft from one central location, its Scott Air Force Base headquarters. Computer-aided scheduling and control of aircraft will be provided. Schedules will be published one year in advance and each aircraft scheduled one month in advance.

General Recommendations

All things considered, it seems apparent that an order of magnitude increase in the effective demand for air cargo transportation will not evolve without considerable effort in the following directions:

- Reduce the cost and the price of air cargo service.
- Encourage potential shippers to organize for total-distribution-cost management.
- Ensure cross-seeding of innovations.
- Standardize shipping containers.
- Reduce the paperwork required for commerce (especially international commerce).

• Organize concerted effort on the part of shippers, airport operators, air carriers, aircraft manufacturers, and government planners to develop suitable facilities and equipment.

SUMMARY OF TRENDS IN GOVERNMENTAL POLICIES

Analysis of a detailed matrix showing the present domestic and international governmental structure that affects air transportation from either the regulatory or promotional standpoint and the interactions between governmental organizations and the several components of the air transportation system has led to a number of conclusions:

1. Many governmental organizations exercise authority over the same air transport function.

2. Since air transportation is a system whose effective function is dependent upon the adequacy of performance and interaction among numerous component subsystems such as airport systems, governmental action or inaction with respect to one component subsystem can have multiplicative impact on the air transport system as a whole.

3. Integration of airport planning into regional planning may be a mixed blessing. While it will lead to recognition of air transport and airport access problems as part of total urban area planning responsibility, aviation interests will have to compete with other metropolitan and regional interests for planning and development funds. Economically viable airports may be expected to depend more upon their own resources in the future, or even to contribute to the development of other airports in the same regional system.

4. Distribution of commercial air services via satellite airports, assignment of pleasure flying and less essential general aviation activities to more remote airports, and the formation of regional governmental authorities, such as airport districts, represent significant trends. The result should provide better protection of airport systems, focusing of regional attention on airport access needs, the development of compatible land uses, and more effective integration of airport and air transport operations into the total community, assuring more solid support.

5. Requirements for control over approach and departure paths may increase airport land ownership or bring pressure for intermunicipal cooperation leading to regional zoning or other protective policies.

6. Positive control of airspace, with clearly defined terminal airspace and access corridors in and out of all major metropolitan areas, as well as positive control of aircraft, appears to be inevitable. One side effect of controlled airspace may be limitation of the use of smaller airports under such airspace, unless and until the aircraft using them are trans-

ponder-equipped and both airports and aircraft are otherwise properly instrumented to receive and respond to centralized area control directives.

7. Reduction in federal aid to airports, partly offset by state financial aid to airport development, will give added impetus to the creation of special airport districts which provide a broader tax base than municipal airports and greater state control.

8. The inadequacy of airport access systems is being recognized as a major constraint on an effective air transportation system. While air transport's urban rapid transit requirements are still quite small as a percentage of total transit volume, aviation officials may be able to demonstrate the community benefits of providing adequate airport access in terms of the overall economic and social needs of the community.

9. Removal from the airport of terminal air transport functions, such as ticketing, passenger and cargo processing, containerization or palletization and break-bulk operations, will be increasingly required if the airport is to effectively perform its primary function of transfer between ground and air transport. Such terminal functions may be relegated to check-in points at urban nodes, which may also serve as rapid transit hubs and V/STOL ports.

10. Trends in the direction of developing common standards and a common system of airspace control and air navigation aids, overseas and internationally, offer socioeconomic benefits that are clear and encouraging. They will bring about safer, more efficient international air transport operations. However, ownership and financing of such facilities are still a problem. A dual system of user charges may be the solution. Terminal air traffic control and air navigation services will normally be charged as a part of the airport usage, leaving in-transit usage to be covered by a separate charge.

11. The upgrading of air safety systems and regulations of most countries expected during the next decade will have an impact on the performance requirements and licensing standards for airmen, mechanics, and those in related fields. These trends will lead to increased professionalization and increased salary levels to attract additional personnel to these activities. Universities and technical schools should be encouraged to perform a more active role in offering training in these areas. Additional efforts will be needed to assure an adequate supply of technically trained mechanics and air traffic controllers.

12. Assumption by the federal government of a major role in the design and development of new aircraft types, such as the supersonic transport, has engendered a trend toward quasi-socialization of the air transport industry, with control over the objective and direction of

production being vested in a government bureaucracy, instead of resulting from economic forces and competitive relationships between producers and air carriers. The air transport industry and the government must both recognize this as a trend that, if continued, will radically alter the balance of competitive forces within the air transport industry.

13. With respect to noncommercial air transportation, it seems obvious that airspace and airport separation of aircraft and pilots having different performance and operating capabilities will further limit their scope or require substantial time and financial effort for qualification. In an era of increasing congestion and scarcity in usable airspace and airports, increased restrictions of the few in favor of the many must be expected.

14. With respect to commercial air transportation, it seems inevitable in the face of governmental trends and economic and technological pressures that the present division of the air transport industry into classes will disappear and give way to fewer, larger, though perhaps more generally competitive organizations. In the international field, present pooling arrangements may be intensified or may in turn give place to supernational carriers on the lines of SAS.

FISCAL POLICIES, SUBJECT TO DATA GAPS IN THE ROLE OF INVESTMENT AND THE ROLE OF PRICING

A systems fiscal approach is inseparable from a total systems approach. Financial management encompasses planning, organization and control at the highest level in the system. The means by which finances are managed are probably the most powerful determinant in the evolution of the system.

Although there is an interface between government and the transportation industry, it is so fragmented that total systems direction is all but impossible. Historical data relative to past expenditures by the many public and private agencies involved in the air transportation system are difficult, if not impossible, to obtain. Current revenue or income data are likewise so fragmented that they are equally hard to assemble for overview. Estimates with regard to future costs and expenditures for various alternative developments in the air transport system appear to be general and lacking in detail essential for good decision-making.

We are now facing bottlenecks at some of the airports, limitations in capability of the manufacturers to produce new equipment, insufficient dollar sources to finance the industry, and difficulties in supplying such items as parts and fuel. An adequate federal fiscal policy must have the information and the flexibility to keep all of the participants in balance if the total system is to function well. Immediate steps should be taken to bridge the fiscal data gaps.

An effective measure that could be taken to contribute to the more efficient use of airport capacity is the use of pricing as a rationing device. For example, most air travelers prefer to arrive at their originating airport by private automobile rather than by taxi or limousine; parking fees at most airports are so low that it costs less to park three to five days than to make the round trip by taxi. As a result, congestion and the demand for parking continue to increase. If airport parking were priced high enough, congestion on access routes would be reduced as well as the need for additional parking facilities.

Similarly, airport capacity would be used more efficiently and less new capacity would be required if higher landing fees were charged during peak hours and such higher fees were passed on to the passengers or absorbed by general aviation. A similar argument can be made for differential landing fees at different airports within the same geographic area.

Doubtless the growth of air travel will call for additional airports in many major hub areas in the next 10 to 20 years. The newer airports will sometimes be less conveniently located and underutilized, while congestion continues to grow at the older airports. An obvious remedy is to charge higher landing fees and premium fares at the more conveniently located airports. Perhaps the greatest contribution to efficiency would be made by a system of pricing that had the effect of separating commercial and general aviation, although many would object to such a policy.

COMPETITIVE PASSENGER TRANSPORTATION TRENDS

The most significant development in the field of surface transportation during the next two decades will be the inauguration of high-speed intercity common carrier ground transportation. Much of this activity will have its greatest impact in the period beyond 1980. However, the initial phases of the development of these systems (between 1968 and 1980) may slow down the traffic growth of air carriers, particularly those with short-haul route structures in highly congested areas.

High-speed intercity common carrier ground transportation systems can potentially be justified only in corridors of high-density population. Only a few such corridors exist in the United States. However, these megalopolitan corridors contain approximately 50 percent of the U.S. population. The three largest — those of the Northeast, Chicago, and California — appear to have the greatest potential for high-speed ground transportation in the next two decades. Since these corridors are important air travel routes, diversion in these markets could significantly affect total air travel volumes.

Completion of the National Interstate Highway program by 1972 or 1973 may be expected to have some impact upon air travel, as the present gaps along major air routes are closed. By 1972, for instance, expressway gaps will be closed between Northeastern cities and Florida, Midwest cities and Florida, Great Lakes cities and Florida, and Northwest cities and the Southwest. On the other hand, it is possible that the development of economically feasible V/STOL aircraft will permit air transportation to compete more effectively with highway transport than it does now.

The principal maritime competitive technological development which may occur during the 1970's could be the inauguration of significant volumes of service with air cushion vehicles. This might have some effect on the volume of short-haul air travel between Florida and the Bahamas, Boston and Nantucket, and similar routes.

COMPETITIVE FREIGHT TRANSPORTATION TRENDS

The most apparent socioeconomic phenomena that might be expected to stimulate changes in the commodity modal split pattern (air versus truck versus rail) are

1. The rapid decentralization process which appears to be at work in most metropolitan areas, resulting in the proliferation of peripheral urban places with 50,000 to 250,000 population.
2. The related dispersal of primary (i.e., "exporting") industry and retail outlets.
3. The trend toward more value added per unit cost of input factors in industrial production.

The implications of these phenomena can be seen grossly to be

1. Dispersal of both production and consumption nodes in a dynamic growth pattern with increased average surface traffic density and longer average intra-area trip lengths.
2. Increased sensitivity of product cost to transportation time, resulting from inventory level minimization by both producers and consumers.
3. Decreased sensitivity of product cost to the transportation component.

These effects will tend individually and jointly to adjudicate against motor carrier and rail commodity transport in favor of air, increasingly as metropolitan dimensions increase and as the cost of providing adequate rights of way for surface transportation increases with the value and extent of land traversed.

Perhaps the most dramatic impact of demographic change on air freight traffic will derive from the expansion of the short-segment-length low-traffic-density airborne collection-distribution system, presently oriented toward passenger traffic but which could at the same time provide an effective terminal collection-distribution system for commodities.

It is not anticipated that technological innovations, other than automated cargo handling and containerization, will have a profound effect on the character or cost of either rail or motor carrier transport within the period being considered in this study.

GENERAL AVIATION TRENDS AND POTENTIALS

General aviation is in the beginning of what appears to be long-term steady growth. Federal Aviation Agency projections indicate a total fleet of 172,000 aircraft by 1975, up from 95,000 in 1965. A straight-line projection suggests a total fleet of 300,000 by 1985.

Of those used for transportation, the fastest-growing segment is the air-taxi group, expected to grow from 5,700 in 1965 to 30,000 by 1985; personal flying is second (50,000 to 200,000); and business flying is third (21,500 to 48,000). The aircraft will be bigger, more powerful, and more sophisticated.

To accommodate this rapidly growing fleet, the 10,000 airports in the nation today should be increased to over 16,000 in 1975 and 28,000 by 1985.

Airlines and general aviation transportation are mutually supporting. Sharply separating the two might be no more than a stopgap solution to airport overcrowding and could severely handicap their mutual support. It would seem imperative in planning the 1975–1985 air transport system that those portions of general aviation that contribute directly to the movement of people must be considered an integral portion of a nationwide net.

In fairness, however, it should be stated that in some respects general aviation is competitive with commercial air transportation and that airport and airspace limitations may impose restraints on the former in favor of the latter. While general aviation is important and should be facilitated, it should also pay its way, and less urgent general aviation activities should give way to more urgent commercial and executive needs.

RECOMMENDATIONS

A More Systematic Continuing Effort Should Be Directed Toward the Collection and Analysis of Industry-Wide Sales and Market Data

Strategic planning for domestic and international air transportation would be materially assisted by

1. Annual in-flight surveys based on adequate statistical sampling techniques.
2. Annual market and motivation studies providing data on the characteristics of non-air travelers as well as air travelers in the population.
3. More detailed local origin and destination surveys revealing the actual suburban or city locations from which passengers originate and to which they are destined, rather than merely the airport origins and destinations shown by the present origin and destination surveys. More precise data of this nature are essential in connection with satellite airport planning and development.
4. Collection and analysis of data concerning the actual local area origin and destination of the principal categories of air cargo, including air freight, express, and mail.

An Organized Effort Should Be Made To Close Important Fiscal Data Gaps

A systems fiscal approach is inseparable from a total systems approach in air transportation. Accurate data on past expenditures (both investment and operational) by the many public and private agencies involved in the domestic and international air transportation system are difficult or impossible to find, and current revenue and expenditure data are so fragmented that they are difficult to assemble for planning and overview purposes. Ideally, fiscal data should embrace all elements of the air transportation system, including aircraft manufacturers, airlines, airports, and the air traffic control system.

General Aviation Data Gaps Should Be Closed

General aviation, with its large present fleet, has a significant impact on airport and air traffic control facilities requirements; yet present information on this important and rapidly growing segment of the air transportation system is incomplete and of questionable accuracy.

To Provide a Better Balance Between the Development of Air Cargo and Air Passenger Service, Encourage Maximum Economical Use of Aircraft and Other Facilities, and Broaden the Revenue Base of Commercial Aviation, a Number of Studies Are Recommended Relating to Trends in Distribution and Air Cargo Movement:

1. Undertake a joint airline/aircraft manufacturer study of ways and means of reducing the cost of providing air cargo service, using systems analysis techniques. The study should consider all possible ways to reduce direct, indirect, and pickup and delivery costs.
2. Encourage potential air cargo shippers to organize for total-distribution-cost management. Provide assistance as needed for such organization and for maximization of sales and profits.
3. Undertake a joint airline/MAC study of ways and means of introducing military airlift system innovations into airline air cargo operations.
4. Undertake a joint government/airline study of ways and means of eliminating some of the documentation required for air cargo shipment.
5. Undertake a joint government/industry/user study of standardized shipping containers, possibly under the leadership of the National Bureau of Standards.
6. Undertake a joint government, airline, airframe manufacturer and shipper study of air cargo facility and equipment requirements.

Airport and Airport Access Planning Should Be Given Greater Attention in the Development of Comprehensive Transportation Plans

Such plans are now required on a continuing basis in urbanized areas by the Federal-Aid Highway Act of 1962. States should be required to develop state airport plans as a condition for federal aid to airports just as state highway plans are required as a condition for highway aid.

1. Actions should be taken to reserve land for future airport requirements. To facilitate this effort, temporary (preferably time-limited) uses should be identified and promoted.
2. Further research should be conducted with respect to aircraft noise levels — their acceptability, minimization, and control.
3. A standard cost/benefit rationale and methodology should be developed for determining airport location and dispersion as related to such problems as the following:

- Population and industrial distribution
- Metropolitan growth patterns and rates
- Elasticity of demand
- Social acceptability of noise, surface traffic, and safety standards
- Destination patterns

There Is Need for Intermodal Cost/Benefit Studies

Huge sums are involved in current proposals for high-speed ground transportation, highway systems, and air transport programs, inclusive of V/STOL. Unfortunately, little has been done to date in the direction of comparative cost/benefit studies applicable to specific routes, corridors, or areas. Such studies must be made if optimum choices of alternatives are to be available to public and private decision-makers.

CTOL TECHNOLOGY FORECAST

The many technologies involved in aircraft design cannot always be sharply differentiated. For this forecast, though, it is convenient to group them into the traditional disciplines of aerodynamics, propulsion, structures, and avionics. Progress in these fields usually finds more than one application. A better power plant, for instance, can be used in CTOL, STOL, or VTOL aircraft. It is therefore difficult to subdivide these disciplines according to their main areas of application. Because of this overlap, the CTOL technology forecast covers several areas of technology that are common to CTOL, STOL, and VTOL applications. This leaves for the STOL and VTOL technology sections the relatively few topics that are special to those aircraft.

The section "CTOL Design Trends" delineates the ways in which the technological possibilities described in this section are expected to be exploited.

AERODYNAMICS

There are two basic areas in which technological development can directly increase the performance and productivity of an airplane: (1) the cruise drag, or more correctly the lift/drag ratio in cruise, and (2) the high-lift capability, which dictates takeoff and landing field requirements. These are dominant factors in selection of the airplane wing area and power plant size. In general, the smallest airplane that can perform a given payload-range task is the most economical.

Maximum Lift/Drag Ratio

The two envelope curves in Figure 3.1 mark the present and future limits of maximum lift/drag ratio. Typical subsonic and transonic transports will continue to use fixed wings; the flatter operating curve of the United States supersonic transport (SST) results from the use of variable sweep. By combining the wing design variables of sweep, thickness, and airfoil sections, it is possible to tailor designs for particular speeds or ranges. Better detail design techniques promise to improve performance by reducing wave drag, induced drag, and profile drag. Some of these techniques are concerned with the wing airfoil cross section; others involve lift distribution over all surfaces of the airplane. Advanced mathematical tools and a better knowledge of empirical processes will help to develop these techniques.

Figure 3.1 shows two subsonic points for the unconventional concepts of laminar flow control and ground proximity cruising. Laminar

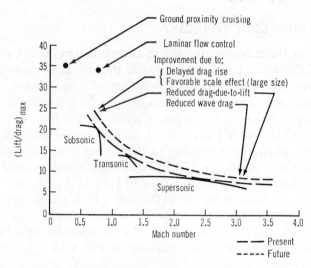

Figure 3.1. Maximum lift/drag ratio—present and future.

flow control results from a sophisticated system that sucks away the boundary layer through a porous skin, greatly reducing skin-friction drag over most of the surface. Ground proximity cruising achieves its performance gains in transoceanic flights; the induced drag of the wing is greatly reduced by flying very close (much less than the wingspan) to the ocean surface. Both these potential improvements will present a challenge to exploitation.

Airfoil Section Performance

Airfoil section performance, as measured by drag-divergence Mach number, has improved steadily through empirical tailoring in transonic wind tunnels. This work has made the state-of-the-art performance envelope (Figure 3.2) significantly better than that of the 707 airfoil. Continuing gains will come from more precisely balanced designs that will minimize both boundary-layer–shock-wave interaction and the supersonic flow that ultimately causes drag divergence. Research into more sophisticated design and analysis techniques and better mathematical methods will help to develop these designs. To implement this approach, three-dimensional wing design and tailoring must be greatly improved.

Improved airfoils could be exploited in several ways in the design of both subsonic and supersonic airplanes. Future airplanes may be able to cruise with less wing-sweep angle at a chosen speed, yielding higher aspect ratios and thus more range and altitude. Alternatively, the cur-

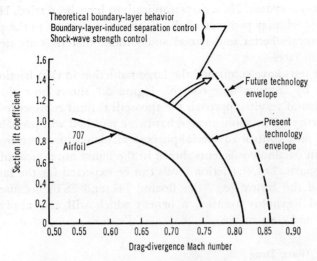

Figure 3.2. Potential gains in airfoil section performance.

rent sweep angle may be retained and the wing thickness increased, resulting in a much lighter wing structure. Direct use of the advanced airfoils for faster cruising will also be possible.

Skin Friction

Figure 3.3 shows typical wing skin friction for turbulent flow and laminar flow. The much lower level associated with the latter is the ultimate goal.

Laboratory research shows promise for some reduction of turbulent-flow friction by use of compliant skins, typical of a passive boundary-

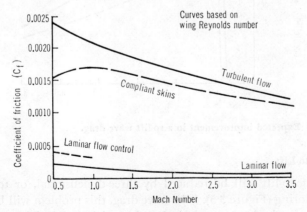

Figure 3.3. Potential reductions in wing skin friction.

layer control system. No serious applications have been tried. However, this approach may prove attractive in the next 20 years as the phenomenon becomes better understood and suitable materials are developed for the surface.

Flight tests have confirmed the large reduction in skin friction made possible by laminar flow control. Figure 3.3 shows how closely the experimental results approach the theoretical limit represented by the bottom curve. The sophisticated hardware required will probably limit laminar flow control to special-purpose airplanes for some time. The wing skin friction coefficients shown in the figure are typical of today's jet transports. Lower friction levels can be expected for the larger airplanes of the future (e.g., the Boeing 747 and SST) because of the increased Reynolds number, a benefit which will also apply to the fuselage and empennage.

Zero-Lift Wave Drag

Improvement in zero-lift wave drag appears quite promising as knowledge is gained about the nature of three-dimensional supersonic flow interactions. Complex mathematical models are now becoming tractable that will permit more direct investigation and control of the complicated flow regions for complete configuration tailoring. Figure 3.4 shows expected gains.

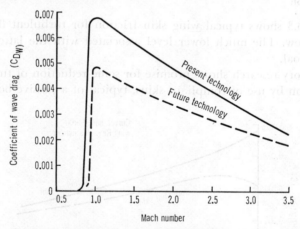

Figure 3.4. Expected improvement in zero-lift wave drag.

Drag-Due-to-Lift

Drag-due-to-lift will be reduced by three-dimensional, or total airplane, tailoring (Figure 3.5). Like wave drag, this problem will be made easier to solve by better analytical and empirical techniques.

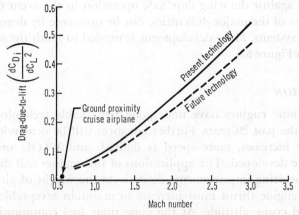

Figure 3.5. Expected improvement in drag-due-to-lift.

Trimmed High Lift

There are many promising new approaches toward achieving high lift. For example, one design limitation can be alleviated by gaining a better understanding of boundary-layer separation due to shock wave interaction or geometrically produced pressure gradients. Another approach involves the mechanical design of variable-geometry devices, permitting the incorporation of surface shapes and curvatures that analysis has shown will improve aerodynamic performance.

Major improvements in takeoff and landing occur when the propulsion system is used to enhance the wing lift according to the "powered lift" concept. Thrust can be used either to add to lift directly or to

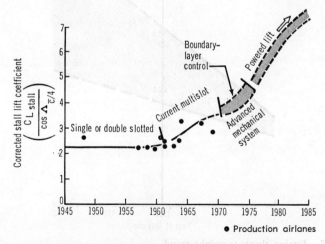

Figure 3.6. Trend in trimmed high lift capability (corrected for sweep).

deflect air against the wing flap. Safe operation in the event of engine failure, one of the major difficulties, can be overcome by demand compensation systems. More development is needed to reach the objectives forecast in Figure 3.6.

PROPULSION

Gas turbine engines have undergone remarkable technological advances in the past 20 years. Further advances will be demanded as airplane size increases, more speed is desired, and VTOL and STOL aircraft are developed. The applications of the engines will dictate the specific operating improvements desired. As the weight of air vehicles increases, engine thrust must increase to maintain acceptable runway length and cruise altitude. At the same time, fuel consumption must remain low without increasing the engine drag and weight, so that operating cost can be kept to a minimum at cruise. To keep the lowest fuel weight for the particular mission, engine thrust must be matched to airplane drag at minimum fuel consumption. In general, higher thrust will be demanded along with a corresponding decrease in engine weight and fuel consumption.

Thrust and Weight

Engine thrust has been increased through higher allowable operating temperatures and increased airflow capacity. Higher thrust has been

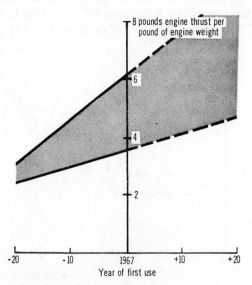

Figure 3.7.   Engine thrust-to-weight trend.

accompanied by engine weight reduction through improved material technology and cooling effectiveness. Figure 3.7 shows the trend of increasing engine thrust per pound of engine weight.

Specific Fuel Consumption (SFC)

As the efficiency of turbine engines improves, the amount of fuel per hour needed for each pound of thrust decreases. Higher turbine-inlet operating temperatures and compressor pressure ratios combined with higher bypass ratios have contributed to this trend for engines operating at subsonic cruise thrust. Figure 3.8 shows that SFC has gone down 30 percent in 20 years and should continue to improve as engine designs with even higher bypass ratios become available. Low SFC has been demonstrated for supersonic cruise thrust with proper selection of compressor pressure ratio and turbine inlet temperature.

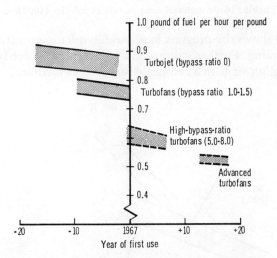

Figure 3.8. Engine performance trend (specific fuel consumption).

Engine Component Technology

The performance of a turbine engine is limited by the permissible turbine inlet temperature, internal losses, and component efficiencies. Substantial progress has been made in the development of turbine blade materials to withstand high temperatures. Figure 3.9 shows past temperature limits of wrought and cast alloys and what can be expected in the future.

Turbine inlet temperatures much higher than the raw-material limits can be achieved through convection and transpiration cooling.

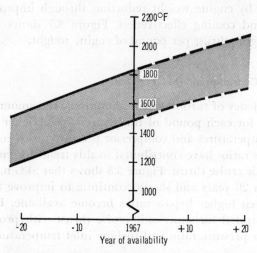

Figure 3.9. Turbine blade material temperature capability (1000-hour life).

Figure 3.10 shows the progress in allowable inlet temperatures realized through cooling. Further gains might be achieved by refrigerating the turbine cooling air with a cryogenic fuel such as methane.

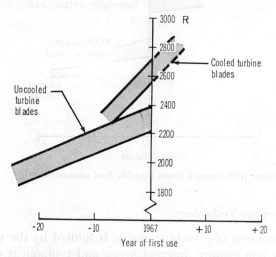

Figure 3.10. Trend in turbine inlet temperature at takeoff.

Lift Engines

The size of a lift engine has an important effect on installation weight and drag. In most applications the volume must be kept small as thrust increases. Technological advances in material strength and

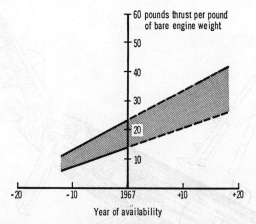

Figure 3.11.   Trend in lift engine thrust-to-weight ratio.

temperature capability, cooling effectiveness, blade tip speed, and stage loading can be applied in different ways, depending on the specific use of the engine. The application of a design improvement depends on the relative importance of weight, volume, and thrust.

Figures 3.11 and 3.12 show the history and expected trends of the thrust-to-weight and thrust-to-volume capabilities of lift engines. Because of the short history of this technology and the varied application of the products, only general trends can be forecast.

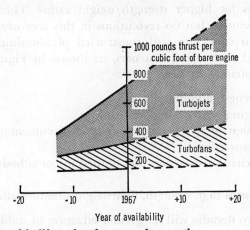

Figure 3.12.   Trend in lift engine thrust-to-volume ratio.

STRUCTURES

With lighter structures, air vehicles can carry heavier payloads and thus operate more profitably. Accordingly, structures research con-

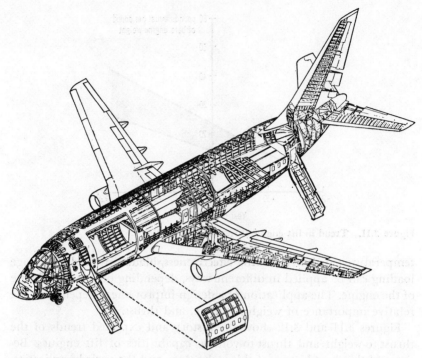

Figure 3.13.   Typical multipart, mechanically fastened airplane structure.

tinually strives for higher strength/weight ratios. There have been steady improvements but no revolutions in this area over the past 20 years. Most airplanes are still constructed of aluminum-alloy components joined with metal fasteners, as shown in Figure 3.13. The chief improvements have been

- Higher-strength aluminum alloys
- Better forgings, extrusions, and castings
- Better design analysis, prediction of environmental effects, and material protection
- Better mechanical fasteners and limited use of adhesives and weldments
- Limited use of high-strength, lightweight titanium alloys

The next two decades will see greater advances in stabilized-element structures and increases in ultimate strengths. Advanced titanium alloys and composite materials, with more strength per pound than aluminum, will be used to reduce weight. New bonding techniques will gradually replace riveting in many applications, permitting greater design stresses and more efficient distribution of the materials.

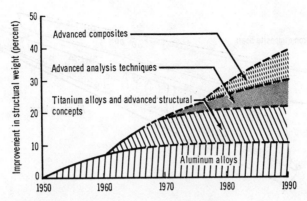

Figure 3.14. Structural weight improvement prospects.

These new technologies should bring about weight savings of 20 to 40 percent, as shown in Figure 3.14. Note that the improvement available with aluminum has just about run its course; titanium alloys now offer greater benefits. Advanced composites have even higher potential than the titanium alloys (Figure 3.15) and are most promising for the rest of this century.

The improvements shown in Figure 3.15 can be realized only in structural members under simple tension. Aerospace structural members are generally subject to different types of loading such as shear, torsion, and compression, which do not allow the full savings. The effect of load magnitude is shown in Figure 3.16, which compares a

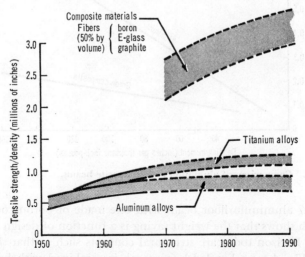

Figure 3.15. Projected improvements in structural material strength-to-density ratio.

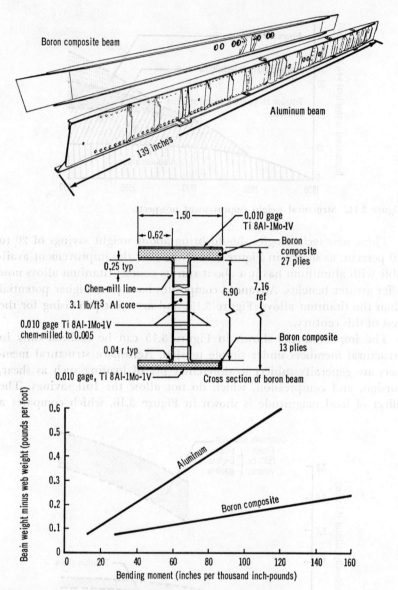

Figure 3.16. Comparison of aluminum and composite beams.

simple 707 aluminum floor beam with one made of boron composite. The graph shows that the weight saving is a function of design load.

On the horizon today are structural concepts such as that shown in Figure 3.17, where a bonded honeycomb is combined with bonded-in extrusions and a bonded frame assembly. This concept results in the

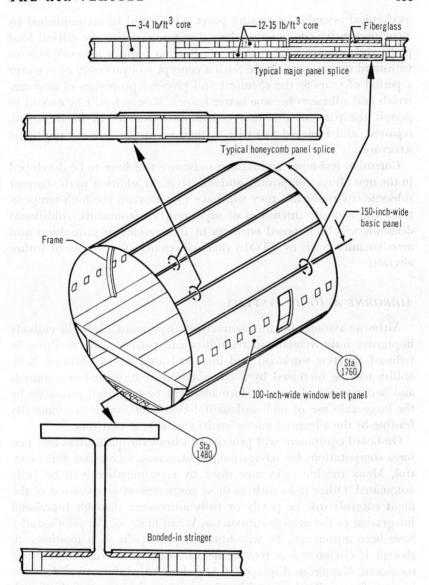

Figure 3.17. Airplane body section assembly—advanced concept.

use of far fewer frames and stringers than are shown in Figure 3.13, and in a 20 percent weight reduction. Factory production of this type of structure will require improvements in construction techniques, using a higher degree of automation.

The next 20 years may see the construction of single complete units incorporating networks of high-strength filaments rather than the mechanical assembly of smaller parts. This could be accomplished by a comprehensive computer analysis that would derive the critical load paths and instruct a fabrication machine to build a network able to withstand the required loads. Such a concept will probably evolve over a period of years as the chemical and physical properties of new materials and adhesives become better known. Research will be needed to permit the parts of this new continuous structure to be inspected, repaired, and replaced as easily as they are in the present multipart structures.

Corrosion resistance and fatigue resistance will have to be developed in the new alloys, composites, and adhesives. In addition to the current subsonic environments, they will have to withstand the high temperatures and acoustic intensities of supersonic environments. Additional demands will be imposed on them by innovations in propulsion and aerodynamics (such as VTOL) that will change the shapes of future aircraft.

AIRBORNE AVIONIC SYSTEMS

Airborne avionics for the commercial airplane of 1985 will embody impressive improvements in reliability and performance, resulting in reduced air crew workload and increased airplane capabilities. Reliability will be increased by a combination of improved components and better system design. Performance will be improved primarily by the large-scale use of on-board digital computers, made economically feasible by the advanced microcircuits available at that time.

On-board equipment will process data from various sources and perform computations for navigation, flight management, and flight control. Many routine tasks now done by crew members will be fully automated. Other tasks such as those connected with operation of the flight controls will be partly or fully automated through functional integration of the avionic subsystems. When many of the pilot's duties have been automated, he will function principally as a monitor, although if circumstances require he will be able to return to direct command. Numerous displays will keep him fully informed and enable him to effect easily the transition from monitoring to manual control.

Aside from the smaller size, lighter weight, and greater reliability of future avionics, the major difference between 1985 systems and those of today will be the advanced integration concepts in use at that time.

Comprehensive functional integration of avionic subsystems is being carried out in airborne military systems under development. These programs point the way for the commercial airlines, but must be followed up by considerable adaptation, as well as commercial research and development. The trend toward avionic integration in civil aviation is already clear; one step being taken in this direction is centralized frequency selection for all airborne communication and navigation equipment. Another example is the industry's concerted effort to develop an all-weather landing system (AWLS). A third example is the thought being given to an automatic flight management system for advanced airplanes like the U.S. SST. This may be a fully integrated avionic system in which most operational functions are computer controlled, and the crew's role in the operating loop is executive management.

Elements of 1985 Airborne Avionic Systems

Airborne avionic systems consist of many components and units performing numerous related and integrated functions. Shown here are the principal elements of a typical 1985 system, arranged to suggest the functions performed by the equipment:

Communication
- Data link
- Interphone communication
- Passenger public address

Passenger entertainment

Navigation
- Inertial navigation system (INS)
- Weather/terrain mapping radar
- Receivers: distance-measuring equipment (DME), VHF omnirange (VOR)/localizer, glide slope, and/or hyperbolic and range-bearing measuring systems
- Microwave receiver for AWLS
- Radar altimeter

Ground surveillance: air traffic control (ATC) transponder beacon

Flight safety
- Collision-avoidance system (CAS)
- Clear air turbulence (CAT) detector
- Weather/terrain mapping radar

Flight management
- Navigation and flight management computers
- Central air-data system

- Flight control system
- Aircraft-integrated data system
- Stall warning system
- Cockpit voice/flight recorder
- Instrument warning system
- Integrated data display
- Head-up display
- Moving map
- Conventional cockpit displays
- Prediction systems

The rest of this section briefly discusses some of these elements.

Communication and Navigation

Present-day communication and navigation have evolved by independent steps, adding new capabilities as black boxes. This has resulted in various isolated types of equipment, many of them specialized for particular segments of the flight path.

The network of ground-based radio aids known as the "ground environment" has evolved in like manner. The constraints imposed by the ground environment make it difficult to reduce the number of airborne radio receivers by integrating communication and navigation. Such integration will not occur until there is a worldwide network of radio navigation aids that combine several communication and navigation functions. Extremely complex political and economic problems make it unlikely that such a worldwide system will be set up in the foreseeable future; thus the airborne receivers of 1985 will still be isolated units developed from today's black boxes. However, they will benefit from advanced miniaturization techniques.

The difficulty of obtaining a standard state-of-the-art ATC environment may result in a countertrend toward airborne avionic systems that can operate without heavy dependence on the ground environment. Such self-sufficiency would permit widespread use of advanced airplanes in many parts of the world that lack sophisticated ground environments.

Air-to-ground communication will be provided by automated or semiautomated VHF and UHF digitally modulated data links; HF may remain as a backup. Reliable air-to-ground communication in remote areas will be provided by a satellite system compatible with the airborne data links. Airline groups as well as numerous avionic and airframe manufacturers are studying digital air-to-ground communication links.

The primary source of en route navigational data for both long-haul and short-haul commercial airplanes will be the inertial navigation system (INS). Anticipated INS improvements will probably not be enough to allow purely inertial navigation in terminal areas and in high-density domestic airspace without periodic comparison with other position data sources. The INS may therefore be used in a hybrid system with other radio navigation aids like DME and VOR. Position updating in remote areas could be done by a navigation-satellite fix. If such satellites are not available, updating could be carried out with hyperbolic navigation systems such as Loran C or OMEGA.

The airborne ATC transponder beacon will continue as a major link between ATC and airplane. This equipment, developed from the present-day transponder, will transmit altitude, identity, and possibly other data in digital form.

The navigational sensors for the all-weather landing system may include microwave receivers designed to operate with a microwave-beam landing guidance system. The VOR receivers will be used for instrument approaches at airports equipped only with conventional instrument landing systems; precision radar altimeters will supply the required altitude information. An all-weather cockpit display of the approach and landing area, nearly independent of the ground environment, may be provided by one of several self-contained radar and optical techniques now under development.

By 1985 radar techniques should be refined enough to provide a combined weather and terrain obstacle-avoidance radar. Other navigational flight safety sensors that may be included are clear-air turbulence (CAT) detection and an airborne collision-avoidance system (CAS). The development of an operational CAT detection system is contingent on a suitable technical approach. Both infrared and radar scanning have shown promise in flight tests. The deployment of a CAS is technically feasible but depends on operational suitability and economic feasibility.

Flight Control Systems

Flight control systems for commercial airplanes in 1985 will have been expanded from simple yaw (oscillation) dampers to include automatic three-axis stabilization. Redundant designs using majority voting or adaptive voting (which eliminates circuits if they fail) will help provide highly reliable automatic landing. Control systems will improve airplane handling characteristics over the expected range of weight, altitude, airspeed, and center-of-gravity changes.

Flight control systems in current use depend on mechanical linkages between the pilot's controls and the controlled elements. Many problems associated with this mechanical transfer will be eliminated or greatly simplified by electrical signal transmission. By 1985 electrical signaling will have had nearly 20 years of development, and its role in airplane control should be well established. Simple mechanical systems may be kept as backup.

Displays

In the 1985 commercial airplane, both conventional and advanced integrated data displays will be in use. Moving-map navigation displays using paper charts or optical projections are expected to be an important development in cockpit instrumentation. The pilot will be provided with a map presentation of information regarding airplane position, heading, track, and possibly other data. Such displays should greatly assist the pilot when flying holding patterns, approaches, departures, or other complex routes. In high-density terminal areas a major benefit of moving-map displays in the cockpit will be the reduction in workload for both pilot and ground controller.

Head-up displays, currently under study, are another potentially important cockpit improvement. Head-up displays superimpose impor-

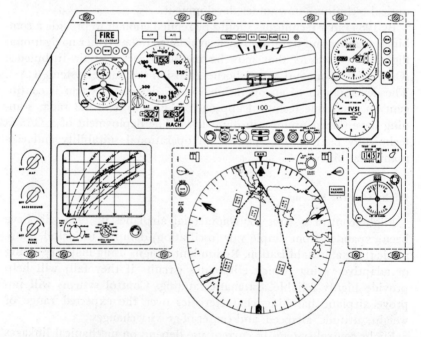

Figure 3.18. Artist's concept of a pilot's advanced panel (based on conventional organization).

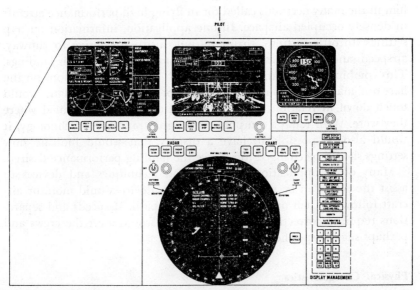

Figure 3.19. Artist's concept of a pilot's computer-assisted display panel (final approach configuration).

tant flight information on the crewman's normal field of view. Thus he can devote full visual attention to the flight environment and at the same time read instrument information previously available only by looking away from the windshield. This feature may be important in all-weather landing systems, where the information rate is high and the transition from instruments to visual contact must be made smoothly and rapidly. Studies are being conducted to determine the requirements for head-up displays in the cockpit and to evaluate the benefits of such systems.

Integrated data displays such as the multimode cathode-ray tube (CRT) proposed for the production model of the U.S. SST may also be employed. With careful attention to reliability, it may be feasible to replace standard flight instruments with more flexible CRT displays. The standard instruments would probably be retained in a backup role. Figure 3.18 is an artist's concept of a panel configuration in which CRT displays are substituted for the conventional electromechanical displays. Figure 3.19 shows an advanced computer-managed CRT display panel currently under study.

Prediction Systems

Even today's aircraft have available many items of flight information that could be combined in new ways and presented to the pilot to assist him in the many decisions called for in flying high-performance aircraft in densely occupied airspace. In one application, information on flap settings, throttle settings, thrust output, altitude relative to runway, airspeed, and rate of descent could be combined to assist in landings. This combined information, together with built-in assumptions on the flare-out maneuver, would show the pilot where the airplane would touch down in relation to the runway if all settings remained where they were. With today's computer and signal processing technology, it would also be possible to have a display that would indicate how settings should be changed to achieve the landing performance desired.

Many other applications of prediction techniques and devices to assist the pilot can be visualized. One such device would monitor aircraft following each other on an approach path. If speeds and separations required corrective action, the device would alert the crews and perhaps suggest specific corrective measures.

Physical Characteristics

The most important physical characteristics of airborne avionic systems are weight, reliability, and volume. The approximate weight breakdown of present-day airborne avionic systems in a large subsonic airplane are as follows:

Item	Weight contribution to system
Controls, instruments, displays	30%
Electronics	25%
Wires and connectors	35%
Racks, hardware, etc.	10%

As shown, the wires and connectors are a large part of the total system weight. Future avionic systems will use various forms in signal multiplexing to reduce cabling and weight. Communication subsystems such as the interphone and passenger entertainment may be completely wireless.

The electronic circuitry is the most amenable area for drastic weight and size reduction. Thus the greatest reductions can be expected in the communication, navigation, and data-processing equipment. Figure 3.20 shows weight decreases for a selected group of nonredundant primary avionic subsystems projected to 1980. The weights of these systems today are one-quarter what they were in 1947; this trend should continue to 1985 but will be partly offset by the addition of new sensors and higher redundancy. Decreases in volume can be expected to correlate closely with the weight reductions. The major trends in microelectronics are toward greater operating speed, smaller size, less cost

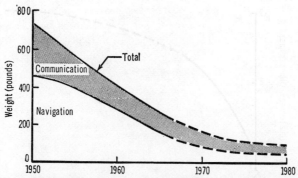

Figure 3.20. Weight trend of avionic equipment (mean of 13 selected nonredundant primary avionic subsystems).

per circuit, and greater reliability. Large-scale digital integrated-circuit arrays will appear in equipment in 1968. Figure 3.21 shows price projections of various semiconductor circuits, based on cost histories. Figure 3.22 shows predicted reliability trends for high-reliability microcircuits.

A commercial avionics reliability study recently indicated that in the decade before 1965 component reliability increased one hundredfold, while subsystem mean-time-between-failures (MTBF) improved less than tenfold. Overall avionic system MTBF, without redundancy, increased three- to fivefold in the same decade. Figure 3.23 shows these findings and their projections. Individual component reliability will continue to improve and will compensate for the rapidly increasing electronic complexity. Overall system reliability will also be greatly increased by designing redundancy into future avionics. The redundancy of an individual component will of course depend on the system

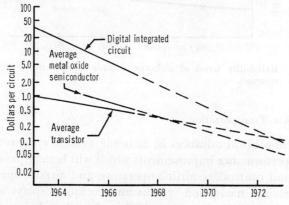

Figure 3.21. Projected prices of semiconductors.

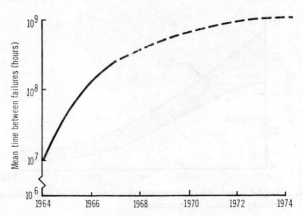

**Figure 3.22. Improvement in high-reliability microcircuits (mean of nine manu-
facturers).**

configuration. As a general guideline, it appears that subsystems
directly affecting flight safety will be triple redundant and others
either double redundant or a high-quality single system with emergency
backup.

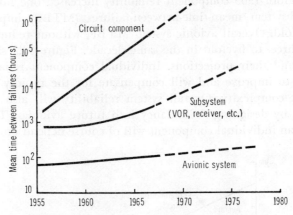

**Figure 3.23. Reliability trend of airborne avionic equipment (mean of 15 sub-
systems).**

Effect on Air Transportation

The technological advances in airborne avionic systems will be reflected in performance improvements which will benefit passengers, aircrew, ground controllers, airline operators, and airport operators. Advanced airborne navigation systems and cockpit displays will permit
the pilot to navigate on an area basis rather than being confined to

present airways. This will result in more efficient use of airspace and fewer delays. With area navigation, more of the navigation function in terminal areas will be performed in the cockpit; this will greatly reduce the communication workload for both aircrew and ground controller. The direct, flexible routes made possible by area navigation will lead to sizable cost savings for the airline. Similar benefits will be obtained on transoceanic and other remote routes. The use of all-weather landing systems will lead to more consistent scheduling and additional cost savings. Other sophisticated airborne elements such as weather radar, collision avoidance, CAT detection, and advanced flight control will enhance passenger safety and comfort.

CTOL DESIGN TRENDS

Progress in civil aviation has been marked by a few significant technological revolutions. Milestones over the past half-century are the single-engine wood-and-fabric biplane, the aluminum monocoque monoplane, the multiengine low-wing airplane, the sweptwing jet, and the fan-jet engine. The periods between revolutionary innovations have been filled with constant improvements of details.

There are no prospects of such major revolutions in CTOL aircraft for the next 20 years. This does not mean that no significant progress will be made. Quite the contrary, it means that the basic CTOL configuration is reaching maturity after a half-century of imaginative and varied experimentation. Progress will be in the form of technological refinements, improved arrangements, and expanded overall designs.

The preceding section has described many technological advances that can be foreseen in the next 20 years. The extent to which these advances will be incorporated into the commercial fleet seems to depend on these four factors:

- How soon these advances become acceptable and desirable from the viewpoints of cost, reliability, maintainability, and installability
- How much they contribute to airline efficiency
- How well they fit the standard pattern of airline equipment and how compatible they are with older equipment
- How compatible they are with the flight and ground environments of the airlines

This section discusses the ways in which current and future technology will be manifested in the overall design of CTOL airplanes. Airplane design is heavily influenced by the desire for economically competitive operations. Prime factors in these operations are the expected passenger loads, the stage lengths between stops, and the airfields to be used.

CAPACITY

In predicting future airplane capacities, one must realize that an airplane program must be targeted somewhat later than the date of introduction, since the airplane must be operational before the market reaches its optimum average load factor. This factor, historically around 60 percent, is a compromise. On one hand, a low load factor accommodates all passengers willing to travel, but at high operating cost per passenger. On the other hand, a high load factor results in more favorable operating cost per passenger, but at the risk of dissatisfying an undesirably large part of the travel market.

Figure 3.24 shows that the Boeing 707-320 Intercontinental, introduced in late 1959, was sized for a long-range route segment with a load factor that did not become prevalent until about 1964. Thus the Intercontinental was somewhat large for its pre-1964 use and could be expected to have a somewhat higher load factor after 1964.

The growth in airplane capacity for a given route segment usually will not match the total market growth, since more frequent service may better meet this demand for a time. Thus, with the current 20 percent yearly growth in the market, airplane size is predicted to increase only 10 to 12 percent by 1975 (Figure 3.24). Allowing about four years for a new airplane to reach a desirable load factor and earn appropriate returns for the airline, it can be seen that the Boeing 747 is sized correctly for its introduction in 1969.

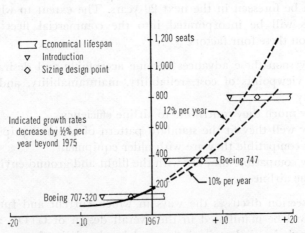

Figure 3.24. Influence of market growth on subsonic airplane capacity (constant frequency and route structure).

Extending the prediction calls for introduction of a two-class airplane carrying 800 passengers in the late 1970's. Such an airplane would have to be anticipated in any significant airport planning done today, in terms of either major modification or new airport design. The same logic can be used to describe the growth in aircraft capacity since DC-3 days.

This explanation of airplane capacity growth is incomplete, since it leaves out many of the variables and potential influences. All the same, it is a valuable aid in perceiving some of the underlying trends. Figure 3.25 shows that the prediction made here is quite compatible with past developments.

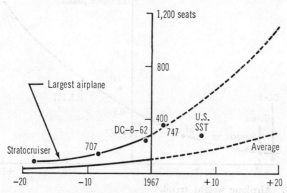

Figure 3.25. Airplane seating capacity trend.

The capacity to handle traffic is just one factor influencing overall airplane design, but its importance is reinforced by the fact that direct operating cost per seat-mile tends to decrease with increasing capacity. The jets are more efficient in terms of cost than the propeller airplanes that preceded them, and each new generation is another step ahead. The SST's of the 1970's will depart somewhat from this trend (Figure 3.26), but their higher speed should prove very attractive and should stimulate traffic growth in a different way.

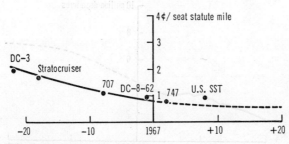

Figure 3.26. Direct operating cost trend.

GROSS WEIGHT

The advent of the turbine engine, especially in the jet and turbofan designs, removed a power ceiling that tended to limit the gross-weight growth of reciprocating-engine airplanes. Thus there has been a steady growth in gross weight from the early 707's to such airplanes as the 747 and the SST, and there is no apparent reason why this trend should not continue. Gross weights of 1,500,000 pounds are predicted for 1987 (Figure 3.27) and may occur sooner if a large enough cargo market develops.

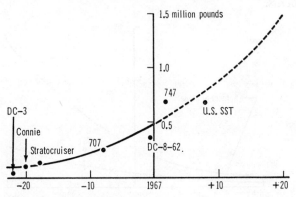

Figure 3.27.   Airplane weight trend.

AIRPORT HANDLING

Since the average airplane size in the fleet is increasing (though not as rapidly as the traffic), and since nonstop service will be available between more and more city pairs, the number of aircraft departures (Figure 3.28) should increase less than the number of passengers. In this way, increasing airplane size improves the use of airport facilities. On the other hand, passengers and baggage will tend to arrive in bigger

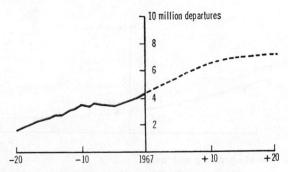

Figure 3.28.   Total yearly airplane departures (U.S. domestic).

"pulses," requiring a corresponding upgrading of facilities. With all the concern about airport congestion and the expected impact of larger airplanes, it is pertinent to examine some consequences of increasing airplane size.

Runway Length

Until 10 years ago, airports were designed to meet the performance requirements of reciprocating-engine airplanes (Figure 3.29). Runways 8000 feet long were adequate. With the advent of jet airplanes, longer runways were needed; the main reasons were less favorable engine thrust characteristics at the lower speeds, swept wings, and heavier fuel load. At the threshold of the era of supersonic and hypersonic flight, it is difficult to foresee the eventual runway length requirements of airliners that will fly at such speeds. It is a sound assumption that the use of present-day runways will be a key design criterion for these aircraft. In the meantime, with the growth in long-range subsonic flights, more airports will need to provide runways of 10,000 to 12,000 feet or more.

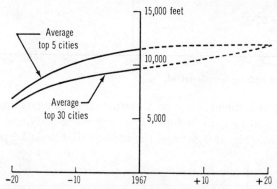

Figure 3.29. Equivalent runway length trend (sea level, 90°F) in cities having the largest number of aircraft operations.

Dynamic Loads

As airplanes become larger, the designers can keep loads within present runway strengths by spreading the landing gear, providing load equalization systems between individual gear oleos, and adding more main landing gears. Although future airplanes can probably use present runways and taxiways, overpasses and other airport structures that support the airplane's full weight will have to be strengthened. Airports that desire modern jet service but do not meet the requirements will of course have to update the length and strength of their runways.

Body Lengths

Body lengths have been increasing consistently (Figure 3.30) as larger passenger capacities are provided. This trend is more pronounced on the SST, where a longer, thinner fuselage is required to reduce drag. Airplane lengths of 350 feet or more may be required in the 1980's. This trend may be stopped, at least for subsonic airplanes, by the introduction of the double- and triple-deckers.

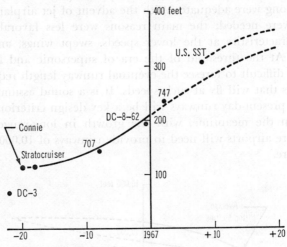

Figure 3.30. Airplane length trend.

Body length influences not only maintenance hangars and passenger bridges but also taxiway layouts. The longer the body, the greater the turning radius (Figure 3.31) and the acreage that must be provided for

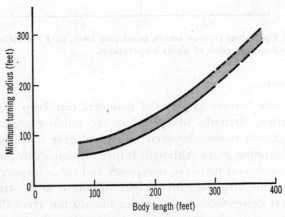

Figure 3.31. Influence of body length on turning radius.

aircraft surface maneuvers—at least in conventional apron layouts. Apron layouts with drive-through docks, such as are being considered for Paris Nord, are less affected by the increasing turn-radius requirements of long-body airplanes.

Wingspan

The growth in wingspan (Figure 3.32) has been remarkably small through the years. For instance, the 700,000-lb 747 has only about twice the span of the 25,000-lb Douglas DC-3. This is partly a result of the change in power plants, but even the largest foreseeable airplanes of the next 20 years are unlikely to have wingspans of more than 300 feet. The technical reason behind this trend is the use of more power, more efficient wings, and more effective high-lift systems instead of large increases in wing areas.

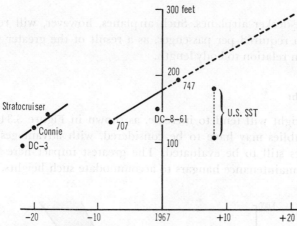

Figure 3.32. Wingspan trend.

An indication of ground-handling gains resulting from the fact that capacity has grown faster than wingspan can be obtained from a study of Figure 3.33, which plots nose-in ramp width per passenger, where the total required ramp width per airplane is assumed to equal the wingspan plus 25 feet for clearance between airplanes. It is possible that folding wingtips will be introduced to reduce wingspan for ground handling. An 800-passenger airplane would have a normal wingspan of about 250 feet and, with tips folded, a span of about 200 feet. It remains to be seen whether the improved ground handling will be worth the increased weight and complexity of folding wingtips.

Great improvement has been made toward more efficient lineal ramp use and little more improvement can be expected even with double-

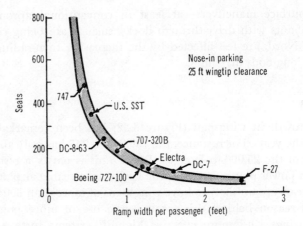

Figure 3.33. Trend in ramp width required per passenger (single deck, all-economy seating).

and triple-decker airplanes. Such airplanes, however, will reduce the ramp area required per passenger, as a result of the greater passenger capacity in relation to body length.

Tail Height

Tail height will tend to increase, as shown in Figure 3.34. Folding tail assemblies may have to be considered, with advantages and disadvantages still to be evaluated. The greatest impact here is on the design of maintenance hangars to accommodate such heights.

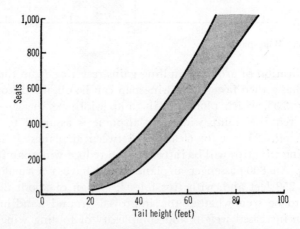

Figure 3.34. Subsonic airplane tail height trend (single deck, all-economy).

Decks

Passenger access will be affected by the number of decks and by the height of the decks. Figure 3.35 gives actual and projected deck heights, including those for a vehicle that might be introduced in 1980. The 1980 airplane's main deck would probably be about 15 feet above ground level, with an upper deck at 26 feet. The lower deck at 8 feet would be close to current deck heights. The implication to passenger bridge design is clear: height versatility will have to be designed in.

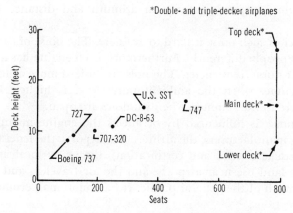

Figure 3.35. Passenger deck height trend (all-economy). The three-decker at right may be introduced about 1980.

COMMUNITY NOISE

Requirements for our society's physical environment are gradually being defined as part of the development of a concept of "quality of living." Noise background is one of the environmental problems receiving attention.

The past decade has been a period of growth: the U.S. population has gone up 17 percent, the gross national product 67 percent, air passenger travel 150 percent, air cargo more than 300 percent. The urban portion of the population increased from 67 percent in 1957 to 72 percent in 1967. As a result of these trends, there are more jet transports flying more frequently and using more airports. Thus airport communities are being exposed to more jet-engine noise.

Compounding the problem is the fact that airports are nuclei for businesses and suburban residences. As the noise level increases, so does the number of people in the vicinity; some of these go to court with the contention that they are being deprived of their constitutional right to enjoy their property. Existing legal principles have had to be extended to deal with these precedent-setting situations.

Definition of the Problem

Jet-engine noise is a relatively new phenomenon, produced by complex mechanisms that have only recently been studied in detail. Its transmission to the ground is complicated by atmospheric patterns of air density, humidity, temperature, turbulence, and winds. Its intensity on the ground depends greatly on azimuth and distance from the aircraft.

The effect of such noise is hard to evaluate. The noise of each engine type affects people differently. Furthermore, each engine has a different spectrum of noise frequencies. The noise is noticed more at night than in the daytime, when the ambient noise level is higher. It is also noticed more in the summer, when windows are open.

Engine noise is influenced by or affects the engine manufacturers, the aircraft manufacturers, the airlines, the airports, the federal government (air traffic control and certification), the many local authorities controlling land use near airports, and the air travelers and shippers, as well as much of the general public. It has emotional, economic, and legal implications.

Sonic boom is quite a different problem; it affects only supersonic aircraft and is generated by the drag- and lift-producing components rather than by the engines. Sonic boom may be reduced to an acceptable level through operation at higher cruise altitudes, but this may not occur until after 1985. Techniques for reducing sonic boom through configuration and other changes are currently under study.

Current Status

A great deal has already been accomplished in the field of airplane noise reduction. It was recognized during the design stages of the first commercial jet transports that noise could be a serious problem. As a consequence, the industry spent millions of dollars to develop exhaust noise suppressors before the DC-8 and 707 entered commercial service late in 1958. The next power-plant development was the turbofan engine, in which the fan, rather than the exhaust, produces the dominant noise. Research on turbofan noise has taken the place of subsonic engine exhaust-noise suppression since this type of engine was introduced.

The airplanes equipped with JT8D turbofans (727, 737, and DC-9)

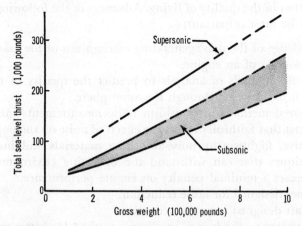

Figure 3.36. Influence of airplane weight on required takeoff engine thrust.

benefit from designed-in reduction of fan and compressor noise. Noise is further reduced in these airplanes by partial internal mixing of fan air and exhaust in fully ducted nacelles. In addition, bands of absorptive material are incorporated in the nacelle inlets of the 727 and 737.

Designs for the next generation of subsonic transports call for the use of advanced turbofans with high bypass ratios. Because more energy must be extracted from the exhaust to drive the larger fans, these engines will run more quietly than present turbofans. Fan noise will also be reduced by omission of the inlet guide vanes, ample guide vane spacing from fan rotor to outlet, and lower fan tip speeds. Acoustic treatment of the nacelles will also reduce noise; the 747, for instance, will carry 2,000 pounds of sound-absorbing material.

The trend toward larger airplanes requires corresponding increases in takeoff thrust (Figure 3.36), which is often assumed to be accompanied by more noise. Because of the advances already outlined, however, the giant 747, even with its greater thrust, will be significantly quieter than the 707-320B. In addition, because it is so much larger, it will make far fewer airport stops to transport the same total number of passengers. This double improvement in noise per passenger must be balanced against the predicted rise in air traffic.

Other noise-reduction techniques such as attenuation of noise at the source and changed flight procedures will be developed in the future as the noise problem is better understood through analysis and test.

Predicted Improvement

Substantial progress is expected in the next 20 years so that the advantages of air commerce can be realized without unacceptable deterioration in the quality of living. Advances in the following specific areas will be most important:

- Knowledge of the noise-generating mechanisms of the many acoustical sources of an engine.
- Reliable methods of analysis to predict the quality of the noise after it has traveled through the atmosphere.
- Improved methods to transform noise measurements into figures of merit that faithfully reflect the effects of noise on the population.
- Effective, flightworthy noise-absorbing materials and installation techniques that can withstand the operating environments and will exact a minimal penalty on engine performance.
- Engines designed for noise reduction.
- Aircraft designed for noise reduction.
- New testing methods (e.g., small-scale testing) for better evaluation of noise reduction techniques.
- Application of recently developed systems analysis methods to obtain balanced solutions to the noise problem.
- Planning of new airports and airport extensions so that land use compatible with airport nearness can be developed and implemented.
- Regulation and legislation to induce rapid improvement in noise control. Wisely drawn, these measures will promote the continued growth of air commerce so that its revenues can finance noise control.

The problem of noise reduction has been recognized by the scientific and engineering communities, and many agencies, public and private, are now pressing for a better understanding of the noise-generating mechanisms. This broad and fundamental approach will provide the basis for many technological solutions to the noise problem that will be evaluated, screened, and applied.

GENERAL AVIATION

General aviation is defined as all aircraft except those of the military and the certificated air carriers. General aviation is subdivided by the Federal Aviation Administration (FAA) into eight classes: executive transportation (professional pilots); business transportation (nonprofessional pilots); personal; aerial application; industrial/special; instructional; air taxi, charter, and contract; and other. For each class, a wide variety of aircraft designs is available. It is therefore difficult to discuss general aviation except in general terms.

The 100,000 general aircraft now in use outnumber airliners 40 to 1. They fly 4 times as many hours, and use 15 times as many airports. With the increasing use of general-aviation air taxis and business jets, these aircraft have become an important supplement to the air transport system. As air travel grows over the next two decades, their relative importance is expected to increase.

The composition of the U.S. general aviation fleet in 1985 is projected as follows:

Type of Airplane	Number
Single-engine, 4 or more places	200,000
Single-engine, 1 to 3 places	50,000
Multiengine piston	45,000
Multiengine turbine	18,000
Rotorcraft	9,000
Other	1,800

By FAA forecasts, the 1985 total will be 50 times the number of airliners flying in 1985. General aviation's percentage of total airborne hours should reach 79 percent by 1977 (compared with 52 percent in 1963).

The fleet's enormous growth will be accompanied by technological advances as these are needed, desired, and economically justified. This discussion concentrates on the technological area of general-aviation avionics, because of its importance to the future ATC system. General aviation and the airlines will present major challenges to that system by 1985.

Until recently general-aviation aircraft have mingled with airliners only at airports and at the lower altitudes. However, the newer pressurized general-aviation aircraft enjoy a greater choice of flight altitudes and, as a result, are more frequently using high-altitude controlled airspace. Since the controlled airspace floor may be lowered in the future, cooccupancy of that space by general aviation and airliners will be increased. Thus, the importance of avionics for general aviation is expected to grow.

Avionic systems are currently being improved in weight, volume, reliability, and maintenance through the application of solid-state technological advances such as transistors. Future generations will use more subminiature components and microcircuits, permitting small aircraft to carry quite sophisticated equipment. The use of digital circuits will improve reliability and accuracy by allowing more self-testing for failure isolation. Modular functional packaging will simplify fault repair, thus reducing requirements for field maintenance. Some of the advanced concepts developed for the airlines will be

adapted for general aviation through the use of low-cost digital electronics. On-board data processing in small planes will permit partial
automation of some flight functions, e.g., preprogrammed digital frequency control, automatic airplane performance monitoring, and automatic position reporting via data link. Area navigation will be provided by a number of systems ranging from low-cost course line computers to advanced pictorial displays. Other cockpit displays and instruments will be simplified and improved through regrouping and combining.

Until recently, general aviation has confined itself primarily to operations under visual flight rules, but a rapid transition to instrument
flight rules (IFR) capability is now under way. Three factors that tend
to accelerate this change are the increase in speed and range of light
aircraft, the emphasis on punctuality regardless of weather, and the
desire to obtain more flying hours from expensive aircraft. Figure 3.37
shows an FAA forecast of the increase in IFR-equipped general aviation; such aircraft could well be the heaviest load on the future ATC
system.

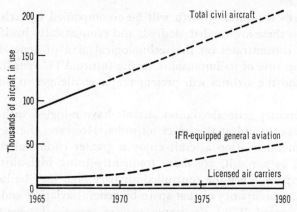

Figure 3.37. U.S. civil aircraft fleet composition.

The major trend in the general-aviation avionics market is toward
greater penetration by airline-type equipment. The rate of this penetration is controlled primarily by the cost of such equipment.

The value of the equipment that will be installed in a given airplane
is related to the operational requirements and the airplane's value.
Heavy twins and business jets usually are fully equipped with avionics
of the same quality as that used by the airlines. Light twins and single-
engine planes are not so well equipped. A survey by the Aircraft
Owners and Pilots Association found the following usage of avionics
in the 1967 general aviation fleet:

Avionic subsystem	Percent of aircraft equipped
Dual omnirange	54
Single automatic direction finding (ADF)	53
Dual VHF transceiver	52
Single omnirange	43
Single VHF transceiver	42
Autopilot	29
DME	12
ATC transponder beacon	6
Dual ADF	2
Radar	1

Increasing traffic density and IFR usage during the next 10 years will contribute to a sharp rise in the use of ATC transponders and DME on light aircraft (including single-engine models). At the same time, there will be an increase in the use of automatic flight control. All major manufacturers of general-aviation craft now offer some type of autopilot, and such systems are rapidly gaining acceptance. More than 50 percent of the new airplanes are being turned out with such equipment; if the trend continues, virtually all new light aircraft will be equipped with autopilots in the near future. The use of stability augmentation systems in light aircraft is being encouraged by the FAA and may be a future FAA requirement.

Additional advanced systems such as collision avoidance, pictorial and head-up displays will be taken up by general aviation when they become operationally necessary and economically feasible.

STOL TECHNOLOGY FORECAST

This section and the next present some of the ways in which STOL and CTOL airplane designs differ. Some key technological influences are pointed out, and the effect of market demand on STOL designs is discussed. Because STOL technology has not seen much commercial use, meaningful trends cannot be established. Design objectives for the next 20 years are given instead.

Figure 3.38 relates approach speed to cruise speed for existing airplanes. A low approach speed is required for landing on short fields. At the same time, if the vehicle is to be economical and attract passengers, the cruise speed should be as high as possible. The figure shows a group of airplanes offering first-generation STOL performance, but with low cruise speeds. The objective of the next 20 years, indicated by the target area, is to design high-cruise-speed airplanes that can approach at speeds roughly half those of today's high-speed airplanes.

Figure 3.39 relates approach speed to wing loading for the same groups of airplanes. Designing for high-speed cruise increases both

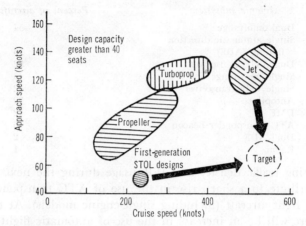

Figure 3.38. STOL speed design objective.

wing sweep angle and wing loading. Both effects translate into higher approach speeds. The development of high-lift devices (flaps, slats, slots, etc.) has kept approach speeds within acceptable limits. First-generation STOL aircraft develop low approach speeds with relatively low wing loadings. The design target is to maintain low approach speeds while providing wing loadings as high as those of the current high-speed jets.

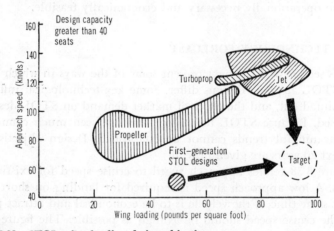

Figure 3.39. STOL wing loading design objective.

Figure 3.40 shows the general operating economics of STOL, CTOL, and VTOL aircraft. Direct operating cost at a typical short-haul trip distance of 150 nautical miles is presented against the field-length capability of various future aircraft designs. Note that STOL airplanes

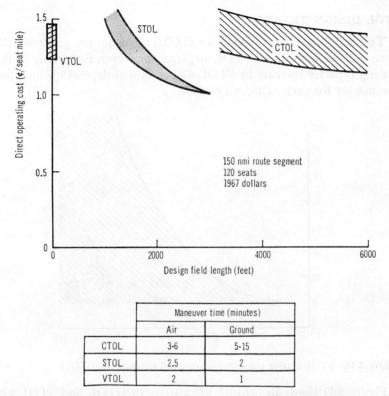

	Maneuver time (minutes)	
	Air	Ground
CTOL	3-6	5-15
STOL	2.5	2
VTOL	2	1

Figure 3.40.   Direct operating cost comparison—STOL, CTOL, and VTOL.

need not suffer an operating cost penalty in relation to CTOL airplanes.

Short-field capability can be used in two ways: a STOL airplane can operate from short runways close to traffic-generating centers, or it can land on a long runway (usually associated with large city airfields), quickly clear the runway, and proceed to its gate position with short ground maneuver time. This potential saving in ground maneuver time depends, of course, on airfield layout.

The technology of lift engines, a type of propulsion considered for STOL and VTOL aircraft as well as CTOL, is reviewed in the CTOL propulsion section.

The technology forecast for STOL airplanes is a reflection of the forecast already given for CTOL in the various design disciplines. Specific trends in past STOL technology are largely buried in CTOL advances. Hence, this section has emphasized the differences between STOL and CTOL designs and has presented the expected trends as goals that must be reached by STOL technology per se.

STOL DESIGN TRENDS

The design trends presented for CTOL airplanes are generally the same as those forecast for STOL airplanes. However, the timing of the seating capacity increase in STOL airplanes will depend on how fast the market for such vehicles develops.

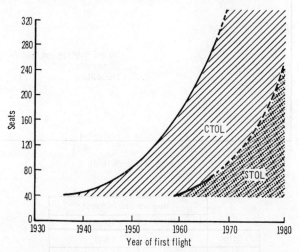

Figure 3.41. STOL seating capacity growth trend compared to CTOL.

Figure 3.41 shows the growth of capacity in CTOL and STOL airplanes with the expansion of commercial service. This expansion has principally affected CTOL airplanes. With STOL operation, the market from one large community will spread over a large number of small airports (STOL-ports). To maintain satisfactory frequency of service, the STOL vehicles will be smaller at first; however, after introduction of the first-generation designs, this market may be stimulated as was the CTOL market. The resulting growth would require larger-capacity STOL designs.

Figure 3.42 shows this trend toward larger capacity plotted against approach speed. The design target is low approach speed (STOL performance) in airplanes as large as the current large commercial jets. Turboprop, propeller, and jet areas are set off in the figure to indicate that, as is true today, a family of each type of aircraft will be required to handle the diversified market.

VTOL TECHNOLOGY FORECAST

Rapid progress in VTOL technology has been made in the last 15 years, and further development in the next 20 promises fast, convenient, and economical short-haul transportation. Improvements in propulsion

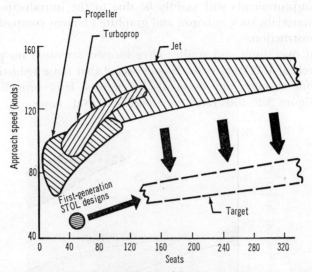

Figure 3.42. STOL seating capacity design objective.

systems, materials and structural technology, aerodynamics, reliability, and other engineering aspects will enhance the capabilities of helicopters, compounds, and other VTOL aircraft.

PROPULSION SYSTEMS

Decreased engine weight and fuel consumption will result from the application of advanced technology. Figure 3.43 shows past and projected improvements in specific weights of propeller and rotor systems.

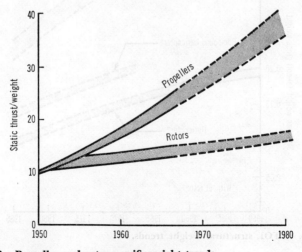

Figure 3.43. Propeller and rotor specific-weight trends.

Future improvements will mainly be due to the introduction of advanced materials, such as boron and graphite filament composites, into blade construction.

Recent operations and studies have focused attention on potential noise levels of VTOL aircraft. It is expected that noise reductions will be possible through improvements in engines, fans, propellers, and rotors. Figure 3.44 illustrates the trend in VTOL noise.

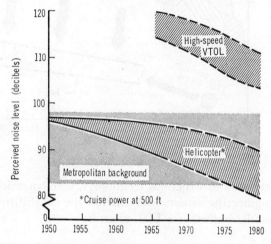

Figure 3.44.   Projected VTOL noise levels.

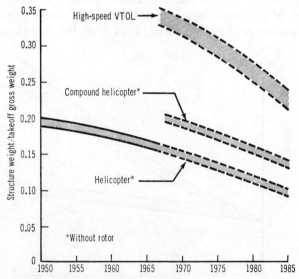

Figure 3.45.   VTOL structural weight trends.

MATERIALS AND STRUCTURAL TECHNOLOGY

The major improvement expected in future structural weight, as shown in Figure 3.45, will be primarily due to the very high strength and stiffness of advanced fiber-reinforced composite materials.

AERODYNAMICS

Improvements in airfoils, lift coefficients, and drag alleviation will result in increased cruise performance efficiency, as shown in Figure 3.46.

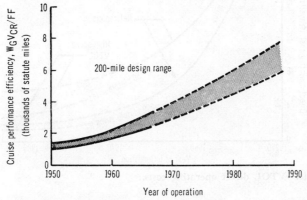

Figure 3.46.   VTOL cruise performance efficiency trend.

Continual improvement over the past 15 years has increased the speed of VTOL aircraft from 100 knots to 250 knots. By combining the advances in propulsion, configurations, and aerodynamics, the trend of VTOL aircraft speed capability can be projected as shown in Figure 3.47.

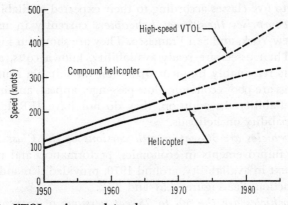

Figure 3.47.   VTOL cruise speed trends.

DIRECT OPERATING COSTS

The direct operating costs of helicopters have decreased spectacularly during the past 15 years of operation. Figure 3.48 indicates the further improvement promised by the advances in technology described earlier.

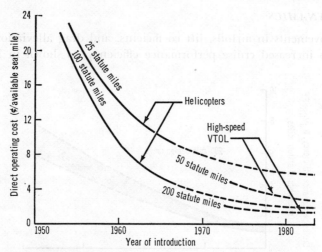

Figure 3.48.   VTOL direct operating costs.

VTOL DESIGN TRENDS

This section presents performance data and three-view drawings of typical existing and future VTOL vehicles. They range from the relatively small twin-turbine equipment now operated by helicopter lines up to the much larger advanced helicopters and advanced V/STOL (vertical or short takeoff and landing) configurations. The aircraft are grouped into five classes according to their expected availability dates.

Class 1 comprises the 25-seat helicopters currently in use in Los Angeles, New York, and San Francisco. They are shown in Figures 3.49 and 3.50. Their assets are ready availability, known costs, and a size that permits reasonably frequent operation on suitable routes. Their shortcomings are poor economics, low passenger appeal, and inadequate schedule reliability. In addition, they do not have IFR takeoff and landing capability on helipads.

Class 2 vehicles are 30-seat growth versions of the Class 1 vehicles with small improvements in economics, performance, and reliability. They are next in availability, around 1970, provided demand warrants their production. See Figures 3.51 and 3.52.

Class 3 vehicles are the 50- to 75-seat versions of current military

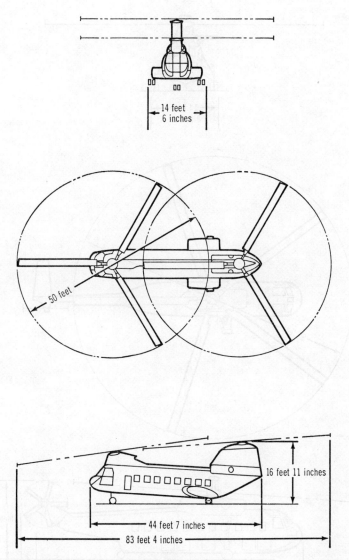

Figure 3.49. Boeing-Vertol 107II helicopter: 25 seats, cruise speed 156 mph, maximum gross weight 19,000 lb.

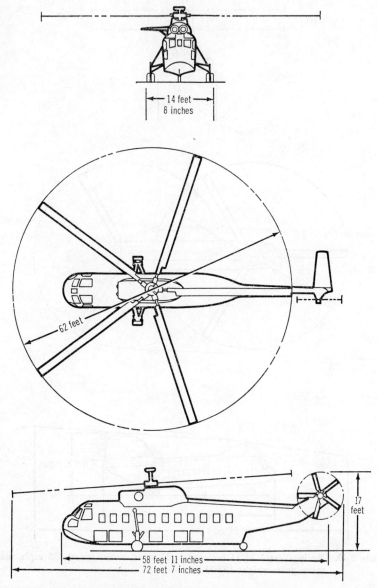

Figure 3.50. United Aircraft–Sikorsky S-61L helicopter: 28 seats, cruise speed 139 mph, maximum gross weight 19,000 lb.

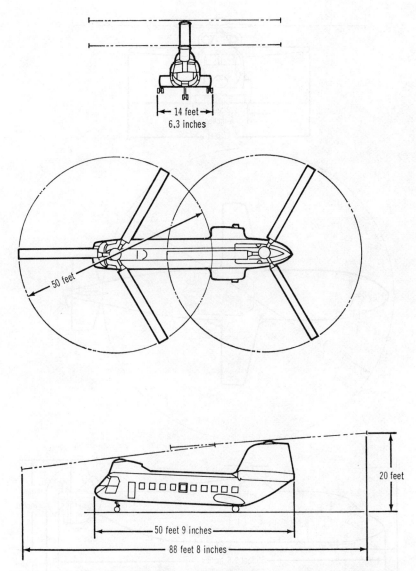

14 feet
6.3 inches

50 feet

20 feet

50 feet 9 inches
88 feet 8 inches

**Figure 3.51.   Boeing-Vertol 107IIA helicopter: capacity, 31 seats, cruise speed 163
mph, maximum gross weight 24,000 lb.**

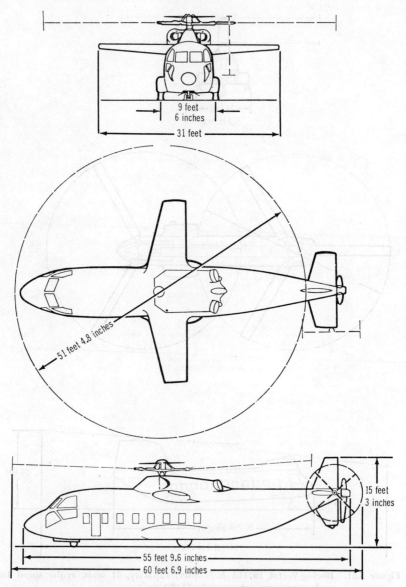

Figure 3.52. Lockheed CL-1026 rigid-rotor compound VTOL airplane: 30 seats, cruise speed 230 mph, maximum gross weight 23,500 lb.

helicopters. They are shown in Figures 3.53 to 3.55. Their economics, performance, and reliability are predicted to be superior to those of Classes 1 and 2, but certification provisions would have to be made for these military derivatives. They are potentially available by 1971.

Class 4 consists of 90- to 100-seat helicopters specifically designed for the commercial market of the 1970's. (Figures 3.56, 3.57.) Their direct operating costs, matching those of the DC-9 and 737 at ranges from 50 to 100 miles, make possible a profitable large-scale VTOL operation. They could be as reliable as current jets, with acceptable vibration and noise levels. Their safety attributes would include IFR takeoff and landing capability on helipads. The large body of testing and operational experience accumulated on helicopters gives confidence that these design goals can be met. These aircraft could be available four to five years after the start of the program.

Class 5 encompasses compound helicopters, tilt wings, tilt rotors, stowed rotors, fan-in-wing, and propulsive wing—advanced configurations that are featured in most V/STOL studies. (Figures 3.58 to 3.64.) If these designs live up to expectations, the tilt-wing and tilt-rotor groups should have the lowest direct operating costs of all VTOL's. These aircraft could be available in eight to ten years.

Development of Class 4 and 5 vehicles can proceed faster if appropriate financial support becomes available.

Current FAA rules covering transport helicopter IFR operations, commonly referred to as Category A rules, limit allowable takeoff weights by engine failure considerations. In the event of an engine failure during takeoff prior to reaching a critical decision point, the pilot must be able to return safely to the heliport. Should an engine fail after the critical decision point, the pilot must be able to climb out safely. Similar criteria apply to landing. During aircraft certification, takeoff and landing procedures with an allowable height and speed envelope are established to meet these rules. Specific procedures in current use are vertical takeoff and landing to the critical decision point or takeoff with acceleration in ground effect along a short runway. The former procedure is usually limiting.

The FAA rules also establish minimum rate of climb with one engine inoperative, and minimum heliport size.

Future rule changes may require the ability to hover with one engine inoperative. Aircraft under 20,000 pounds maximum gross weight may be certificated for visual flight rules operation only under Category B rules, which are somewhat less restrictive in regard to engine failure.

Because of the narrow experience base in IFR VTOL operations, it is difficult to project future certification requirements and the extent

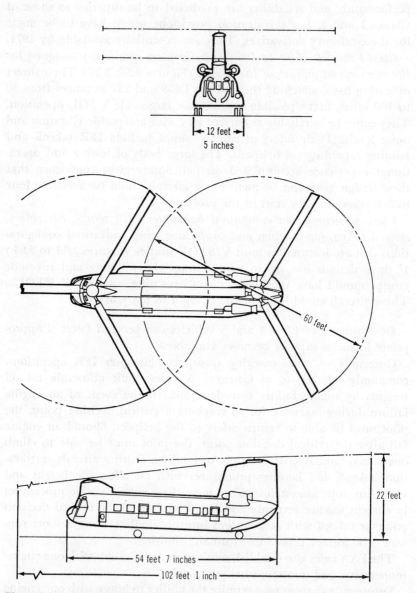

Figure 3.53. Boeing-Vertol 157 helicopter: 49 seats, cruise speed 181 mph, maximum gross weight 41,600 lb.

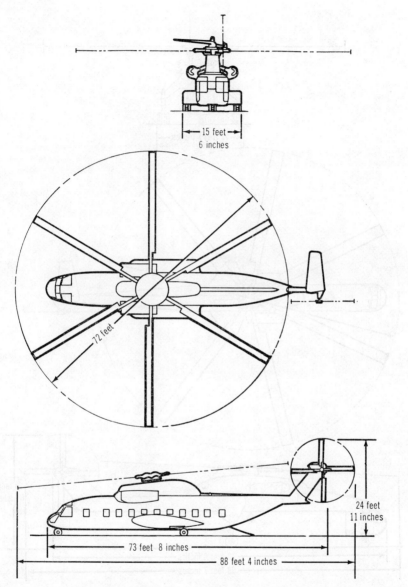

Figure 3.54. United Aircraft–Sikorsky S-65 (CH-53) two-engine helicopter: 60 seats, cruise speed 175 mph, maximum gross weight 39,300 lb.

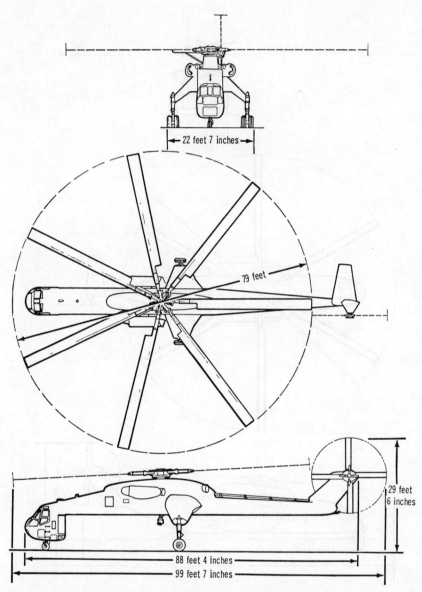

Figure 3.55. United Aircraft–Sikorsky S-64B crane-and-pod helicopter (pod not shown): 73 seats, cruise speed 157 mph, maximum gross weight 55,000 lb.

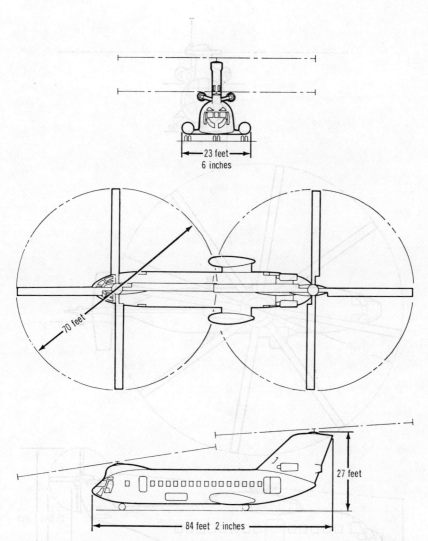

Figure 3.56. Boeing-Vertol 177 helicopter: 94 seats, cruise speed 215 mph, maximum gross weight 71,500 lb.

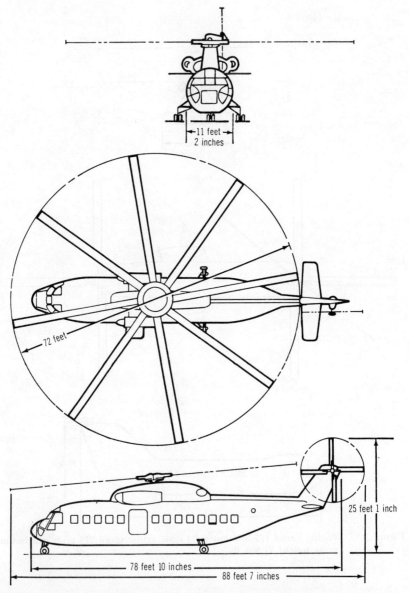

Figure 3.57. United Aircraft–Sikorsky S-65 three-engine helicopter: 90 seats, cruise speed 175 mph, maximum gross weight 54,300 lb.

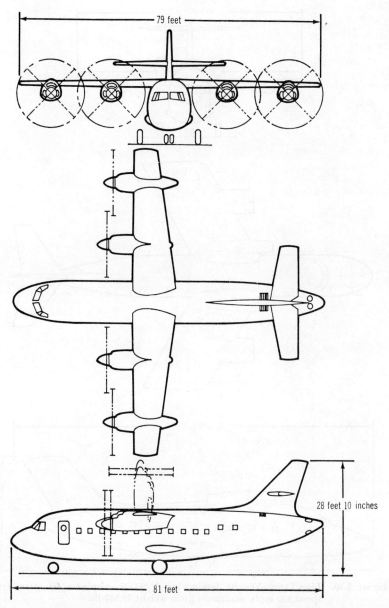

Figure 3.58.   Ling-Temco-Vought turboprop V/STOL airplane: 60 seats, cruise speed 450 mph, maximum gross weight 62,115 lb.

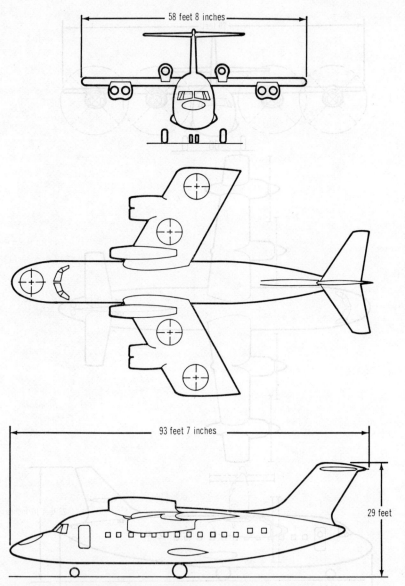

Figure 3.59. Ling-Temco-Vought fan-in-wing V/STOL airplane: 60 seats, cruise speed 530 mph, maximum gross weight 79,587 lb.

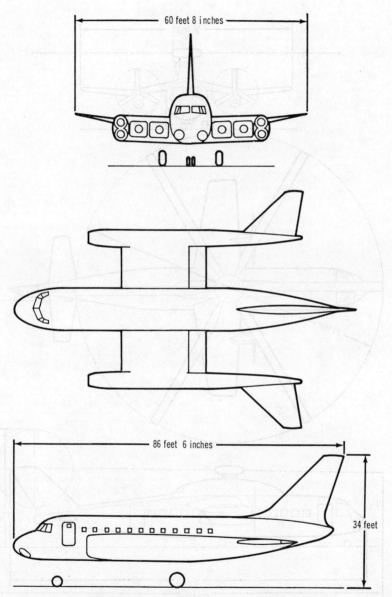

Figure 3.60. Ling-Temco-Vought propulsive-wing V/STOL airplane: 60 seats, cruise speed 600 mph, maximum gross weight 73,300 lb.

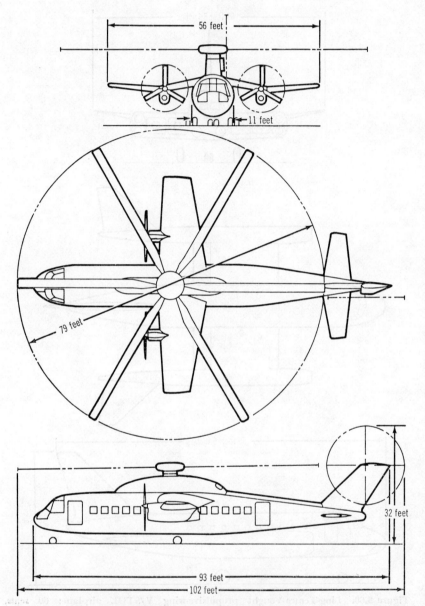

Figure 3.61. United Aircraft–Sikorsky commercial compound V/STOL helicopter: 70 seats, cruise speed 272 mph, maximum gross weight 57,000 lb.

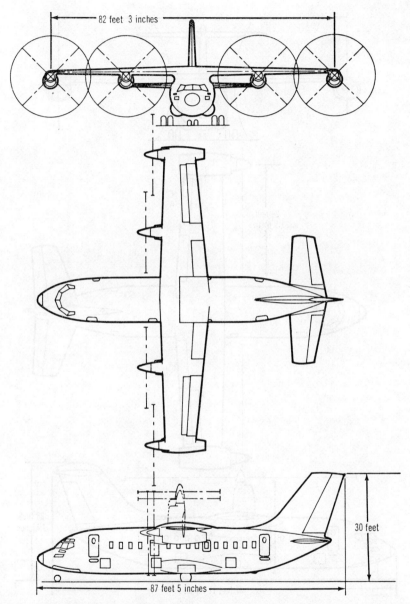

Figure 3.62.   Boeing-Vertol/NASA tilt-wing airplane: 90 seats, cruise speed 450 mph, maximum gross weight 84,500 lb.

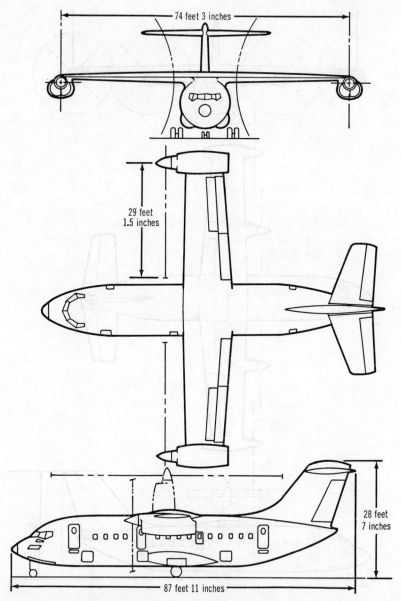

Figure 3.63. Boeing-Vertol tilt-rotor airplane: 90 seats, cruise speed 404 mph, maximum gross weight 83,000 lb.

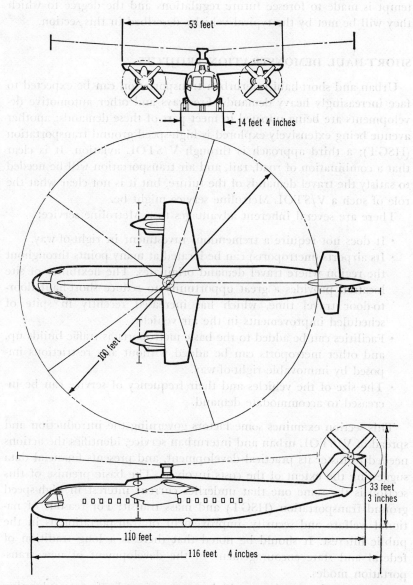

Figure 3.64. Lockheed CL-879 rigid-rotor compound VTOL airplane: 98 seats, cruise speed 288 mph, maximum gross weight 78,800 lb.

of their departure from existing regulations. For this reason, no attempt is made to foresee future regulations and the degree to which they will be met by the typical vehicles described in this section.

SHORT-HAUL DEMONSTRATION PROJECTS

Urban and short-haul interurban transportation can be expected to face increasingly heavy demands. Freeways and other automotive developments are being pursued to meet part of these demands; another avenue being extensively explored is high-speed ground transportation (HSGT); a third approach is through V/STOL aviation. It is clear that a combination of road, rail, and air transportation will be needed to satisfy the travel demands of the future, but it is not clear what the role of such a V/STOL Metroline service might be.

There are several inherent advantages to a Metroline service:

- It does not require a tremendous investment in right-of-way.
- Its airports (metroports) can be located at many points throughout the region where travel demand originates. The flexibility of site location provides a great opportunity to reduce short-haul door-to-door travel time, which has increased recently in spite of scheduled improvements in the air vehicles.
- Facilities can be added to the basic metroports as traffic builds up, and other metroports can be added without any restrictions imposed by immovable right-of-way.
- The size of the vehicles and their frequency of service can be increased to accommodate demand.

This section examines some factors governing the introduction and spread of V/STOL urban and interurban service, identifies the actions needed to foster its practical development, and presents financial data suggesting the extent of the costs involved. The basic premise of this section is the same one that underlies current interest in high-speed ground transportation (HSGT) and mass transit: For reasons of national welfare and security, improvement of transportation is in the public interest. It should be noted that there is a long tradition of federal and state encouragement in the development of new transportation modes.

The Metroline service would have a profound effect on planning the facilities required for the nation's transport system. It would allow access to air transportation at a number of new city-center and suburban terminals. It would require changes in major airport buildings for rooftop loading, revised use of terminal-area airspace, and new ATC procedures. Multiple-access interurban transportation would probably attract new travelers and shift short-haul passengers away from present fixed-wing airport facilities. When and where Metroline service will be introduced are significant uncertainties in air transport planning.

This application of V/STOL technology seems remote at present for reasons other than technical, as outlined later in this section. It would cause a far greater revolution than did the introduction of jet transports. It is essential that those who plan this nation's future transportation facilities have more detailed knowledge of full-scale systems, so that V/STOL may develop as an integral part of the overall transportation network.

FULL-SCALE METROLINE SERVICE

A description of a general Metroline system is necessary to delineate the role it could fill. Figure 3.65 shows typical routes, both urban and interurban. The vehicles (metroliners) would be best suited for interurban service. Local service would be provided by helicopters of the present type.

The distances traveled would range from 10 to 250 miles. At these distances the metroliners and metroports have a decided door-to-door trip time advantage, as shown in Figure 3.66. This advantage would have to be supported by frequent service, particularly on the shorter routes. Flight times would be less than half an hour, permitting simpler cabin furnishings, no meal service, fewer toilets, and other savings.

The system would be used by a variety of travelers. By interfacing with major airports, it could quickly and conveniently collect and distribute medium- and long-haul passengers from both the urban area and the outlying cities and towns. This might obviate the construction of major airports in the smaller cities in favor of metroports. Another use would be interairport transfer in areas having more than one airport. There is also the possibility of intermodal transfer between bus or rail stations and the airports.

The existing helicopter services in New York, San Francisco, and Los Angeles already partly fulfill some of these functions. Los Angeles Airways provides a collection-distribution service to the airport from multiple sites within the Los Angeles urban area. New York Airways provides interairport transfer as well as airport access for the New York airport system. These would be relatively small parts of a full-scale Metroline system.

The major use of the system would be interurban travel between large cities less than 250 miles apart, as in the megalopolitan or corridor areas developing in the United States. Short-haul air travelers would find frequent service from multiple access points in each city

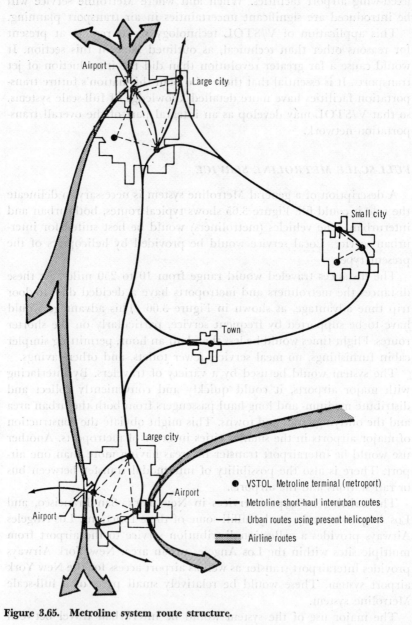

Figure 3.65. Metroline system route structure.

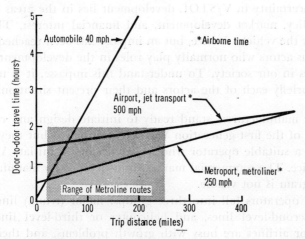

Figure 3.66. Metroliner travel time comparison.

to be quicker and more convenient than using the fixed-wing airports.

The system would relieve short-haul airports by diverting much of the predicted air traffic. Because of the time saving, it might also divert traffic from other modes such as train or auto. Introducing new routes and services could generate much new traffic as well, since business travelers would be able to make new types of interurban trips.

The interurban portion of the Metroline system does not exist today. Future V/STOL aircraft will be particularly suited for this type of service.

THE IMPASSE

The system promises many advantages in time saving, convenience, and flexibility. The technical feasibility of suitable V/STOL vehicles has been indicated, and future technology promises much-improved direct operating costs. Operational feasibility seems assured, although there are problems of site location, community noise level, design and construction of major terminals in city centers and urban areas, ATC, and all-weather operation. These problems are soluble, but they require some operating experience.

Determination of economic feasibility requires marketing experience at various levels of service and fares, and some operating experience to determine station-operating expenses, maintenance costs, block times, and daily vehicle use. Operating experience is also required so that the operator can guide the designer by specifying vehicle sizes and configurations, interior arrangements, fuel reserve requirements, and stabilization requirements.

The uncertainty in V/STOL development lies in the areas of regulatory policy, market development, and financial interest. The technology for the vehicles is here, but an impasse has been reached among the various actors who normally play roles in the development of new enterprises in our society. To understand this impasse, it is useful to describe briefly each of the actors and their present situations.

1. The manufacturers stand ready to initiate design and construction of the first generation V/STOL transports, but they cannot find a suitable operator who has any plans to initiate V/STOL service. The commercial market to justify a costly manufacturing program is not visible.

2. The operators fall into three groups: major (trunk) lines, local or second-level lines, and helicopter or third-level lines. The major airlines are busy with growth problems, and their fixed-wing experience tells senior management that there is no profit to be made on short-haul traffic. Because of the poor performance of present helicopters and the uncertain performance of military experimental vehicles, they are reluctant to gamble on new V/STOL transports. No fixed-wing trunkline has a suitable route structure for Metroline service, and the operators are uncertain as to whether they would be allowed to add new short-haul routes. If they do consider a new route structure, they find they are talking about extensive development of markets where air travel does not now exist. A few years of promotional service would be required to develop the full traffic, indicating an initial financial exposure of millions of dollars in operating expense where market potential is unknown. The operators find it difficult to divert the capital and manpower required by their growing operations into expensive, long-term development of an uncertain new area of business. Their boards of directors and financial backers can always find a better return at less risk in buying fixed-wing airplanes and developing their present long-haul system.

3. The local airline operators who perhaps do have suitable route structures and who might feel that they could get new routes for Metroline service are on federal subsidy. It would require a clear statement of support from the Civil Aeronautics Board (CAB) to let them start planning such a service, and with no market information they would face severe problems in raising financial backing.

4. The helicopter carriers, who might logically expand their heliport services into a Metroline system, are losing money. They

have neither the financial nor the management resources to contract for the large initial order that the manufacturer would require. Like the local airlines, they could not take action without the support of the regulators and legislators.

5. The investors who might be attracted by the long-term returns of a Metroline service must have some idea of the investment requirements and the period of development until a profit can be made. They need a strong demonstration of market response and assurances of economic viability before they will lend their support to any operator.

6. The public, whose response is essential to Metroline development, has not had a chance to sample this type of service, aside from the airport feeder and transfer operations of present helicopter lines. The public will not get this chance unless an operator can persuade himself, the regulators, his investors, and local authorities of the long-term viability of the service.

7. Local authorities, who will be responsible for siting and constructing metroports, will await the request and assurances of an operator before they give approval and funds. They will need to coordinate their actions with nearby cities to get the service started.

8. The regulators have only recently faced up to the possibility of a new mode of air transport. The lack of any regulatory framework for developing a new system is a gap that needs to be filled. A statement of policy that somehow defines the rules of the game for the various actors is needed before the operators and investors can act. This policy has not been set, since the technical and economic feasibility of V/STOL aircraft has only recently been recognized. It is not clear whether national transportation policy will include the development of such systems, but an important first step was taken by the CAB on October 4, 1967, when it decided to institute "an investigation to determine the need and the feasibility of metropolitan area to metropolitan area VTOL, V/STOL, and STOL service on a subsidy-ineligible basis, between certain major cities of the Northeast Corridor" (Docket 19078).

9. The legislators' experience with subsidies to helicopter services has left them with a strong impression of unprofitability. While subsidy is one avenue to V/STOL development, it can blunt the profit incentive and cost consciousness of management. Furthermore, the pressure to minimize subsidy expenses often leads to minimal service and avoidance of experimentation in marketing or operation. Such experimentation may be the only way to

obtain the basic market data needed to guide decisions concerning the new system's development.

Thus the actors are at an impasse. The manufacturers will not build until a market is visible. The operators will not provide the service because they have other interests and because they lack suitable route structure, financial backing, and market information. Investors are wary because of the amount of capital required, the risks involved when there is no clear evidence of public response, and the uncertainty about future government action. Since the operators show no interest, the regulators and legislators have been slow to investigate V/STOL development and methods of encouraging it.

RESOLUTION OF THE IMPASSE

What is the key to breaking the impasse and enabling the actors to play their parts in developing a system? There are two critical steps, both of which must be undertaken by government.

1. A policy statement should be made to declare the goals of Metroline development, define the Metroline service of the future, and outline the government's interest in finding ways for the political, regulatory, financial, and industrial groups to work together toward testing and developing V/STOL service. Perhaps the Metroline service should be recognized as a new mode of air transportation and the rules of the game made clear regarding the roles of trunklines, locals, helicopter lines, and new entries. The policy statement could come from the Department of Transportation (DOT) in coordination with the Department of Housing and Urban Development (HUD), the Department of Commerce, or the CAB. At the same time, a serious government/industry study of developmental alternatives should be initiated.
2. The Department of Transportation should invite proposals from teams of manufacturers, operators, and local authorities to run demonstration projects in suitable areas. The market response needs to be demonstrated to the operators, investors, regulators, and legislators as soon as possible. Portions of a full-scale system can be operated in carefully controlled market tests to show who and how many of the traveling public will use this service and why. This information is vital for stimulating the interest of all actors in the game and for selecting the channels of development. It would be valuable in defining the role of the Metroline service relative to the proposed HSGT system.

DEVELOPMENTAL ALTERNATIVES

Some of the channels being considered for development of Metroline service are listed here to indicate the broad range of possibilities.

• Trunk airlines

Present practice has shown that it is feasible for a trunkline to underwrite an expensive air feeder service to its own separate terminal at a major airport. The revenue diverted from other carriers, particularly when handling long-haul passengers, justifies the expense. If a large enough market develops, other trunklines might be forced to start independent feeder services, both to meet competition and to disperse their ticketing and boarding at congested terminals. As these feeder systems grow, the trunks might consider interurban services in competition with themselves and other airlines.

• Local or regional carriers

Local carriers have traditionally handled feeder and short-haul interurban routes. They could be called on to introduce V/STOL aircraft into their present systems, expanding their route structures as required. These routes would not compete with the trunk routes. Although their costs would be less, the level of service would be distinctly lower than that generally available from the trunklines. These carriers are still on subsidy and would need financial support.

• Trunkline consortium

In the Washington-Baltimore helicopter case considered by the CAB, major trunklines formed and financed a corporation to provide airport feeder service in that area. This is one way to set up Metroline service; an allied concept is the creation of a separate division of an airline to operate with its own identity and profit incentives and separate cost reporting to the CAB. The availability of this cost information is vital in guiding the development of new facilities for the system.

• New entries

Several large corporations and financial interests are considering entry into Metroline service because of its long-term attractiveness. Their ability to hire airline personnel, along with the possibility of acquiring or merging present third-level carriers, creates an attractive potential for a new system designed specifically for economical, efficient service.

• *Comsat-type corporation*

The federal government could be involved in financing the initial development and perhaps underwriting demonstration programs. One mechanism for such involvement is the creation of a federal/industrial corporation similar to Comsat.

• *Other transportation companies*

Some bus or rail lines might consider acquiring and operating a Metroline service. A bus line, for example, could install metroports on the roofs of its terminals and use the buses as feeders.

OBJECTIVES OF DEMONSTRATION PROJECTS

If it is in the public interest to develop V/STOL service, demonstration projects should be undertaken in the next few years. These projects would not be a simple subsidy program; instead, federal "seed" money would be used to develop a new transportation system. The required data cannot be obtained from present services such as the helicopter lines because the Metroline system is quite different. Moreover, the existing trunkline subsidy program was not intended to allow enough experimentation with fares and service frequencies to determine market response. The V/STOL demonstration projects should be experimental, using systems that are prototypes of the final system. The projects should be scheduled for finite time periods, with arrangements for termination agreed upon in advance.

The objectives would be

- To acquaint the public with this new mode of common-carrier travel and measure acceptance vis-à-vis HSGT at various fare and service levels.
- To study the problems of locating new metroports in megalopolitan areas (e.g., community acceptance).
- To show the manufacturers and operators the vehicle characteristics needed for this service.
- To improve and develop the ground support system (e.g., automated passenger terminals).
- To develop ATC procedures at major airports so that V/STOL and fixed-wing aircraft will be segregated.
- To show investors the long-term economic viability and potential growth of an efficiently operated system.

The first objective implies that any project should demonstrate a complete new transportation system. It should not be principally a

showcase for a new product like a STOL airplane, hovercraft, or helicopter; their technical and operational feasibility can be quickly and
easily shown in less expensive ways. The more difficult task is to demonstrate the economic viability of an overall service.

Demonstrating an entire system requires a long-term effort by an
operator interested in developing the market and in maintaining and
expanding the service after the project is ended. He should be willing,
with federal support, to invest time, effort, and capital in the project.
Likewise, the manufacturers should be willing to spend money to
supply and maintain their vehicles in the demonstration. Local authorities interested in having a demonstration project should share
costs of land acquisition and construction of terminals.

The administration of the projects could be controlled by DOT
through a series of programs in which the various parties can propose
to participate (similar to HUD's urban development programs). The
projects could be integrated by an agency designated by DOT.

POSSIBLE PROJECTS

Demonstration projects for the years 1968 to 1973 are restricted by
the types of vehicles that can be available and certificated for passenger
travel in that time. Table 3.1 lists some vehicles that might be used.
Public acceptance will be sensitive to the vehicle used, and a demon-

**TABLE 3.1 METROLINER VEHICLES AVAILABLE NOW OR
THROUGH 1973**

Class	Model	Capacity (seats)	Speed (mph)	Availability date
Currently available				
STOL	DHC Twin Otter	19	180	
	Short Skyvan	18	175	
VTOL	Bell Jet Ranger	4	140	
	FH 1100	4	125	
	Hughes 500	4	125	
	Bell 204B	8	125	
	Bell 205A	14	120	
	BV-107 II	25	156	
	S-61L	28	139	
Available in future				
STOL	Breguet 941	55	250	1969
	DHC Buffalo	50	250	1969
VTOL	Advanced BV-107 IIA	31	163	1970
	BV-157 (CH-47)	49	181	1971
	S-65 (2-engine CH-53)	60	175	1971
	Canadair CL 84-1	16	285	1971
	LTV C-142	52	400	1971
	Lockheed CL-1026	30	230	1972
	S-65 Compound	70	272	1973

stration vehicle that makes a poor showing in terms of size, comfort, speed, safety, or noise may retard the acceptance of V/STOL transportation.

The projects should be carried out in markets where present ground and air congestion can be eased by the timesaving of a Metroline system. This restricts them to megalopolitan areas and initially favors the Northeast Corridor.

City Center to City Center

There is a need to determine what kind of traffic can be persuaded to use city-center service at fares consistent with future vehicles and a full-scale Metroline system. A good route for such a project would be downtown New York to downtown Philadelphia. After an introductory period, fares and frequency of service could be varied to get an idea of traffic response. The project would have to start with presently certificated transport helicopters or STOL aircraft, but could go on to adaptations (with restricted certification) of present and future military V/STOL vehicles.

Logically, an operator would be supported by one or more manufacturers (e.g., United Aircraft-Sikorsky, Lockheed, or Boeing-Vertol), and under contract to DOT. For the three to five years of the demonstration, DOT would control the project and retain the revenues. The various authorities at New York (Port of New York Authority, Department of Marine and Aviation, State of New York) and the local Philadelphia authorities would participate in arranging and supporting the ground facilities.

If the service looked promising, it could be extended to Baltimore and Washington in direct competition with the high-speed rail demonstration project. It would then connect with a future helicopter system in the Washington-Baltimore area as well as with local New York helicopter services. This is only one example; other city pairs like Cleveland and Detroit, Chicago and Milwaukee, Los Angeles and San Diego could also be considered as sites for similar projects. Perhaps a program should be offered that is widely available to other markets and participants.

The program proposals should be clearly directed toward the six objectives listed in the previous section. A New York–Philadelphia project, with thorough planning and analysis, could work toward all these objectives. For example, the problems of starting the service would provide a case study in site location, terminal construction, and rearrangement of ATC procedures. Planning and analysis in this area

should be fully documented to assist in working out other developments.

Instead of fixing fares and frequency of service, the operator should
vary them to test market response. After allowing a year to establish
the service in the public's mind, the frequency could be doubled; this
would test actual versus predicted traffic and would indicate (through
passenger surveys) whether the added convenience generates new traffic.
Businessmen might find, for example, that instead of making an all-day
trip to the other city, they could conveniently schedule a morning or
afternoon away from the office. A strong response of this nature would
argue for smaller vehicles, even at a higher unit operating cost—a
datum of utmost importance to the manufacturers. Similarly, systematic changes in fares, if they remain in effect long enough, would
permit evaluation of the results of fare elasticity.

Helicopter Airport Taxi

To start a collection-distribution system for major airports, a program could be offered to help develop helicopter taxi service at airports
where ground access is a problem. Most helicopter systems use 25-
passenger vehicles and fly a fixed schedule from relatively few urban
sites. They cannot offer the convenience of a taxicab; frequencies are
too low, the sites too far apart.

Another type of service can be provided with small helicopters
operated on a dynamic schedule from many small urban sites. Air
General of Boston is a model; it offers pickup and delivery every 15
minutes between Logan Airport and 44 small heliports at shopping
centers, motels, industrial parks, and individual business offices. The
fares are high in terms of cost per seat mile, but the service competes
with single-passenger cab or rental car. The price of $12 is low enough
so that the convenience and timesaving make the service attractive to
the business traveler.

Most of Air General's customers use the service to and from electronics firms in the Route 128 area (the circumferential highway). This
is a very small part of the total airport traffic, but it is interesting to
speculate whether the demand could grow to include a much larger
fraction of Boston business travel. Would reduced fares attract passengers? Are still more sites needed for convenience? Could the service
be extended to outlying cities whose travelers go through Logan Airport? More needs to be known about the costs of this type of air taxi
system and the market response to it.

Helicopter taxis could be proposed for all the major airports, perhaps with different demonstration objectives at different airports. One certain result would be to acquaint the populaces of major cities with the idea of having numerous heliports in the urban area.

Small heliports are easy to establish and do not arouse much local antagonism. They are generally managed by a local motel or shopping center. The current commercial versions of light observation helicopters would be excellent initial vehicles, but some operations analysis in particular markets is needed to determine whether a larger (e.g., 10-passenger) helicopter can run economically on dynamic schedules. Scheduling strategies can be constructed and tested with computer simulation, but real-time field testing is advisable to see the travelers' reactions.

Extending the area of coverage would eventually lead to some interurban service. For example, a New York system might bring in travelers from Trenton, Princeton, and New Brunswick in New Jersey, while another system could feed the Philadelphia airport from Trenton. The two systems should merge at Trenton and provide multistop through service from New York to Philadelphia. Such a route would eventually use larger VTOL equipment, but could well be broken in by an airport taxi service using present small helicopters.

Regional STOL Air Taxi

Some current STOL vehicles (Twin Otter, Short Skyvan) are suitable for use within a 250-mile radius of major airports. New ATC procedures and new 2000-ft runways would be needed to segregate them from the congested fixed-wing traffic patterns.

A STOL taxi program would logically use low-cost third-level carriers. By selecting ideal markets and spreading their overhead into the other fixed-base operations, these new carriers have become the only form of short-haul air travel that shows a profit. They could begin a new service and maintain a high frequency for several months at very low costs.

None of these carriers are large enough to embark on large-scale expansion of their markets, but federal aid would sharply enhance their growth and the entry of new operators. The expansion of the field could lead to mergers and acquisition by larger airlines interested in developing a full-scale Metroline system. This process would be subject to control by the CAB.

As traffic density and interconnections increased, larger V/STOL vehicles would be needed. The system would eventually provide multistop regional service, using STOL at small outlying airports and VTOL at major airports and city centers.

An example of a STOL project would be service to the three major New York airports from Long Island and the north shore of Long Island Sound. With initial federal help, one of the operators now using Twin Otter vehicles could provide a high frequency of service and build some simple outlying terminals. The system could pioneer low-level helicopter airways and an IFR all-weather ATC system. It could extend to major airports at Hartford, Providence, and Boston, as steps toward an eventual Boston–New York multistop service.

SHORT-HAUL DEMONSTRATION RECOMMENDATIONS

1. Government transportation policy should recognize V/STOL interurban short-haul service as a long-term goal, along with HSGT and mass transit. It should declare a broad program of support for development of this service in megalopolitan areas.

2. The V/STOL development alternatives should be studied to define the problems, advantages, and disadvantages of each. This would allow the formation of a policy framework within which the manufacturers, operators, investors, and regulators could operate.

3. The government should immediately call for detailed proposals of demonstration projects possible within the years 1968 to 1973. These proposals should be made by teams of operators, manufacturers, local authorities, investors, and others, and should include the following:

- Market studies and projections
- Data gathering and analysis methods
- Vehicles to be used
- The cost-sharing method
- The duration of each project and financial arrangements for termination

CONCLUSIONS

Projected improvements in CTOL vehicle design appear more than adequate to meet the challenge of the rapid increase in air travel over the next two decades. The potential economic advantages of these design improvements may be lost, however, if air vehicle technology does no more than compensate for the lag in operating and supporting environments.

Figure 3.67 shows the transportation snarl that looms in the years ahead. Air vehicle advances are being increasingly offset by overcrowded airways, insufficient and inadequate airfields, underdesigned terminals, and a haphazard approach to moving passengers and cargo

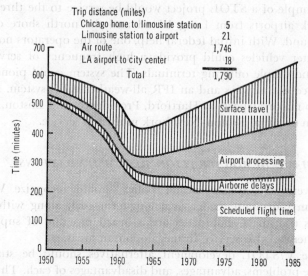

Figure 3.67. Door-to-door travel time projection for a typical air route (Chicago to Los Angeles).

between the terminals and their ultimate points of departure or destination.

In the next decade, medium- and long-haul aircraft will probably undergo their greatest improvement in the area of avionics, including guidance. Refinements in propulsion, structures, and aerodynamics will be continually introduced in subsonic aircraft. The U.S. SST will see service toward the end of that period and will induce intensified application of these technologies.

Avionics, until now principally exploited in military aircraft, is just beginning to make its impact in modified form on commercial aircraft. Extensive applications are foreseen in navigation, automated checkout, airborne computation, instrumentation, aircraft control, and communication. Better integration with the ATC environment should allow more operations in bad weather and greater safety in a much more crowded airspace (provided that all aircraft in that airspace are suitably equipped).

The growth of CTOL aircraft in passenger and cargo capacity will continue. Gross weight will increase. Body length and height, wingspan, and tail height will also increase, but the extent of the increases will be set by design approaches. More consideration will have to be given to multiple decks and folding wingtips and vertical fins. Ground developments to cope with passenger and baggage surges at airports will have more and more influence on aircraft designs.

Today's CTOL jet transports are the result of a "natural selection" that has standardized the most desirable design features; it takes a keen eye to distinguish a Douglas DC-8 from a Boeing 707. This selection was brought about by years of interaction between technology and demand for air travel: better airplanes increased the demand, which in turn spurred more technological progress, and so on. Many design features were tried out; those that suited the market survived, the others were abandoned.

Such a growth process has not yet occurred for V/STOL aircraft. There is a multitude of varied designs, each of which has received only a small amount of technological concentration. This makes it difficult to pinpoint trends for these aircraft as sharply as can be done for CTOL airplanes. Nevertheless, military requirements have stimulated the development of some of these vehicles. Advanced systems will probably be available for commercial use within the next decade; it remains to be seen, of course, whether they will meet the requirements of the market. To date, commercial experience with helicopters has provided only a limited amount of the information needed to support extensive plans for commercial competitive exploitation of these machines, and operating conditions have not been such as to yield compelling evidence of their economic viability. For both technical and operational reasons, it is not possible to draw firm conclusions on the prospects for V/STOL vehicles in either the urban or interurban transportation markets.

Supersonic transports will be used extensively over long-range routes; however, the sonic boom problem may limit overland flights at first. Research currently under way is already suggesting airplane shapes that may produce substantially less noticeable boom signatures.

Subsonic aircraft noise will remain a problem, although to a reduced extent. The most hopeful approach to subsonic noise control is through coordinated action by the following participants:

- Power-plant manufacturers, by controlling the sonic output of their product.
- Airframe manufacturers, by keeping noise levels in mind at the design stage.
- Aircraft operators, by adopting noise-control flight and operations practices.
- Airport planners and operators, by designing and operating airports so as to lessen the community's exposure to noise.
- Local government units, by using zoning, redevelopment, and other measures to induce compatible land use near airports.
- The federal government, by promoting progress in all these aspects

in such a way that air commerce can continue to add to the national economy and thereby make financially possible the desired control of air transport community noise.

RECOMMENDATIONS

Almost all the elements supporting air transportation need intensive attention to bring about immediate improvement. Most of these elements have not been keeping pace with either CTOL vehicle technology or the passengers' and shippers' demand for air service.

Integration of these elements and coordination of air transportation with the total transportation system are required. Realistic long-range planning must be intensified and correlated. Effective methods must be developed to identify the most desirable and practicable solutions. The data base to apply these methods must be enlarged and improved in coverage and accuracy.

The evolution of short-haul V/STOL vehicles must be speeded up to match that of CTOL airplanes over the past 30 years. First, studies are required to narrow down the numerous vehicle concepts to the most promising, so that these can be given the benefit of intensive application of technology. Second, after the first step has reached at least a preliminary stage, demonstration projects should be conducted. These projects should be designed to obtain the reliable economic and operational information required by the investors, manufacturers, and operators before they can commit themselves to a full-scale short-haul system.

4. AIR TRAFFIC CONTROL

INTRODUCTION

If air traffic is to grow with the national economy, airspace must be treated as a national resource. Thus the air traffic control (ATC) segments of the national airspace system (NAS) must be continuously developed to provide for the expeditious movement of all aircraft. Consideration must be given to all users of the airspace, i.e., military, airlines, and general aviation.

The Air Traffic Control Panel was given the objectives to identify, analyze, and evaluate factors affecting the future NAS, including airspace utilization, en route control, terminal area control, meteorology, navigation, and communications.

DEMAND FOR TRAFFIC CONTROL

The continuous development of a responsive air traffic control system should be predicated on demand and aircraft characteristics. The demand for air transportation has been delineated in the chapter on socioeconomic trends. Anticipated en route IFR traffic control activity for future years is shown in Figure 4.1. It is evident that greater attention will need to be given to allotment of airspace and compatibility of equipment between the airlines and general aviation. Likewise, such new types of aircraft as STOL, VTOL, and SST will require ATC system alterations. Chapter 3 gives details for each type of air vehicle.

SYSTEMS ANALYSIS

In order to develop an adequate air traffic control system, the systems analysis or building-block approach must be taken. Table 4.1 outlines

265

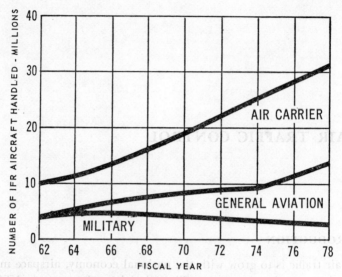

Figure 4.1. Projections of en route traffic control activity.
Source: FAA.

some of the basic factors that must be considered either in developing or modernizing the ATC system. In addition, problem areas must be identified. The present report analyzes some of the basic ATC components, outlines problem areas, and provides specific conclusions and recommendations for implementation.

BACKGROUND

Historically the federal aviation policy has tended toward dependence upon aircraft operators to avoid collisions under all conditions. In the past the government, either local or federal, has assisted with traffic control measures after the need was demonstrated by individual failures. Initial measures were air traffic "rules of the road," followed first by terminal traffic control measures, then by traffic control en route. In the terminal area, traffic was first controlled only on visual flights within sight of the airport. Later, control of instrument flights was undertaken.

En route control traditionally has been imposed only on instrument flights, although early procedures allowed for voluntary inclusion of visual flights, and radar advisory service has been available on request since about 1960. It is probable that increasing traffic problems will require further regulation of traffic, primarily through ground-managed traffic control measures.

TABLE 4.1. ATC SYSTEM FACTORS

	Airspace utilization	Aircraft	Information links	ATC services	Airports
Primary	Departure En route Arrival	Cockpit displays Airborne equipment	Navigation Communication Meteorology	Air Route Traffic Control Center Control towers FSS Satellites	Aircraft surface handling Runways/taxiways Landing/takeoff aids Terminal/transfer
Secondary	Noise abatement Restricted areas and ADIZ	Utilization procedures	Intermodal data processing	Funding Rules and procedures	Real estate expansion factors Airport access/egress Parking Baggage handling Ticketing/reservations
Operations	—	Flight crews	Automation	Controllers	

SOURCE: W. H. Arata, Jr., Northrop Nortronics.

PROBLEM AREAS

To illustrate a few of the problem areas already identified in ATC operations, the following examples are given.

All-Weather Landings

In order to eventually achieve all-weather operations, a concerted effort is being made to permit Category II operations at a number of airports in 1968. When equipment developments are completed, it is anticipated that Category III operations will be possible by the 1970's. The landing categories are shown in Table 4.2.

TABLE 4.2. ICAO/FAA CLASSIFICATIONS FOR LANDING VISIBILITY

Category	I	II	IIIA	IIIB	IIIC
Decision height, ft	200	100	0	0	0
Visibility, RVR, ft (Runway Visual Range)	2400	1200	700	150	0

SOURCE: FAA.

Delays

In improving the present ATC system, it is evident that the terminal area needs the most attention. Figure 4.2 is based on information compiled to forecast the average delays at the J. F. Kennedy airport. Some airlines are now experiencing delays greater than the forecast. If the projections prove to be even generally accurate, the advantages of high-speed air transportation will be lost.

Airport Capacity

It is not always necessary to find real estate for new airports in order to improve the operating capability. A number of improvements could be made at existing airports to increase the number of arrivals and departures. For example, towers can be automated; more ILS runways, and terminals can be added. Airport layouts should consider the feasibility of directing an aircraft to turn off an active runway and go to a terminal building without crossing a second active runway.

Landing Accidents

In order to highlight the importance of adequate air traffic control aids, Table 4.3 draws attention to the fact that although only 17 per-

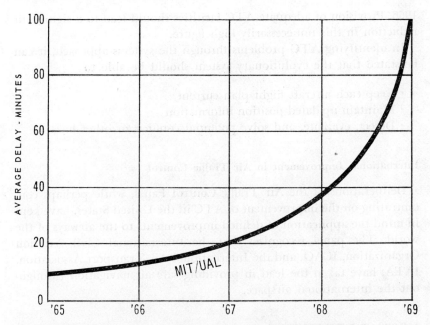

Figure 4.2.   Projections of average delays at J. F. Kennedy airport.

SOURCE: R. W. Simpson, Mass. Inst. of Technology, and United Air Lines. *Operating Dependability in Air Transport.* AIAA Paper No. 66-943, December 1966.

cent of the world landings of jet aircraft take place outside of North America and Europe, 63 percent of the accidents have occurred in such areas. The data presented cover the time period from 1958 through

**TABLE 4.3.   DISTRIBUTION OF JET TRANSPORT APPROACH AND
LANDING ACCIDENTS WHERE NAVIGATIONAL OR
ATC FACILITIES ARE INVOLVED**

(1958–1966)

	Percent of world's landings	Percent of accidents	Approach or landing accidents
North America	62	23	5
Europe	21	14	3
Asia	7	36	8
South and Central America	6	18	4
Africa	3	9	2
			22
North America plus Europe	83	37	
Remainder of world	17	63	

SOURCE: W. W. Moss, Pan American Airways.

1966. Provision of adequate ATC facilities should lead to a significant reduction in this unnecessarily high figure.

In identifying ATC problems through the systems approach, it can be stated that the evolutionary system should be able to

- Keep each aircraft flight plan current
- Maintain up-dated position information
- Detect, evaluate, and solve potential conflicts or other hazards

International Improvement in Air Traffic Control

Deliberations of the Air Traffic Control Panel, while perhaps concentrating on the improvement of ATC in the United States, have kept in mind the application of defined improvements to the airways of the world. The panel recognizes that the International Civil Aviation Organization, ICAO, and the International Air Transport Association, IATA, have taken the lead in providing safe air navigation throughout the international airspace.

AIRSPACE UTILIZATION

Two basic factors in airspace utilization are safety and efficiency. Safe airspace utilization in a controlled environment entails the requirement that aircraft be provided sufficient airspace protection to avoid the risk of collision with other aircraft as well as with the terrain. However, the efficient use of the airspace requires that no airspace be wasted and that aircraft be allocated only that amount of airspace required for safety. Achieving the proper balance between safety and efficiency is one of the chief problems in airspace utilization. In addition, demands for the nonaeronautical uses of airspace must be considered.

The number of aircraft in use today by military, airlines, and general aviation is such that any inefficiency, particularly in the terminal areas, immediately results in delays in aircraft movements and other adverse effects. With the projected increase in numbers of aircraft, efficient airspace use becomes more imperative each year.

Ideally all aircraft should be operated along the optimum route and at the optimum altitude for the particular flight in question. Deviations from this ideal lead to a commensurate derogation in the efficient use of the aircraft. Some planes, for example 707's and DC-8's, are so similar in operational characteristics that the optimum route and altitude on a given flight for one are usually the optimum route and altitude for the other. Congestion thus increases for that particular route and altitude and stringently requires the efficient use of airspace. The penalty for inefficiency is greater for jets than for piston aircraft and will be even greater for the SST than for jets. At the other end of the scale, it is just as important to meet the airspace requirements of V/STOL aircraft so that their unique characteristics may be fully exploited. Because of the shorter ranges of V/STOL aircraft, inefficiency in airspace utilization will have a magnified effect on the use of these vehicles.

AERONAUTICAL USE OF AIRSPACE

With increasing numbers of aircraft, the division between controlled and uncontrolled airspace shifts toward more controlled airspace with the present type of ATC system. There are no designated categories of uncontrolled airspace but there are, of course, numerous categories and designations of controlled airspace. Starting generally at the lower altitudes and going up, there are control zones, transition areas, additional control areas, control area extensions that are being phased out, airways, continental control areas, jet routes, jet advisory areas, positive control routes, and positive control areas.

In addition to these designations, there is a rather extensive list of airspace used for special purposes. Examples include restricted areas, military climb corridors, caution areas, warning areas, prohibitive areas, controlled firing areas, student jet training areas, and flight test areas. In each case the specific question is whether it is necessary to set aside a designated portion of valuable airspace for a particular use that might deny the use of that airspace to aircraft during certain periods. Sometimes it is necessary to set aside airspace in this manner simply because it is the only way that safety can be maintained while the necessary mission is performed. However, where airspace is set aside for special use it is imperative that every effort be made to designate only that airspace required for safe operations of these missions and not unnecessarily restrict nonparticipating aircraft.

Joint Use of Airspace

With the growing demands on the use of airspace for routine aircraft operations, there is an increasing need to find ways to share airspace jointly on an equitable basis. Radar is an example of an excellent tool that has been widely used to permit use of airspace. Other means must be found. One of the problems hindering more effective application of the joint-use concept is the fact that communications permitting rapid coordination between special-mission activity and routine aircraft movements are limited. The air traffic control system as it develops between now and 1975 must make such coordination easier. The introduction of computers and the semiautomatic air traffic control systems that accompany them, together with improvements in high-speed communications, should provide some relief.

With regard to the airspace routinely used by aircraft, it is mandatory that techniques and equipment ensure safe operation. The key point in this respect is the prevention of collisions between aircraft as their number increases. When the weather is clear and the speeds of the aircraft are slow, the see-and-be-seen principles may be adequate. However, even under these relatively ideal conditions, it seems almost inevitable that in certain areas the sheer numbers of aircraft, even at slow speeds, will require some organization to minimize the risk of collision. Such concentration will probably occur by 1975 in terminal areas used only by slow aircraft. In view of the numbers of turboprop and turbojet general aviation aircraft being delivered, the problem becomes compounded in the many concentrated areas which will have a mix of slow and high-speed aircraft. Also, the separation and sequencing criteria for various aircraft types, e.g., VTOL and SST, must be considered in effectively using the airspace corridors.

Positive Control Airspace

Because of the volume and speed of airline and military operations, confidence in the see-and-be-seen method of collision prevention is rapidly dwindling. Planning must now be directed toward elimination of the see-and-be-seen method of separation insofar as airline aircraft are concerned. The designation of positive control areas has started the process. Discussions have taken place concerning how this should be extended to the lower areas in ways which will not impose an undue penalty upon other aircraft. Enough is known now to designate positive control airspace in the present ATC system down to at least 15,000 feet where needed. Plans must be developed on an expedited basis for the further designation of positive control airspace. For instance, positive control transition route segments in high-density areas should be designated to connect terminal areas with the floor of positive control areas. Plans must be made, on an urgent basis, for positive control in terminal areas. Care must be taken to see that such designations are not extravagant so that they will not unduly penalize anyone. On the other hand, in spite of protests that may occur, the overall public interest has to be considered, and legitimate positive control designations should be made. The public depends upon safe air transportation, and the growing numbers of aircraft make it imperative that safety not be dependent upon the pilot's visually sighting another aircraft.

NONAERONAUTICAL USE OF AIRSPACE

There are several nonaeronautical uses of the airspace that deserve attention. Probably the most important of these are television towers. Although the physical dimensions of the towers themselves are insignificant when related to the total amount of airspace, their effect on the use of airspace at the lower levels is often very significant, since the airspace surrounding an obstruction becomes sterile as far as aircraft use is concerned. Although the television industry can be expected to expand in the future, it is possible that a practical means of using communication satellites to relay television programs or some other technique which will contain the height and number of television towers may be developed. In the meantime one of the most practical solutions is the concentration of television towers in antenna farm areas so located as to have a minimum adverse effect on aviation.

Other obstructions to navigation are buildings on and around airports. These buildings must be limited in height and located at sites where they pose no hazard to the movements of aircraft and have the least impact upon aeronautical utilization of airspace.

We have discussed the important physical impediments to the use of airspace by aircraft. In addition, there are airspace areas prohibited to the use of aircraft, together with disaster areas and controlled firing areas. As there are only four prohibited areas in the United States, these have little effect upon aeronautical airspace utilization. Disaster areas are temporary and can be penetrated with proper authorization. Activities in controlled firing areas are conducted under conditions designed to eliminate any hazards to aircraft.

Airspace Lost to Weather Blocks

Weather blocks are those volumes in the airspace where utilization is substantially reduced for safety because of known or suspected hazardous weather within those volumes. For the most part weather blocks are associated with severe convective turbulence in squall lines or thunderstorms, severe clear-air turbulence, or heavy icing. Because these hazardous weather conditions are associated with moving storm systems, the weather blocks are transient. Furthermore, the size and shape of the weather blocks change continually with the changing nature of the storms.

The volume of the airspace temporarily lost in a single weather block can be as much as 50,000 cubic miles or more, depending on the meteorological situation. This loss of airspace is especially critical when the weather blocks occur over or near airports, terminal areas, and/or holding fixes for terminal approaches. Such blocks can completely disrupt the orderly flow of terminal traffic, and it is thus important that the ATC system be continuously advised by the weather system of their present and future state. The more accurate these forecasts can be, the more efficient the use that can be made of the airspace. The improvements called for elsewhere in this section will help to minimize these weather block problems.

Noise Abatement and Use of Airspace

It should be noted at the outset that noise abatement is discussed here only with regard to its effect on airspace usage. In many major cities the use of the available airspace, and for that matter the available runways on airports, is seriously curtailed because of aircraft noise. It has been estimated that under certain wind conditions the capacity of Kennedy Airport in New York is reduced by more than 50 percent solely because of noise abatement procedures. Such limitations not only cause serious delays to aircraft movements today but also concentrate those operations which do take place in certain limited airspace, thus causing further restrictions.

Many proposals for improving airports by the construction of new runways are dropped solely because of aircraft noise problems. Airspace congestion could be reduced in many terminal areas if it were not for noise abatement problems. It is imperative that all practical solutions to noise problems be implemented at the earliest possible date. Failure to do this will cause undue airspace congestion.

CONCLUSIONS

Because of the tremendous growth in air traffic, safe and efficient use of airspace both takes on new significance and becomes more complicated. Because of the new types of aircraft being developed, further demands are being made on airspace utilization. In addition, the factors of nonaeronautical use of airspace, weather blocks, and noise abatement are affecting the solutions necessary for efficient aircraft movement.

RECOMMENDATIONS

1. Continue to expand positive control of airspace where needed.
2. Accelerate noise reduction research and development so that noise abatement has a lesser effect on air traffic.
3. Continue takeoff and landing flight-path tests for various types of aircraft to improve noise abatement.
4. Improve measurement and prediction of severe weather to lessen the impact of weather blocks on air traffic.

ATMOSPHERIC ENVIRONMENT

Over the past few years the public has become more and more aware of the impact of weather on our activities. Air transportation and all its supporting services are conditioned by the weather. In particular, weather necessitated the present air traffic control system. As each new type of aircraft is placed in the inventory and the traffic density increases, the ATC system becomes more sensitive to weather.

More timely and accurate knowledge of existing atmospheric conditions and a more dependable prediction of future trends would increase the capacity and efficiency of the air traffic control system. The weather system providing this intelligence is a national asset and must serve and satisfy the requirements of all aviation user groups. It is fundamental that the weather intelligence should come from a single, well-coordinated weather system so that a standard product can be provided to all of aviation.

THE WEATHER PROBLEM

Weather effects on air traffic movement are cumulative. A sluggish terminal, slow en route flight movement, aborted takeoffs or landings, deviations in hold due to turbulence and icing, slow climb-outs due to ice or winds, VFR traffic that becomes lost in IFR weather—all cause congestion of the airspace. This is true not only where the weather occurs; the effects can back up and cause costly delays in large segments of the system. In some cases the effect is so great as to make unscrambling of the overall system a long and tedious process. The airline system may become so unbalanced as to cause mass flight cancellations, ferrying of aircraft, and deadheading of crews, to say nothing of great inconvenience to the traveling public and a resulting impact on the economy.

One of the most difficult problems is the control of traffic and the regulation of its flow in and out of high-density terminal areas. Solving the navigational problem and the airports problem will not completely solve the traffic control problem. In spite of the most advanced electronic means available, weather in the terminal area is and will continue to be one of the major factors of concern to safety and the orderly flow of traffic. In addition to imposing operational minimums, heavy snow, heavy rain, and freezing rain may render runways unusable and create congestion problems not only in the air but on the ground. More accurate and timely terminal forecasts would better permit ATC to adjust traffic flow to airport capacity and would provide a better basis for en route decision-making.

Unplanned Delays

There are many factors that make airspace management and the control of traffic difficult, but some of the most troublesome are unexpected delays of aircraft in the air or delays feeding into the system. Most of these are caused by weather, and the weather does not have to be severe. During rain, snow, or other marginal conditions, aircraft ground movement at the terminal is slowed down, as is also the flow of approaching and departing aircraft, owing to more cautious actions on the part of crew and controllers. Passenger- and cargo-handling also slow down, and changes in plans for hundreds of aircraft may result. If these unplanned delays continue for any length of time, segments of the system become congested and delays gradually spread throughout the system. It is important, therefore, that weather conditions affecting surface operations as well as those in the air be accurately presented and planned for in advance to bring about a better ordering of events.

Coordinated Flight Planning

When widespread areas of instrument weather exist or when winds, clouds, and turbulence are significant to flight, operators frequently request the same altitudes and optimum routes. Since airspace is limited, each operator cannot be given exactly what he wants. Here a need exists for coordination of flight planning between the meteorologist, air traffic controller, and operator. The users of the system, as well as the air traffic controller, must employ the same fundamental set of variables in their planning to eliminate confusion and expedite traffic movement.

Still another problem of both flight planning and air traffic control is the allowance for the influence of winds and temperatures in the accurate prediction of arrivals over en route fixes. The weather system must provide accurate analyses and predictions of winds and temperatures for all altitudes used by the operators under the cognizance of air traffic control.

Even more demanding is the need for accurate predictions of landing times at airports. Landing time should be determined in advance of each aircraft's approach, and the pilot must land within a few seconds of the predicted time in order to allow for the clearance of the runway for the next aircraft in the sequence. An approach from 90 miles or so usually involves a descent from 20,000 feet or more through layers of the atmosphere having varying conditions of wind and turbulence. Accurate information on winds and turbulence is necessary if landing times are to be predicted within tolerable limits. This information must be provided by the weather system to air traffic control.

Effect of Weather on Noise Propagation

Airport noise and sonic boom are not meteorological in nature, but the propagation of this noise is affected by the atmosphere. It is doubtful that the meteorological services can play an important part in relieving this situation. It is quite probable that under certain conditions of wind, temperature, and atmospheric turbulence, the airport noise and sonic boom would be within tolerable limits, and the approach and takeoff patterns as well as the SST transition and cruise routes could be adjusted accordingly. If this becomes the case and if the noise and sonic boom problems cannot be solved by design, the ATC will have to take these meteorological factors into consideration on a day-to-day basis, using the weather system to make decisions.

Solar Flares and Radiation

One aspect of the environment that has had only an indirect effect on aircraft operations to date but that may play a more important role as operating altitudes increase to the 60,000–80,000-ft range is that associated with the eruption of solar flares on the sun. These flares reach a maximum in times ranging from a few minutes to a few tens of minutes, and have lifetimes that vary from minutes up to, on extremely rare occasions, seven or eight hours. The primary effect of solar flares on the current air traffic control system is to cause a degradation or complete blackout of high-frequency communications for periods up to several hours, owing to the increased ionization of the lower ionosphere from the X rays and ultraviolet radiation that emanate from the flares. As increasing use is made of the higher frequencies, which are not dependent upon the vagaries of the ionosphere, this problem will disappear.

As operating altitudes increase to the 60,000–70,000 ft proposed for the SST, problems may arise relating to the biomedical effects of the radiation environment at these altitudes. Excluding exposure to major solar proton events, SST passengers probably will receive radiation doses roughly comparable to those received by passengers in present-day subsonic jets since, although the radiation level at 70,000 ft is approximately 3½ times that at 40,000 ft at polar latitudes, the passenger will travel about three times faster at SST altitudes. These considerations do not apply, however, to the case of the very infrequent giant solar proton events (eruptions). These could subject passengers in one hour to dosages comparable to the maximum permissible yearly dose. This problem can be alleviated by flying at a lower altitude, and thus provision must be made within the weather services to give the pilot adequate warning of such events. The worldwide solar patrol now in operation, its planned expansion, and the real-time communication of solar conditions that is commonplace now will certainly not only enable adequate warning to be given the en route pilot but will also enable the air carrier and the air traffic control system to take these giant solar events into account in their flight planning.

The World Weather System

The national meteorological system and the meteorological systems of other nations make up the world weather system. It is through this world system that the dynamic state of the atmosphere over the globe (temperature, wind, and pressure) is determined and predicted, and this basic information is vital in the prediction of the specific weather elements (ceiling, visibility, precipitation, turbulence, winds, and temperature) important to aviation.

The weather system, producing vital intelligence concerning the atmosphere, must be considered an important adjunct to the air traffic control system. Since each system is autonomous, and since both have some mutual weather responsibility, there must be an effective means of communication between them to apply, distribute, display, and present the operationally significant weather information on a timely basis for the controllers, pilots, and operational planners. Such communication does not presently exist. If this system gap is eliminated, noticeable and immediate improvements in the orderly flow of traffic can be realized.

In the post-1975 period the national meteorological system should have greatly improved capability, including a nationwide weather radar network, improved data from weather satellite systems, and the analysis and prediction of the state of the atmosphere up to 100,000 ft, utilizing high-speed computers. Radar will be capable of detecting severe weather and providing conflict displays to air traffic control. Poor terminal visibility as a result of fog can be improved by weather-modification techniques so that minimum visibility for control purposes can be obtained under most conditions.

However, there exist technical gaps that must be eliminated for future improvements in the light of increased traffic after 1975. The terminal area is defined as the air volume within a cylinder of 90 miles diameter extending to 20,000 ft. This area is the most critical from the viewpoint of traffic planning by dispatch and air traffic control, and the elements of most serious concern are visibility, turbulence, and icing. Accurate short-range forecasts (up to two hours in advance) are imperative in the years ahead. The inability of the weather system to provide this service by producing forecasts with the accuracy and detail required in the future is a serious technical gap demanding attention by the research community. The following areas are in need of better understanding and more accurate forecasting:

- Terminal area visibility for approach, landing, and takeoff for the ranges of three miles or less, with special emphasis on the very low visibility of less than one mile.
- Turbulence in the free atmosphere in the terminal areas regardless of the cause, with special consideration given to thunderstorms and squall lines including areas of hail.
- Freezing rain and areas of moderate and heavy icing in clouds for the terminal area.

CONCLUSIONS

1. Weather intelligence is one of the essential tools for management of air traffic. Aviation weather services must be considered an integral part of the national air traffic system, providing detailed and up-to-the-minute information in a form that will precisely define the environment as it is and will be.

2. The meteorological elements having the greatest impact on ATC and airspace utilization include

- Restricted visibilities at terminals, particularly as a result of fog, heavy rain, and snow.
- Turbulence in the free atmosphere as a result of thunderstorms, mountain waves, and wind shears.
- Heavy rain, snow, and freezing rain on runway surfaces.

3. The meteorological elements indirectly affecting airspace utilization and contributing in a cumulative sense to delays and "sluggishness" of the ATC system include

- Low-level wind shears in the approach zone.
- Strong winds en route.
- Unusually high surface and en route temperature.
- Restricted visibilities in the air hampering VFR flight.
- Strong and gusty surface winds.

4. The special meteorological elements affecting airspace utilization and ATC related to the SST include

- Cosmic radiation levels at cruise altitude (not meteorological, but environmental).
- Precise temperature information for transition (20,000–50,000 ft) and cruise altitude.
- Precise information on the existence of rain, hail, and turbulence for transition and cruise altitudes.
- Absolute tops of clouds along the route.

5. If the airport noise and sonic boom problems cannot be solved by design, ATC will have to consider these problems on a day-to-day basis using meteorological information in the decision process.

6. For V/STOL operations, no unique weather problems are identified. However, the same information will be needed for more airports (heliports), and quicker. These factors will be important because of the handling of these aircraft by ATC in a mixed environment.

7. The national meteorological system, if adequately funded, will provide necessary improvements in the measurement, analysis, and prediction of the large-scale features of the atmosphere.

8. A system gap exists in both the weather and ATC systems, namely, the lack of effective communications between the two systems to apply, distribute, display, and present the operationally significant weather information on a timely basis for the controllers, pilots, and operational planners.

9. A technical gap deserving the attention of the research community relates to the measurement and prediction of terminal area visibility, turbulence in the free atmosphere in the terminal area, and freezing rain and areas of moderate and heavy icing in clouds for the terminal area.

RECOMMENDATIONS

1. Support the funding required to improve the overall national meteorological system.

2. Work toward the elimination of the systems gap by supporting the establishment of an effective means of communication between the weather and ATC systems.

3. Begin to bridge the technical gap by stimulating scientific interest in, and encouraging support of research concerned with, short-period forecasts of visibility, turbulence, and icing in the terminal area.

AIRCRAFT EQUIPMENT

Major advances in aircraft technologies have continued in recent years, following the impetus given them during and immediately following World War II, in such areas as high-performance jet engines, variable-sweep wings, composite materials, and moving map displays. However, the past decade has seen a decrease in the rate of application of the new technologies to the private sector of the aviation economy. This situation has arisen largely because of the great reduction in the number of new military aircraft under development. There has been a corresponding reduction in the means whereby the new technologies may be proved sound, both technically and operationally, and whereby industry is given an opportunity of assessing the profitability of applying them to commercial practice. Furthermore, the new military aircraft that are under development are so specialized that little of the advanced, sophisticated technology being developed for them is applicable to commercial use, although their potential applicability is extremely high, provided they become sufficiently cost-effective. As a consequence, civil aviation has had to develop its new aerodynamic and structural designs, propulsion systems, electronic components, materials, and manufacturing processes and techniques largely on the basis of evolutionary improvements in the technology of a decade or more ago.

At the same time, the extension of both commercial and general aviation to a more nearly year-around, all-weather type of operation and the expansion into a greater airspace, together with the ever-increasing performance capabilities, are all contributing to increases in the complexity of vehicles and are compounding the demands on the pilot and the air traffic controller alike.

The equipment carried on board the aircraft itself plays a major role in determining how safely, economically, comfortably, and conveniently people or goods may be transported. Such equipment, particularly that wherein new technologies and a systems approach may contribute most significantly to the air traffic control problem, is the particular concern of this section and will be discussed in terms of each class of aircraft. However, inasmuch as the two major functions of navigation and communication have great impact on the air traffic control problem, and one that is common to all classes of aircraft, these will be treated separately.

GENERAL AVIATION

General aviation aircraft are assuming a progressively greater role in the national economy and as a national resource. Over the past decade the number of general aviation aircraft increased from approximately 63,000 to about 105,000 and is projected to increase to possibly 180,000 by 1975. With this increase in numbers there has also been a significant improvement in the performance of general aviation airplanes; however, this increased performance normally has made the airplanes more difficult to handle, particularly under turbulent or adverse weather conditions. The problem is compounded by the fact that the general aviation instrument-rated pilot is generally able to maintain only a minimal instrument-flying proficiency. As a consequence, almost two-thirds of the accidents involving general aviation aircraft were attributed to pilot error, with weather being the next largest contributor.

Consequently, many air traffic problems could be lightened by devoting major efforts toward providing the pilot with an aircraft in which his workload has been reduced to a point allowing him to manage the aircraft efficiently and safely in flight. One such area is flight dynamics, where much can be done to provide the pilot with an airplane that is stable against outside disturbances, under all flight configurations, and yet has an acceptable response to his control inputs. Aerodynamically, almost everything in this direction that can be done in a practical manner has been done, so stability augmentation systems will probably be increasingly relied on for acceptable flight control.

Presenting Information to the Pilot

Major reductions in pilot workload may also be anticipated from improvements in cockpit displays and particularly in the basic understanding of how, when, and in what form to best present available information to the pilot. The increasing number of operating hours that the general aviation pilot performs far from his home port, under severe weather conditions and increasing traffic density, is placing an ever-expanding requirement on his information needs to the point that a true systems approach to the total problem is required. This would encompass examining the role of the general aviation pilot in the air traffic system, his information needs, and his relation to the air traffic controller and the airline pilot.

Underlying all this concern for pilot workload and aircraft-handling qualities is a growing national concern about aviation safety, with particular emphasis on collision avoidance. While the principal concern of general aviation aircraft manufacturers should still be improving pilot visibility and enhancing the conspicuity of aircraft under various background and lighting conditions, major efforts should also be directed toward developments in airborne equipment that will detect intruder aircraft and bring them to the attention of the pilot. Such equipment must be of minimum weight and volume, generate a minimum of false alarms, and be relatively inexpensive (so that any general aviation pilot who might want to operate in heavy-traffic areas could afford it). It must also function well in a controlled traffic environment and with the more sophisticated collision-avoidance systems of the air carriers. Again, a systems orientation is required in order to evolve an approach that will properly incorporate all of the factors that must be considered.

Small Jet Engines

A final area that actually transcends a discussion of equipment but that certainly merits major technological effort is that of small jet engines for general aviation aircraft. Developments that lead to an inexpensive form of small gas turbine will, because of the high reliability of such engines, go far toward alleviating those increasingly frequent accidents that occur through the failure of current highly complex, finely tuned reciprocating engines.

V/STOL AIRCRAFT

The introduction of Vertical and Short Take-Off and Landing (V/STOL) aircraft into the short-haul transportation market should contribute significantly to the alleviation of the ground traffic problem that is growing more burdensome daily. Care must be taken, however, that such an introduction will not further aggravate the air traffic control problem. Hence, the timeliness and efficiency with which this mode of air travel is introduced into a total transportation system will be dependent upon the route structure employed and the degree to which the terminal area complex is tailored to these types of operations, as well as upon the success achieved in solving certain major technological problems with the aircraft themselves.

One of the major technological problems that must be overcome before V/STOL aircraft become a safe and economical means of air transport is associated with their inherent instability during the transition and hover phases of flight. The problem involves consideration of the flight dynamics of this type of aircraft, the proper matching of man and machine through a thorough analysis of human factors, and determination of the avionics aids that are required to best accomplish this match. Furthermore, many problems arise because the propulsion system must provide both lift and control functions during the vertical takeoff and landing and transition modes. For example, a rather slow-responding turbojet engine and/or control fan will generally be used to generate control moments, and this slow response will degrade vehicle handling qualities and reduce the flight control system stability margins.

VTOL aircraft offer the promise of operating from small terminal areas such as building tops, or spaces between buildings. As a consequence, an invaluable means of access to city centers should develop that would aid materially in the handling of urban traffic flow to and from the main air terminal. Similarly, at the air terminal end, minimal real estate and airspace that might conflict with conventional aircraft will be required. For a system to function economically and with no delays, however, accurate, point-to-point navigation via multiple flight paths under all-weather conditions will be a necessity.

The high degree of blending of control parameters involved requires that the role of the pilot in the aircraft control loop be reassessable. Only after a complete system study of the problem has been made, including the human factors, can the optimum approach be determined. For example, is the solution a highly reliable, automatic landing system, with the pilot functioning as an off-line, parallel monitor and optional operator of the machine; or a head-up display system which keeps the pilot in the loop at all times and yet permits him to react with minimum transition time if conditions external to the system so dictate?

An even more basic problem, particularly for VTOL aircraft, is that of precisely defining those aircraft characteristics that will enable such craft to land and take off quickly, quietly, and precisely from small areas with great regularity. Newer VTOL types have achieved good cruise performance but without having solved the low-speed objective, while helicopters have been moderately successful at attaining low speed but at the cost of a substantial penalty in cruise performance. These are not air traffic control problems, however, and will not be discussed further here.

COMMERCIAL AIR TRANSPORTS

The phenomenal growth in commercial air travel, particularly since the introduction of jet transport aircraft into airline operations, has been a major factor in both the cause and current solutions to the ever-increasing air traffic control problem. Between 1957 and 1967 the number of free-world jet transport aircraft increased from zero to approximately 1800 and passenger traffic increased from about 50 billion revenue passenger miles to approximately 180 billion. An added factor relative to air traffic control has been the change in mix of these jet transports, from all long-range aircraft initially to over one-third medium- and short-range aircraft at present.

Even what are believed to be conservative projections into the 1980 time period indicate that commercial air travel will have an even more drastic effect on the air traffic control picture of the future. By 1980 the jumbo jets and supersonic transports that are expected to be operating will have provided an enormous increase in per-aircraft productivity; it is expected that, although free-world revenue passenger miles will increase to possibly 550 billion by 1980 and air cargo traffic from approximately 4 billion ton-miles today to possibly 70 billion ton-miles, the rate of expansion of the total jet population will actually decrease during the 1970–1980 period. Nonetheless, a total free-world jet transport population of over 4,700 aircraft is expected by 1980, of which about one-fourth are expected to be short-range and another one-fourth medium-range aircraft. Thus, major concern must be given to the complete mix of aircraft of all types that will be operating in the airways of the 1980's, as well as to the sheer numbers involved.

Stability Control

Major technological problems, for whose solutions significant technological advances in the on-board equipment will be required, are those associated with the safe and efficient management of jumbo jets and supersonic transports or other aircraft of like size and performance. For example, in the flight control area, the speed, noise, and sonic boom of supersonic transports (and considerations of economy) will impose stringent requirements for precision flight control from takeoff through landing. Similarly, completely new problems will be posed for supersonic airline crews by the constraints of aircraft skin temperature, sonic boom, and inlet geometry control on aircraft operations. As a consequence, advances in flight control technology will be needed to ensure, for example, that surface overpressures due to sonic booms are not magnified locally by the focusing effect of an erratic flight path and that the narrow corridors determined by the constraints previously discussed are followed closely. At the same time, this problem is magnified by the size and distribution of mass of supersonic transports that lead to pitch sluggishness, roll-yaw coupling difficulties, and structural fatigue due to aircraft flexing. To alleviate these problems, the flight control system must employ a stability augmentation system about all three aircraft axes and at the same time provide for structural mode control and gust alleviation.

CAT Detection

Another important area, and one that is closely related to these last problems, is that of clear-air turbulence (CAT). One possible solution would be to incorporate real-time advisories as to the turbulence levels to be encountered en route. Such information would be received both from an expanded weather service and from real-time transmissions of turbulence-level information obtained by other aircraft as they encounter it. A different approach that would involve a major technological advance in on-board equipment is that of remotely detecting clear-air turbulence by means of sensors carried on the airplane itself. To be effective, such detection should occur at least two and preferably up to five minutes in advance of an encounter with CAT in order that steps may be taken to avoid such areas smoothly and efficiently or to penetrate them as safely as possible. Such a warning time implies, at supersonic transport speeds, a detection range of from 60 to 150 miles, which certainly poses a major technological challenge.

New Display Concept

As a consequence of this need for precision flight control, coupled with the greatly expanded environment within which these aircraft must operate safely, efficiently, and reliably, the complex interrelationships between the pilot and the aircraft need to be completely reexamined. The role of the pilot in the control, guidance, and management of the advanced aircraft may best be as an off-line, parallel monitor and optional operator of the aircraft. The collective task that will be imposed upon him will require that masses of accurate information be made accessible rapidly and concisely. Moreover, one can logically anticipate that operational decision time will be shorter, that the number of alternative courses of action will be greater, and that determination of the effect of a decision on a host of related actions will be more complex and time-consuming.

At present the pilot-aircraft interrelation is mechanized through the displays and controls available to the pilot, all oriented toward presentation and actuation of discrete parameters. As the parameters have multiplied, displays and controls have proliferated to the point that several hundred dials, knobs, and switches vie for the attention of the crew on a present-day airliner. Since interest at any one time is centered on a fraction of these displays and associated actuators, the pilot is confronted with the dual problem of identifying the pertinent display or control while avoiding those not requiring immediate attention. Unfortunately, continuously presented, discrete information concerning all parameters of interest cannot be organized on the panel in such a way as to cope with this problem because the hierarchy of the pilot's interest varies with flight phase. Thus, an entirely new display concept is required that, optimally, should provide the following:

- Real-time display of all parameters necessary to system monitoring and aircraft management.
- An interchangeable graphic, alphanumeric and/or symbolic display format, and possibly a true pictorial format as well, to assist the pilot while he is maneuvering the aircraft on the ground.
- A computer-generated, serial digital pulse train capable of driving the aircraft.
- Self-storage of information.
- Actuation command signals simply presented.
- Acceptable failure modes.

Since the entire display is continuously generated and controlled by a computer, the roster of parameters to be included, as well as their placement and scaling, can be varied as required. At the same time, the pilot retains the ability to call up for display any information that he desires for exercise of his optional control. Normally the display will function as a monitoring device, but it becomes an active part of the control and guidance loop at the instant the pilot exercises his command option.

The degree to which such revolutionary display requirements, together with those of the automatic flight control system, are met will be determined by established FAA and airline considerations of safety, dispatch and inflight reliability, maintainability, mean time before failure, cost effectiveness, and the human engineering considerations of pilot acceptance.

Collision Avoidance

Another area of equipment technology that is directed at a major national problem is that of collision avoidance. Current developments are concerned with protecting commercial transport aircraft from each other, simply because no feasible system that would protect all aircraft with simple and inexpensive equipment has as yet been developed. Such a partial solution is certainly warranted on economic grounds alone, since a reduction of this type of accident from the present frequency of about one in three years to, say, one in ten years would result in a net saving on the order of $50 million per year through reductions in equipment loss and settlements. This saving does not include the cost that would be incurred if a 500-passenger jumbo jet or an SST were to be involved.

However, it is still essential that the total problem be attacked, incorporating all of the factors which must be included in a proper solution. Such an approach requires a thorough examination of basic information, methods of data acquisition, collision prediction and warning criteria, and avoidance logic and command action for all types of aircraft, from general aviation to advanced transports, with proper consideration for how the system will function in the total ATC environment. Major effort is needed in attacking the problem from a total system viewpoint and in solving the technical-economic aspect that is peculiar to the general aviation side of the traffic.

CONCLUSIONS

The major increases in air traffic density that have occurred in recent years and the even more rapid increases foreseen for the future dictate the need, in the interests of both national safety and the national economy, to increase controlled airspace and the degree of control over all aircraft operating in that airspace. This need in turn places new technological requirements on the airborne equipment of both general aviation and commercial carriers, in order that all aircraft types be able to operate safely, reliably, economically, and with the maximum amount of freedom commensurate with national interest.

Significant technological advances are consequently required so that precise flight control may be maintained over any type of aircraft under a wide variety of atmospheric and operational environments and constraints, flight configurations, and pilot capabilities. Even greater flight control is required for supersonic transports and V/STOL's if they are to attain their potential.

Furthermore, the systems approach dictates a reconsideration of the role of man in the control, guidance, and management of all types of aircraft that may be operating after 1975 and a reevaluation of which air traffic control functions and responsibilities should be on the ground, which in the cockpit, and which shared.

RECOMMENDATIONS

1. Initiate systems studies directed toward defining

   • The roles of the general aviation pilot, the commercial pilot, and the air traffic controller in the control, guidance, and management of aircraft in the transportation system of the post-1975 time period.

- The on-board equipment required to automate those flight management functions that become defined by the roles just listed.
- The optimum allocation of crew assignments, their needs for information, and how it should be displayed.
- A collision avoidance system that could encompass general aviation and solve both the en route and terminal area problems. Consideration should be given to those systems that might simultaneously satisfy requirements for navigation and communications.

2. Carry out research and development to provide advanced technology in the areas of

- Automatic control systems for V/STOL aircraft.
- Cockpit displays.
- Detection of clear-air turbulence.

3. Conduct flight tests of the most promising of the preceding systems under real air traffic conditions, to determine operational feasibility and to demonstrate proof of concept.

NAVIGATION

Traditionally, navigation has not been of major concern in the air traffic control problem, both because sufficient margin for navigational error was allowed for in the vertical and horizontal separation standards that were established and because the pilot generally had sufficient time to devote to navigation so that he could know approximately where he was at all times.

This picture is currently undergoing significant change for several reasons. The rapid growth in air traffic is dictating a thorough examination of all possible means for coping with the great increase in airspace congestion, including the possibility of markedly reducing separation standards. Such an action would require much higher navigational accuracy than is currently available in civil aviation, and in the general aviation sector in particular. In addition, the increasing pilot workload is aggravating the problem to the extent that less and less time is available for navigation. Furthermore, a greater percentage of all traffic is operating under adverse weather conditions, and this places much greater demands on the navigational equipment, the pilot, and the air traffic controller.

It is apparent that improved navigation technology can contribute to alleviating the air traffic problem. The present section deals with various possible improvements in this technological area.

CURRENT RADIO NAVIGATION AIDS

The characteristics of various types of radio navigation aids that are currently either operational or in experimental use, and that are expected to still be used in the post-1975 time period, are summarized in Table 4.4. Low-frequency systems such as the Automatic Direction Finder will be particularly useful in the post-1975 period in the under-developed areas of the world, where more sophisticated and expensive systems such as VHF-Omnirange (VOR) will generally not be available. As with all low-frequency systems, however, the atmospheric propagation is highly dependent upon the vagaries of the ionosphere and may be blacked out during periods of high solar activity; in addition, the low-frequency signals can be rendered useless by both the excessive atmospheric noise generated by thunderstorms and the cancellation of the direct wave at the vehicle by the skywaves at long ranges at night.

Day-night, all-weather, static-free measurements are possible with any of the VHF systems since propagation at these frequencies is not affected by ionospheric or atmospheric conditions. However, VHF facilities are limited in range to line-of-sight, and hence not only are there long periods of flying time during which no VHF signals are available even on heavily traveled routes such as the north Atlantic, but SST's and other future high-flying aircraft will suffer mutual inter-ference as a result of seeing simultaneously (because of their greater radio horizon) stations that are not separated by frequency. The latter is primarily a frequency management problem, and since the VHF spectrum is already overcrowded, it may very well be that only critical points such as the terminal area will be frequency-isolated for such types of aircraft.

Loran-C and Omega

Difficulties are encountered in applying the two hyperbolic naviga-tion systems, Loran-C and Omega, to aircraft navigation, since in high-performance aircraft they both require velocity aiding to keep the receiver accurately locked to the incoming signal. In addition, the Loran system does not provide worldwide coverage at the present time and would be expensive for the user.

With regard to the first problem, the velocity required is the line-of-sight velocity to the Loran or Omega transmitter and as such must be determined from data supplied either by an inertial system or an air data system, which are then used in appropriate computations. As a consequence, if an inertial sensor and computer are required to main-tain lock, the wisdom of having Loran or Omega on board at all is

TABLE 4.4. SUMMARY OF RADIO NAVIGATION AIDS

Navigational aid	Function	Unit cost	System accuracy	Range (nautical miles)	Remarks
Automatic Direction Finder (ADF)	Determines bearing to LF beacon stations and LF radio stations	$ 8,800	±2° (2σ); very low frequency random error	50–200 nmi depending on signal strength and noise level	A general purpose aid suitable to the post-'75 environment.
VHF Omnirange (VOR)	Determines magnetic bearing to VOR facility	11,400	±3° (2σ); very low frequency random error	Line of sight $R \approx 1.23\sqrt{h}$ h = altitude, kft	This unit is a combination VOR, localizer, and glideslope navigation unit. For high altitude operations, mutual interference among VOR facilities may limit usefulness to critical areas; e.g., terminal area.
Distance Measuring Equipment (DME)	Measures slant range to DME facility	7,800	±0.2 nmi or 1% of range; very low frequency random error	0–192	As with the VOR, mutual interference among facilities at high altitudes may limit usefulness to a few critical areas, e.g., terminal area.
Loran-C	Determines aircraft position	80,000	±1500 ft (2σ); ground wave at extreme range not on baseline extension	Night ∼ 1000 Day ∼ 1800	This system early operational in subsonic aircraft. Tests in supersonic aircraft at high altitude underway at Shaw AFB. Velocity aiding essential on high performance aircraft and must be derived from external sources such as air data and heading or an inertial sensor.

TABLE 4.4. *(Continued)*

Navigational aid	Function	Unit cost	System accuracy	Range (nautical miles)	Remarks
Omega	Determines aircraft position	$15,000–65,000 depending on automation (two frequencies)	±2 nmi (2σ); night ±1 nmi (2σ); day low frequency random error	6000	This system is still in experimental stage, with two frequencies; lane ambiguity every 24 nmi; not acceptable for supersonic transports. More than two frequencies have not been implemented or tested and hard to say when they will be.
Doppler Navigator	Determines vector distance traveled	$40,000	±0.5% (2σ) of distance traveled or 1 nmi; very low frequency random error		Use for SST altitudes and speeds would require more transmitter power and a more directional antenna.
Air Traffic Control transponder	Provides identification and altitude reporting to air traffic controllers	4,600		200	Altitude reporting in 100-ft increments up to 100 kft. For identification 4096 codes are available.
Instrument Landing System (glideslope and localizer) (ILS)	Provides directional information for poor weather landing (Cat. I and II)	11,400	Not readily defined; pilot flies down beam center to runway.	≈20	Due to low carrier frequency of operational ILS wide beams susceptible to reflections buildings, hangars, terrain, etc. As a consequence, reliable Cat. III landing cannot be accomplished with this system.

| Marker beacon | Indicates to pilot distance to end of runway | 700 | | This equipment not necessary in an advanced instrument landing system (AILS) except for redundant alert. |
| Advanced Instrument Landing System (AILS) | Provides directional and distance information for all-weather landing (Cat. I, II, and III) | AZ $\approx \pm 0.05$ deg
EL $\approx \pm 0.03$ deg
DME$=\pm 100$ ft or 1% | ≈ 20 (hvy rain) | This advanced system utilizes microwaves and very narrow beams making it impervious to multipath. As a consequence this system has the potential for Cat. III and automatic landings. It is still experimental. |

SOURCE: FAA.
SOURCE: NASA Electronics Research Center.

questioned, particularly since the inertial unit itself could perform the navigation function. These factors, coupled with the high cost, complexity, and low airborne reliability of the systems, would tend to preclude their being introduced into an operational status in air carriers.

Despite the difficulties mentioned above, present VOR-DME and ADF equipment is generally satisfactory for commercial aviation and the more completely equipped segments of general aviation and hence will undoubtedly still be in general use in the post-1975 period. It will be needed particularly in order that the navigation system remain compatible with the ATC environment in terminal areas. However, in order to increase the navigational accuracy and reduce pilot workload in the terminal area, major improvements are needed in the displays that these navigation-aid systems drive.

Vertical Navigation

Traditionally, navigation has been concerned only with the horizontal situation, but with vehicles like the supersonic transport a precise vertical path will also be necessary to limit sonic boom overpressures. In addition, changes in upper air temperatures may dictate precise climb-out and cruise procedure for best fuel economy or minimum direct operating costs. One single flight path cannot be used because conditions affecting these two points vary from place to place and from day to day. Climb-out and cruise procedures must accommodate change as often as each takeoff must. Hence, there will be strong interaction between horizontal navigation, vertical navigation, and fuel management that will require sophisticated computational treatment.

Position information will be required for latitude and longitude over the earth, bearing-to-a-station, distance-to-a-station, and outputs for ground track, ground speed, and drift angle. The problem on supersonic vehicles is to display the pertinent information sufficiently rapidly that it is current and usable. Hence, one system concept might consider the primary navigational display to be pictorial in nature, displaying the aircraft's present position by reference to a moving chart and clearly indicating the relationship between actual position and planned position. The display must be flexible, permitting the crew, for example, to extrapolate in time and see on demand the aircraft's position at any desired time in the future. It should present, in relation to the chart, the present position as indicated not only by the navigation sensor currently being used for flight control by the automatic system but also by any additional fixes used for updating by the system or requested by the pilot.

In the vertical plane, the integrated avionics system concept might also use a dynamic pictorial display showing present position in relation to planned position and in relation to performance, structural, noise, or sonic boom limits in climb, acceleration, and cruise. During the approach phase, however, a range-to-touchdown versus altitude display showing present position with relation to the glide path would be preferable.

SEPARATION STANDARDS

As an example of present-day procedures, ATC maintains a 15-minute longitudinal, 120-nmi lateral and 2000 ft vertical separation between jets flying en route airways between New York and London, where the airways and altitude levels are assigned before takeoff.

It is to be anticipated that within the next decade or so new High-High (H-H) sectors having diameters of possibly 600 miles will be established at major Air Route Traffic Control Centers (ARTCC's). These would provide multiple great-circle airways, but with provisions for deviations from the standard routes to take advantage of winds or of temperature variations with latitude.

An improvement in flight efficiency could be obtained with an advanced ATC concept that abandons vertical separation (which is difficult to implement even with advanced ATC displays) and obtains required traffic density by tight control of longitudinal airspace. This tight control, providing separation times along airways of as little as one minute, implies that each flight has precise navigational information (horizontal position uncertainty of, say, 2 nmi), and the means for precise automatic guidance to an airway would have to be so equipped. Multiple one-way airways may still be needed for supersonic aircraft of different cruising speeds in order not to restrict departure times unduly. Crossing airways would not require altitude separation at intersections, since an aeronautical satellite should be available by the middle 1970's to allow ATC monitoring and control of oceanic traffic. It is also assumed that conventional ATC procedures would apply below 40,000 ft, even in this time period. Thus, while takeoff times for aircraft scheduled to enter a time-space slot of an H-H airway would have to be controlled to within about one minute, adjustments to meet the time-space constraint at the entrance to the H-H airway could be made during the ascent. For example, radius of turn on the ascent could be varied to adjust to insertion time.

Other possible ATC systems that may be operational in the post-1975 period should be examined. One approach would be essentially to eliminate the control function from ATC for high altitudes, leaving only a monitoring function. An aeronautical satellite would furnish on demand to every flight a situation display of all air traffic at selected altitudes. Each flight could navigate at will from point to point in the most efficient manner consistent with traffic. Widespread use of collision-avoidance equipment could lead to similar systems. These concepts will require most careful analysis before any consideration is given to their adoption, however, because ground control of air traffic has proved effective and thus will almost certainly be retained.

Inertial Navigation System for SST's

With respect to on-board navigational aids, the SST will use an inertial navigation system, with a radio navigation system for in-flight backup and for use in terminal areas. To provide inertial system updating in the absence of ground-based facilities, automatic star-angle sensing could be incorporated as well. The aided-inertial navigation system can be manually updated in flight, using externally obtained position-fix information. A weather- and ground-mapping on-board radar also provides a navigation capability.

In the normal automatic inertial mode, the crew monitors the horizontal and vertical pictorial flight path displays to be sure that the aircraft is following the commanded path. In the event of discrepancies between navigational sensors (a planned VOR-DME updating fix disagrees seriously with the inertially determined position, for example), the crew may request additional confirming VOR-DME or ADF fixes if available, a stellar fix, or a ground radar fix. On the basis of their analysis of the overall situation, they may accept the update and continue on inertial, or they may switch modes and continue with radio navigation.

In the event that the original flight plan must be changed, the crew inserts the new objective and interrogates the guidance system concerning the resulting effects on fuel reserves and the corresponding revised command flight path for various alternative solutions, accepting the best solution which meets with ATC approval. Inherent in this concept is the use of the guidance section of the computer system to perform the energy management performance computation in the existing configuration and atmospheric environment to specify the most suitable path from one flight condition to another.

LANDING AIDS

In a similar way, on-board system technology could be used to achieve an all-weather landing capability; however, dependence on ground-based cooperation for this critical phase of flight is particularly important from the viewpoint of flight safety. Low-visibility, automatically controlled approaches and landings are technically feasible and are being demonstrated continuously in modern jet aircraft. The main impediments to the full operational deployment of automatic landing systems involve questions of assuring equipment reliability and defining operating procedures for normal and emergency situations.

Approach guidance provided by the present ILS system is satisfactory for most automatic landing requirements. However, there are cases where the lateral guidance provided by localizer beams is marginal at best, because of the accumulation of tolerance errors in the localizer alignment, receiver linearity, and spurious radiation phenomena that produce beam-bending effects. These tolerance factors, combined with aircraft flight path control errors in the presence of windshears and other disturbances, can result in marginal lateral positioning accuracy for automatic touchdowns. However, performance deficiencies in the 1967 state-of-the-art automatic approach and landing systems are not, in general, caused by inadequacies in the control concepts but by inadequacies in the primary guidance information available to define the desired flight path. Adapting systems to operate with deficient information results in performance compromise.

Guidance schemes that can be considered as alternates to the present ILS should provide the ILS equivalent of a fixed "highway in the sky." Concepts that allow any approach flight path provided that terminal conditions are met must be considered objectionable because there is no way to monitor performance of such systems with raw position-measurement data. In general, a ground-based, precision-approach radar should have the capability of monitoring an automatic approach by comparing the measured aircraft position with an allowable window.

The methods of using the crew to monitor performance of the automatic equipment and a definition of crew procedures for various failure situations are critical problems which remain to be worked out for Category IIIA. The solutions are intimately related to the types of displays that are used to present flight situation and equipment status information. Since all-weather-landing flight control displays used on present-day jet transports are evolutionary improvements over the instruments that have been used for less critical flight control tasks, questions exist regarding the compatibility of these head-down instruments with such tasks as manual takeovers from the automatics immediately after touchdown. In addition, a fundamental dilemma arises in regard to the increasing use of automatic guidance and control to land aircraft and the use of the pilot as a systems manager. The pilot is assumed to control the aircraft under abnormal and adverse conditions, but perhaps it is no longer possible to afford him the opportunity to acquire the manual-control proficiency that comes with flight experience. It appears that new concepts in pilot training will be needed for the era when automatic equipment will be allowed to exercise a dominant role in aircraft flight control.

V/STOL TRAFFIC CONTROL

The growth of "megalopolis corridors," such as those extending along the Eastern Seaboard, the Gulf, the West Coast, and the upper Midwest, has created the need for rapid, urban-center-to-urban-center, flexible transportation of people. These corridors represent significant potential markets for vertical and short takeoff and landing (V/STOL) aircraft. Because V/STOL landings are much slower than those of conventional aircraft, these craft can land under conditions of visibility lower than the usual minimums. However, there is a need for ground-based equipment (equivalent to the ILS system of conventional aircraft) that will allow the pilot to take advantage of his increased landing time. At present such equipment is limited.

Aircraft making conventional takeoffs and landings in the 1980 time period will, in all probability, fly today's familiar approach patterns. V/STOL flight operations at the same terminal will involve approach and takeoff patterns that are either nested within, or contiguous to, these conventional patterns. Efficient flight paths for V/STOL operations in the 1980 short-haul system will involve descent paths steeper than the 3-degree paths presently being flown. On the basis of vehicle performance and noise abatement, angles of at least 6 degrees will certainly be employed.

Intercity V/STOL operations will use the same terminals and blend in the same air route structure as conventional aircraft, jumbo jets, and SST's. Intracity operations will involve separate low-level flow patterns that should not interfere with intercity air traffic flow. Although the V/STOL intracity traffic will feed the main air terminals of the city which handle the intercity traffic, the V/STOL vehicles will normally be shuttling from specially designed V/STOL terminals strategically located throughout the city.

The STOL mode of short-haul transportation will involve nominal runway lengths of 1200 ft to 2500 ft, depending on the particular vehicle employed. Such aircraft could be operated on the main runways of the general terminal, although this would make for an inefficient system. Alternatively, adjacent short supplementary runways could be provided. More logical, however, is the concept of satellite STOL facilities, where runways of appropriate length are strategically located at the city outskirts. The short-haul intercity traffic could be handled at these terminals, while other conventional suburban airports could serve the intermediate-range (500 to 1500 miles) traffic. The VTOL aircraft could then serve the main city aircraft terminal and thereby alleviate the heavy traffic concentration at a single central terminal. Again, regularly scheduled operations are contingent upon all-weather capability.

In terms of navigation aids, an efficient short-haul transport system requires a navigation system that allows for point-to-point flight paths. The 1980 V/STOL short-haul system may fly with an evolutionary present-day navigation system. On the other hand, an objective analysis of the total system may indicate that the combination of accurate self-contained inertial flight navigation systems and a ground computer-supported ATC would provide significantly greater flexibility in traffic handling and efficient flight path generation. In developing the system concept, an effective balance must be sought between on-board and ground-based equipment. The on-board systems augment the capability of the pilot, relieving him of routine tasks and allowing him to operate in his primary role of aircraft commander and decision-maker. Ground-based systems correspondingly relieve the air traffic control operator of routine tasks and cast him in the role of policy-maker and broad decision-maker in overall system operation.

In establishing the system design, the navigation, guidance, and control needs of individual aircraft in the transportation net could be met by self-contained inertial measurement and computation equipment. In addition this equipment could provide for integration of all the aircraft into an effectively operating traffic control system wherein movement of the individual aircraft is known and controlled more accurately than the movement of trains in an automated railroad dispatch system. The computer and software needs of an airbus system of this type are complex but within the capability of commercially available computing equipment. In addition, electronic updating of position as the individual aircraft enters the terminal area increases the reliability of the overall system by closing the loop around the self-contained system just prior to the entry of the aircraft into the area of highest traffic density.

CONCLUSIONS

1. One of the most critical navigation problems lies in the interface between the aircraft and air traffic in the environment. For safe,

economical, and undelayed operations in the congested airspace envisioned for the post-1975 period, significant improvements are required, including automation in ATC procedures, establishment of a few major control centers capable of worldwide aircraft surveillance and communication, and a correspondingly greater airline freedom in the selection and assignment of specific airlanes for most economical source-to-destination flights. Similarly, the air traffic control in the terminal areas should be automated and new, all-weather landing systems implemented in order to reduce or eliminate the delays in holding patterns.

2. An immediate implication of an advanced ATC system is a much greater freedom in the selection of flight profiles, together with a requirement that such profiles be followed with precision in assigned air-time space. The selected profiles should not only provide the most economical source-to-destination flight but should also encompass the optimum climb and descent profiles within whatever constraints might be dictated.

3. In order to achieve the required flight precision at supersonic transport speeds and to conform to sonic-boom and noise-abatement constraints, the aircraft guidance and steering functions of this class of aircraft will have to be automated.

4. The required flight safety and precision will have to be implemented by careful selection of equipment, redundancy concepts, failure-detection techniques, and back-up modes. Furthermore the crew, which will be responsible for the overall system operation, surveillance, and performance, will have to be provided with display and control equipment and perform functions consistent with their new role.

5. Present inertial navigation systems can meet the predicted horizontal navigation requirements for the spectrum of aircraft from V/STOL's to supersonic transports, in the post-1975 era. Furthermore, inertial equipment costs could be reduced significantly by the proper mixing of navigation satellite data with data from a lower accuracy inertial system, and possibly by providing for necessary redundancy at the sensor level rather than at the inertial navigation system level.

6. Measurement and display of vertical situation information need to be improved for all classes of aircraft, particularly during operation under instrument weather conditions. In fact, to reduce pilot workload and to realize the capability of V/STOL aircraft for safe operations at reduced weather minimums, major effort needs to be directed toward the development of practical precision instrument approach techniques and vastly improved dis-

plays, as well as toward improvements in aircraft handling qualities.

7. Landing safety and performance under all-weather conditions could be significantly improved if advanced ILS data were used in conjunction with inertial data to provide completely automatic approach and landing. This would need to be accompanied by a new approach to the ATC system if V/STOL and conventional aircraft are to operate effectively in the same high-traffic-density terminal areas.

8. Precision altimetry is another major problem area, particularly for unsophisticated general aviation aircraft, albeit not so much a technological problem as a regulatory one. That is, the long-established, inexpensive pressure altimeter would generally satisfy all but the most stringent altimetry requirements if means were developed for maintaining and calibrating the system on all aircraft at regular intervals and for assuring that the correct sea level barometric pressure was set in at all times.

RECOMMENDATIONS

Major research and development should be directed toward new operational concepts in guidance and navigation, such as multifunction satellites en route. Furthermore, to help overcome the all-weather data from the barometric altimeter and inertial reference unit with VOR-DME in departure and terminal areas and possibly with navigation satellites enroute. Furthermore, to help overcome the all-weather approach and landing problem for either V/STOL or conventional aircraft, inertially aided landing systems should be developed to operate in conjunction with the autopilot and the navigation-aid data from precision DME, advanced ILS, and the radar altimeter.

Inasmuch as it may be anticipated that the barometric altimeter will still be heavily relied upon in the post-1975 period, means for assuring the accuracy of the system need to be developed.

COMMUNICATIONS

The communication network is obviously an essential part of any air traffic control system. Without it no control could be exercised over aircraft en route between terminals.

The required capacity of the communication system, however, depends on several factors such as the amount of direct control to be exercised by the control centers vis-à-vis the responsibility of the pilot to adhere to a precalculated and determined flight profile. As aircraft speeds increase, the period for which weather and traffic forecasts are required decreases and precalculated flight profiles, even for transcontinental flights, come closer to reality. This will tend to lower the required communication capacity per aircraft.

But the same factors that tend to diminish the required communication capacity, i.e., higher speeds and shorter flight times, increase the demand for reliability and speed of communications. Traditional voice communication procedures, often requiring several contacts to ensure that communication has been established, will no longer be acceptable. Systems in which this assurance is automatic and quick will be required. It will also be necessary to process and display the data so that it can be assimilated and used in the shortest possible time.

The number of communications per aircraft may decrease in the future for these reasons, but if the air traffic forecasts are correct, the total amount of air-ground-air communications will increase appreciably. The FAA forecasts that the number of aircraft contacted by FAA Flight Service Stations and Combined Station/Towers will rise from 9.3 million in 1967 to 18.3 million in 1977.

In addition to the communications traffic relating to air traffic control, there will undoubtedly be an increase in the traffic concerned with company business and other functions not related directly to the ATC system, including reports of meteorological information; customs, immigration, and health functions; and the reporting of aircraft status. The larger aircraft being designed now will place increased loads on passenger-handling facilities at terminals, and advance information will become increasingly important if maximum use is to be made of available facilities. High-performance aircraft such as the SST will require a special effort to reduce the time required to service them if economical operation is to be achieved. Knowledge of the status of the major systems in the aircraft prior to its arrival will allow proper preparation to be made, thereby reducing the time required for servicing. This information could be made available by equipping each aircraft with a telemetry system to transmit sensor outputs automatically on command from the ground.

The communications system of the future will be required to handle, process, and display more information and to function more automatically and faster than the present system. Furthermore, this will have to be done within the present frequency allocations; the chance of obtaining additional frequency allocations in time to make any contribution to the solution of this problem is decreasing rapidly. Fortunately, however, the application of digital techniques now available should afford a solution that will be sufficient for some time to come.

DATA PROCESSING

It is difficult to determine data-processing requirements for post-1975 air traffic control in the absence of even a conceptual system design. It is possible, however, to develop a "peak-load" notion against which present and foreseeable technology can be matched to ascertain technical constraints on system capacity and capability. This approach immediately focuses attention on the ground control system. If potential system loads are considered, the projected 180,000 aircraft in the general aviation fleet cannot be ignored, and even the most optimistic view of developments in integrated circuitry and electronic economics does not place self-contained navigation and flight control equipment in any large portion of these planes. Also, if the aim is to probe the technical base, we must assume the highest possible degree of automation. In fact, this is not a particularly speculative position. It is quite obvious that projected traffic loads cannot be handled without a largely automatic system. The real question is not manual versus machine control, but whether data-processing technology — hardware and software — will permit economical and orderly evolution of the required capability.

The basic data-processing load (and the degree of automation that can be achieved) depends largely on the precision with which all aircraft in the control area can be located in time and space. FAA projections of peak-minute traffic above 9000 feet (IFR and VFR) suggest for 1980 a peak instantaneous load of some 10,000–12,000 aircraft over the continental United States. The maximum density over a 300 × 300-mile control area would be on the order of 600 — sufficient to preclude any presently contemplated radar surveillance system.

This load does not, however, appear beyond the capabilities of a cooperative time-frequency position-fixing system. Systems of this type are presently being proposed for air collision warning, and the basic concept (time-multiplexed radio transmissions from which slant range may be determined on the basis of highly accurate time measurements) can plausibly be extended to a ground triangulation system. The key to any such system is precise time synchronization. This is not a trivial technical problem over continental areas, but it is not impossible. A ground-based synchronization system could reduce requirements for airborne equipment and their costs to a point where the great majority of general aviation fleet aircraft could be equipped for precise position monitoring.

If the proposed 1500-μsec "time-slice" per aircraft transmission is accepted, position fixes could be updated once a second on all planes in a control area under estimated peak loads. This is equivalent to every .16 mile for a 600-mph aircraft and is clearly an overdetermination. The computational load would not, however, challenge one of today's small, medium-priced computers.

The estimated peak continental load (12,000 aircraft) could probably be handled by such a system through judicious adjustment of transmission repetition rates to reasonable control or hazard volumes for different classes of aircraft and/or by going to multiple channels. The point to be made here is simply one of plausibility. Such a system could evolve and would represent an upper bound on the input information rate to the traffic control system.

To assess the potential strain that might be imposed on the data-processing facilities, it is necessary to postulate a few more numbers. Assume a 300×300-mile control area; x, y position determination to .1 mile; and altitude to 50 ft (aircraft report). Following the proposed collision warning system message format (75 "message" bits, plus 8 bits assigned to heading information and 6 bits to altitude rate), these assumptions yield 124 bits per aircraft. Assume an average repetition (updating) rate of 2 sec, and a basic information input rate of 62 bits/sec/aircraft is obtained. For 21 control areas, 5 bits must be added for area identity. Somewhat gratuitously, 18 bits of aircraft identification can be added for overall system control. At peak continental loading (12,000 aircraft) a total system input rate of 1.2×10^6 bits/sec could be anticipated. For a given control area, peak loads would probably not exceed 40,000 bits/sec.

Under these conditions there would be no problem of maintaining real-time flight files with present-day equipment. It could probably be done in a single large machine.

Maintaining flight status is, of course, only one of the data-processing functions involved in air traffic control. With appropriate inputs, it is perhaps the least demanding in terms of computation and processing requirements. Once such a capability exists, however, the possibility of automating other traffic management and control functions also exists. Indeed, some degree of automation — for instance, computerized optimization and assignment of time slots — will be required simply to handle expected traffic loads.

If a two-way system is postulated in which ground transmissions are interleaved with air transmissions, the way is open to complete automation, including optimization of flight plans, continual correlation of flight with flight plans, en route speed control to alleviate stacking at terminal, detection of emergency conditions, automatic rerouting, and collision avoidance. How many such computerized functions will be implemented and how soon is not important. Assuming precise flight status information, the capabilities of automating all readily foreseeable control functions exists with today's data-processing technology. In short, the technology can support an automated air traffic control system that will handle projected requirements, including demands for safety, runway utilization, and efficiency.

This is a strong conclusion; it requires one cautionary note. Monolithic integrated systems (e.g., SAGE) are extremely expensive, highly inflexible in practice if not in principle, and difficult to introduce into an ongoing operation. Consequently, a multicomputer environment (including specialized processors with access to a common data bank), computer netting, program modularity, and evolutionary acquisition of capability have been tacitly assumed. These are commonly advertized capabilities of modern data systems that, in fact, have not been successfully and effectively implemented in any current large system. It seems reasonable to assume, however, that the appropriate techniques and engineering practice will be available in the 1970-1975 era.

There is still the assumption of competent system design. Computers per se are no solution to anyone's problem. Technology in the form of machines, programming systems, displays, and gadgets cannot substitute for detailed, realistic systems analysis and design. There is nothing in the technology that precludes or strongly constrains the development of an adequate post-1975 ATC system, but the application of that technology will take a large and concentrated effort that is not, at the moment, visible.

THE COMMUNICATIONS SYSTEM

To take full advantage of the data-processing techniques just discussed and to reduce to a minimum the amount of processing required, the information should be put into digital form as soon as possible and handled in that form as long as possible. A digital communications system would, therefore, be indicated.

There are three questions, however, that must be answered before the system can be designed:

1. What (or how much) information is to be transmitted?
2. In what form can this information be most efficiently transmitted?
3. What is going to be done with the information after it is received?

When the answers to these question are made available to the communications system engineer, he can design a system; in fact, he can design a large number of systems. Herein lies the greatest problem: which system?

Present-day technology is sufficiently advanced to allow the design and implementation of a digital communications system that would be adequate for the foreseeable future. Modern communications theory permits the design of a system with extremely low error rates, high capacity, and the ability to handle a large number of users. Computers, both airborne and ground-based, are available to process the data into usable form. For a digital system to be useful, however, all users must use compatible formats, bit rates, and coding levels. These characteristics must be agreed upon by the users before the system is designed. A standardized system is required.

The gap, then, is not technical but one of implementation. A decision should be made now to go to a digital system, and steps should be taken to define the system parameters so that the necessary hardware can be developed to function in a compatible manner in the system. This must be done through a concerted, cooperative effort involving government, the airlines, the aircraft industry, and the communications industry. The importance of this step cannot be overstressed. If such a system is to be implemented by 1975, it must be started now.

The type of standard required is set forth in two publications: *Tactical Communications and Control Systems Standards,* Volume 1 (Joint Chiefs of Staff, JCS Pub. 10) and *Universal Air-Ground Digital Communications Systems Standards* (Radio Technical Commission for Aeronautics, March 12, 1964). The former is a military standard; the latter is primarily concerned with civil applications. Before any such proposed standard is generally accepted it should reflect the latest state-of-the-art and be as responsive to future requirements as possible. RTCA currently has special committees working on proposed standards.

Nothing said to this point should be interpreted as meaning that no equipment developments are required. Particularly difficult problems exist with the data displays. As the amount of data increases, it is going to become more and more difficult to make it available as required to the pilot in the aircraft or to the interested person on the ground. Unless the present concept of the pilot and controller's role in the system is changed, it may be found that control breaks down through an overloaded human link. Undoubtedly more stress will be put on greater reliability, lighter weight, less power consumption and lower cost. All these are amenable to solution if the designer can be given the system characteristics that must be satisfied.

One of the most serious problems that will be faced by the communications engineer is the need to phase over gradually from the present system to the digital system. Unless this is done carefully, the requirement for compatibility of the two systems can result in the imposition of unreasonable constraints on the new system, and many of the advantages that could be realized from the shift to a digital system may be lost.

The digital techniques will allow a more efficient use of the spectrum but will not solve the frequency problem completely. The use of satellites as communications relays will complicate the situation, because the frequencies used must be set aside exclusively for this purpose, since the satellite can be seen from a large portion of the earth's surface. The same consideration will limit the geographical extent to which frequency allocations can be shared, as the altitude at which aircraft operate increases. Thus as the operating altitudes are increased, no advantage results from using frequencies providing line-of-sight propagation. These factors must be considered in future planning and are independent of the type of system used.

Integrated Systems

A communications system employing digital techniques and a time division multiplex technique to accommodate a number of aircraft simultaneously on a single channel has the inherent capability of furnishing identification and information for navigation (more properly, position-fixing). The present state-of-the-art in stable-frequency generators makes it feasible for each aircraft to carry a frequency source stable enough to allow the determination of distance from another source by measuring the time delay encountered in transmission. For ATC purposes, aircraft position relative to another point is vital, whether with respect to a terminal area or to another aircraft. There are several ways in which this information can be derived from the timing data inherent in a digital communications system.

Traditionally the functions of position determination, identification, and communications have been performed independently. This has necessitated the carrying of several separate systems by each aircraft, with the cooperating ground equipment tending to congest and complicate the control centers and terminals. Further, the separation of these functions has required the use of additional parts of the electromagnetic spectrum so that an increase in the efficiency of spectrum utilization could be expected from an integration of these functions.

If such an integrated system is to be utilized, it is important that it be designed from the beginning with these functions as requirements. Thus a coordinated effort of government, the airlines, and the electronics industry is required if maximum use is to be made of the techniques available.

CONCLUSIONS

1. A communications and data-processing system capable of meeting the needs of the post-1975 period is feasible using techniques that are within the present state-of-the-art.
2. Such a system should employ digital techniques and a time division multiplex arrangement to accommodate multiple aircraft.
3. Communications with the aircraft must be automated to the maximum extent possible consistent with pilot requirements. This includes the use of "canned" messages where appropriate, the automatic transmission of routine information without attention of a crew member, the display of information both in the aircraft and on the ground in an easily interpreted form, and the telemetry of aircraft system status on command from the ground.
4. It may be possible to integrate the functions of communications, navigation, and identification — an improvement which could result in more efficient use of the radio spectrum and a decrease in the amount of airborne and ground equipment required in the ATC system.

RECOMMENDATIONS

An appropriate body with government, airline, and communications/electronics industry representation should

1. Determine the requirements for an integrated communications, navigation, and identification system.
2. Establish the standards of such a system to ensure proper interfacing of the aircraft and ground equipment, at the same time leaving the standards flexible enough to allow improvements to minimize obsolescence of equipment already in use.
3. Establish a plan for an evolutionary change from the present to the future system, with minimum expense to the users and the government.

The urgency of these requirements should be recognized, and action should be taken at the earliest possible time.

ATC FACILITIES

The vast air traffic control system now operated by the FAA in the United States and its territories and possessions includes 327 control towers, 127 terminal radar control facilities, 28 Air Route Traffic Control Center (ARTCC) facilities, and 333 flight service stations. These facilities are manned by more than 17,000 operating and support personnel.

Of the 127 terminal radar control facilities, 91 are directly associated with specific control towers. The remaining 36 are separate Radar Approach Control (RAPCON) and Radar Air Traffic Control Center (RATCC) units at Air Force or Navy bases. There are 89 long-range air route surveillance radars serving the ARTCC's. Many of these are remotely located and connected to the appropriate center by microwave links. In both terminal and en route systems, radar data are displayed in analog fashion, either on low-brilliance plan position indicators or scan-converted television bright displays.

In the main, air traffic control services are provided manually with handwritten records and voice communications. When automation was first introduced in air traffic control in 1958, it was not considered feasible to apply it to the basic air traffic control conflict detection and resolution process. Therefore, attention was directed solely to minimizing the clerical workload of controllers. Initially six air route traffic control centers were equipped, one with an IBM 650 and five with UNIVAC File II computers. The IBM was later replaced with a UNIVAC File II for standardization, and a center-consolidation program initiated in the early 1960's reduced the number of equipped centers to five. In this application of automation the computer accepts manually inserted flight plan data, calculates estimates over specific reporting points en route, and prints flight progress strips for controller record-keeping. A major disadvantage of this system is that strip printing is performed at a central "flight data" operating position, from which the strips have to be distributed to the 30 or 40 operating sectors at each center by clerks.

In 1963 the UNIVAC in the New York center was replaced with an IBM 1401-1410 combination. This system uses what is referred to as distributed flight-strip printing. Individual strip-printing typewriters are located at the sector operating positions so that strips are printed where they will be used. The computer is programmed to address strip-printing messages only to printers at sectors concerned. An additional feature of this installation is Computer Updating Equipment (CUE), which enables flight plan data to be retained in storage until a flight departs; then entry of the departure time causes flight strips to be printed with current data based upon the actual time of departure and air traffic clearance issued to the flight. The UNIVAC in the Cleveland center has been replaced with an IBM 9020 system incorporating features similar to those at the New York center. Studies have definitely proved these systems to be worthwhile in expediting flight data handling and in reducing requirements for clerical personnel.

Only two facilities are presently equipped with automatic data processing to aid radar control. The Atlanta terminal radar has a small tracking computer operating through a display processor which permits the labeling of selected radar and radar beacon targets with alphanumeric identity, altitude, and other data. A recent installation in the New York center provides for such labeling of only radar beacon targets with aircraft identity and automatically reported altitude information. Such data are derived through the Air Traffic Control Radar Beacon System (ATCRBS), which is an outgrowth of military IFF systems.

NATIONAL AIRSPACE SYSTEM AUTOMATION PROGRAMS

Current programs are directed toward application of automation techniques to whatever task shows promise of increasing controller productivity. It is now recognized that a large number of operational functions can either be automated entirely or significantly improved through automation. However, to attempt to apply automation to all these tasks in the first step is recognized as being practically impossible. Therefore, a step-by-step approach has been decided upon, with the first step in the en route system being National Airspace System (NAS) En Route Stage A. This stage provides for development and implementation of most of the hardware needed by later stages, and will form the foundation upon which the system for the 1970's will be built. The operational functions to be provided in Stage A are

1. Flight plan receipt and processing.
2. Flight progress strip printing and processing.
3. Two-way transfer of flight and control data between control centers and terminal control facilities.
4. Two-way transfer of flight and control data between centers.
5. Local computer entry and cathode ray tube readout.
6. Translation of analog radar data to digital, and input to computers.
7. Display of all radar and other data on digital air situation plan view displays.
8. Radar updating of flight data.

The central processor is an IBM 9020 computer. Peripheral equipment includes sector flight-strip printers and alphanumeric data entry devices, together with digital displays with full alphanumeric capability. Each radar display console will have its own alphanumeric input capability, and each controller will have a small cathode ray tube computer output device displaying data entry preview, flight data updates, error messages, terminal weather data, and notices to airmen.

The radar tracking program provides for manual initiation on primary radar and nondiscrete radar beacon targets. Automatic initiation is used on radar beacon targets of aircraft with 4096 code transponders assigned discrete codes. A program interface between the flight-plan data-processing and radar-tracking program components provides for automatic updating of reporting point estimates on the basis of radar progress information. When an aircraft drifts off course beyond a set parameter, the controller is alerted either to direct the aircraft back on course or to amend the flight plan route.

A parallel automation system has been defined for major high-activity terminals such as New York and Los Angeles. These systems will offer essentially the same assistance to the controller as described for En Route Stage A. In addition, provision is included for entry and processing of short-distance flights not involved in en route traffic control.

Later stages of these highly complex en route and terminal systems will add such functions as

1. Automated sequencing and spacing of arrival aircraft, and sequencing of departing aircraft among the arrivals.
2. Feedback of arrival sequencing data into the en route system to allow terminal delays to be partially absorbed by speed reductions en route.
3. Advanced planning functions to provide automation assistance for minimizing peaking of radar control conflict problems.
4. Improved flow control to regulate traffic demands according to fluctuations in system capacity.
5. Traffic conflict detection to assist controllers in foreseeing potential situations where separation minimums are likely to be breached.
6. Conflict resolution in which, once a potential conflict is detected, the computer would quickly evaluate several alternative ways of resolving the conflict and recommend the least objectionable alternative to the controller for implementation.

Less complex automation systems are planned for medium- and low-activity terminals. Primarily these will label radar targets with identity and altitude information and permit some automation of radar hand-off. In the smaller facilities this equipment will process only radar-beacon-derived information. On targets of transponder-equipped aircraft, the label will include aircraft identity and automatically reported altitude information.

In the first stage of automation, medium-activity terminals will process only radar-beacon information, providing essentially the same target labels as at the lower activity terminals plus tracker-derived ground speed and limited manually inserted data. Expansion of these systems will provide for a less complex form of automatic sequencing and spacing assistance than at the high-density locations as well as automatic tracking and labeling of primary radar targets.

COLLISION-AVOIDANCE SYSTEM

The aviation community has long been intrigued by the concept of an airborne collision-avoidance system (CAS). Collision avoidance under visual conditions has always involved the pilot's sighting another aircraft, deciding upon the collision hazard, and making his own decision with respect to any avoidance maneuver required. As the speeds of aircraft have increased, the pilot's ability to perform this function has become less and less effective. At high altitudes, near-field myopia problems seriously interfere with the pilot's ability to sight converging traffic. Other psychological factors lower his ability to react to collision hazards.

An electronic device for collision avoidance would minimize most of these factors and provide the further advantage of being omnidirectional. Research by Bendix Radio, the Sperry Division of Sperry Rand, the National Company, and Collins Radio Company, conducted since 1956 under contract to the FAA, has identified the most promising approach. Two years ago the McDonnell-Douglas Corporation demonstrated a practical collision-avoidance system, based upon a cooperative radio receiver-transmitter operating in conjunction with a small computer and a precision crystal clock using the time-frequency (T/F) synchronization technique. The air transport industry, with FAA and DOD, is now defining the desired technical characteristics for a CAS, and implementation should be carried out in the near future. It is planned to use CAS to complement the ATC system, as well as for protection in areas where ATC service is not available.

THE OUTLOOK BEYOND 1975

The NAS automation program just described, augmented by limited CAS capability, is considered to afford adequate ATC system expansion until the mid-1970s. Forecasts indicate that controlled traffic will double between 1965 and 1975. The following decade could see it double again. The question now being asked is: will expansion and augmentation along current lines satisfy the greater demand should it occur, or will a new approach be required? If a new approach is needed, experience decrees that any new devices be defined 8 to 10 years in advance if system characteristics are to be standardized worldwide and if implementation is to be underway when the need arrives. Second, the approach must allow evolutionary transition from the old to the new over a period on the order of 10 to 15 years.

Realistic examination of current ATC philosophy reveals that collision protection under instrument flight conditions depends solely upon ground management of each aircraft on an individual basis. Under visual conditions responsibility for conflict detection and separation is shared between pilots and controllers. Airport capacities under visual conditions can be shown to be roughly double those under instrument conditions. The relationship of airspace capacity under the two conditions is more difficult to predict, but the ratio is believed to be even greater. Consequently, the goal should be to increase instrument capacity so that it approaches visual capacity. Logically, a system which provides that pilots share some of the separation responsibility under instrument conditions, as they do under visual conditions, should have the potential of so increasing instrument capacity.

To permit the pilot to share this responsibility under instrument conditions, the system must provide for aircraft to have electronic capability for pilots to detect and identify other aircraft in their vicinity and to space their aircraft with respect to the others. ("Identify" in this sense means only that the pilot be able to tell one aircraft from another on a discrete basis.) CAS equipment can be designed with this "station-keeping" ability, and ATC procedures would then be modified to require pilots to effect their own separation in circumstances specified by the controller. Under this concept ATC could deal with groups of aircraft rather than with individual aircraft, detecting and resolving potential group conflicts.

Applying the system approach, it would be advantageous for the technique selected for CAS and station-keeping functions to provide, also, for service in other functional areas such as

- Navigation
- ATC aircraft position determination
- Ground-air-ground digital communications

The benefit of such an approach would be to achieve CAS or PWI (pilot warning indicator) and station-keeping ability at the cost of replacing existing navigation and radar beacon transponder equipment. Acceptance of any new system by general aviation users would thus be facilitated. Lacking this, the system would need to treat most general aviation aircraft individually under current procedures while handling equipped aircraft under the new procedures. The result would be a lowering of the effectiveness of the overall system.

Transition to such a new system would require an additional input to the NAS computer of aircraft position using the new technique. If a digital communications function were included, the NAS computer would logically handle it. Present radar and radar beacon inputs would remain during transition. Eventually, at least the radar beacon input would be phased out. If it should not prove feasible for all general aviation aircraft to participate in collision-avoidance and station-keeping capability, the NAS computer possibly could be programmed for these functions. It would then transmit avoidance and other maneuver instructions digitally for cockpit display.

PROBLEMS WITH ENHANCEMENT OF ATC CAPABILITY

Many problems pertaining to expansion and implementation of ATC facilities are in the nature of normal management problems of fiscal policy, logistics, personnel availability and training, and timing. While serious, they are solvable by ordinary means. A more difficult problem is that of the advancement of the basic state-of-the-art of air traffic control — the need for refinement of tried and proved practices to improve efficiency and safety, and the need for a breakthrough in effective movement of V/STOL aircraft. A discussion of some of these problems follows.

Advanced Planning

Automation assistance is needed to regulate traffic in a manner that will maximize controller capacity. System error analysis reveals that controller overload is a consequential contributing factor in many control incidents. The system needs a better means of predicting when a radar controller will be required to resolve more potential conflicts at a given time than he is capable of handling effectively. It should also assist in determining means of reordering traffic (by horizontal or vertical rerouting) to smooth peaks of potential conflicts. Or, alternatively, it should aid in determining when and how personnel should be shifted to better distribute workload.

Flow Control

More effective methodology and measures are required to meter or limit demand on the ATC system when capacity will be exceeded. Frequently demand so far exceeds capacity that excessive, unacceptable delays are incurred, especially at busy terminals. A process is required whereby demand and capacity are monitored dynamically in various segments of an ARTCC's control area. When demand in a given segment is foreseen to exceed a certain criterion (probably a percentage of capacity), measures would be instituted to regulate traffic flow on an aircraft-by-aircraft basis, rather than by gross metering as is done today.

Automated Sequencing and Spacing

Automation of final approach sequencing and spacing promises significant system gains. Tests have shown that landing rates can be improved 10 to 15 percent with no procedural changes. Calculations indicate that improvements as high as 47 percent are achievable under some conditions with different separation minimums. The greatest gain entails a change from distance to time separation. (The study considered a change from 3 miles to 60 seconds.) Some of these changes are attainable only with automation assistance. An automated process has been developed and tested to sequence and space aircraft landing on one runway. This needs to be sophisticated to provide for

- Landings on multiple runways — parallel and intersecting
- Service to small VFR aircraft not being controlled en route
- Interspersing of departures on the same and other runways
- Service to several airports in the same terminal area

Conflict Detection and Resolution

Automation of the most difficult part of the air traffic control task, conflict detection and resolution, is essential for greater safety as well as for increased controller productivity. The possible consequences of human error in ATC are catastrophic. Many inadvertent errors occur on the part of controllers and pilots. While procedural improvements minimize their effects, a much better solution would be the nonhuman system monitoring which could result from automation of conflict detection. A refinement would be for the computer also to test several alternative solutions and recommend the best to the controller. Lightening of these burdens on the controller should significantly increase his productivity.

V/STOL Considerations

More effective means are required for handling vertical and short takeoff and landing (V/STOL) aircraft operating on very-short-route segments. Interactions with fixed-wing aircraft at regular airports limit the maximum utility of such aircraft. Navigation facilities must provide for operation on approach and takeoff paths segregated from fixed-wing aircraft.

Steep-gradient takeoff and approach paths introduce unique spacing problems. Line-of-sight VHF communications limit the effectiveness of traffic control provided from the ground. Each of these problems would tend to support the use of station-keeping devices in the vehicles, so that spacing of same-direction traffic could be a pilot function. In such a case, spacing of opposite-direction traffic could be achieved by adherence to parallel one-way airways. Ground traffic control might then be required only for regulation of flow at intersections where "over-and-under" procedures could not be followed.

Although not presently provided, control will no doubt be needed in the future at segregated V/STOL terminals where traffic density warrants. However, if station-keeping proves feasible on approach and takeoff, it should minimize the need for ground management at all but the busiest pure V/STOL terminals.

Control of higher speed (200 to 300-knot) V/STOL aircraft operated on relatively long route segments should be identical to that for fixed-wing aircraft. At such speeds there is expected to be no effective difference between the two types of vehicles from a maneuverability standpoint.

Obstruction clearance en route will remain a function of the barometric altimeter which is standard for all IFR flight. It is questionable whether an operational requirement will exist for V/STOL vehicles to cruise at altitudes below those where barometric altimeters are satisfactory. Serious problems could occur in the application of vertical separation if V/STOL's were to use altimeters different from those of fixed-wing aircraft.

RECOMMENDATIONS FOR TECHNICAL STUDIES AND SYSTEMS ANALYSIS

Systems analysis should be applied to the problem areas identified in the previous section. Additional technical studies are specifically required in respect to the following areas.

ATC Separation Criteria

The spacing or separation minimums used by controllers establish a fixed limit on airspace and runway capacity and therefore need to be as small as practicable so as not to waste airspace. Studies show that gains in runway capacity of between 10 and 47 percent should be achievable with appropriate reductions or redefinition of separation minimums. The minimums currently in use were derived empirically over many years. A scientific analysis is needed to determine what reductions are possible without unduly compromising safety.

Perhaps the most critical need is for reduction of spacing between aircraft using different runways for landing and takeoff. Currently, 5000 feet is required between parallel approach paths. But real estate costs and other problems preclude such spacing at many airports needing greater capacity. Effective operation of V/STOL aircraft requires much closer spacing.

System Performance Measures

New technology on the horizon offers opportunities for solving a number of pressing problems. However, a common yardstick with which to compare and select the most suitable candidates is lacking. A program is needed to define the system characteristics required in order for the national airspace system to accept the traffic loads anticipated in the post-1975 period.

Navigation

It is necessary to determine what will be needed in the way of course-selection versatility and other operational characteristics, track-keeping accuracy, along-track-position accuracy, and vertical-position accuracy. It is expected that these characteristics will differ in the terminal area from those required en route. Low-traffic-density areas would probably require less stringent en route characteristics than high-density areas. Finally, the rate at which data displayed to the pilot is renewed could differ in various circumstances.

ATC data acquisition

Specific required characteristics of aircraft-position determination include horizontal- and vertical-position accuracy and discrete identification of position with respect to each aircraft. A question regarding this latter requirement is: should the number of discrete identities be virtually unlimited, or should airborne selection be provided to allow use of a limited number? At what rate does such position data need to be renewed? As in the case of navigational characteristics, requirements may vary in areas of differing traffic densities as well as between en route and terminal positions.

Collision-avoidance system or proximity warning indicator

Characteristics need to be defined for accuracy of relative position, range rate, bearing (if needed), and identification and data renewal rate.

Automatic digital communications

Types of messages need to be identified, also addressing standards, modes of error checking, data rates, and access conditions.

Technique Analysis

Various promising new techniques need to be examined for potential applicability in solving airspace problems. The FAA is currently investigating the time-frequency (T/F) technique. The Autonetics Division of North American Rockwell is currently seeking to define more clearly the role of T/F for application to the total National Airspace System in CAS, navigation, ATC position data acquisition, and other functions. The Arcon Corporation is studying the most suitable techniques for resolving the navigation, communications, and ATC position-data-acquisition problems in over-ocean and remote-area air transportation.

Component Obsolescence Analysis

Existing components of the national airspace system (navigation, communications, ATC equipment) are known to have limited usefulness. It is important to know when each component is reaching obsolescence in sufficient time to identify, design, and procure replacements. This is especially vital where a new technique will be involved requiring international standardization of characteristics. In such instances, 20 years or more lead time is required between determination of a need and full implementation. Continuing studies are required to determine when and under what circumstances NAS components will become obsolete.

CONCLUSIONS

Rapidly expanding air traffic promises to overwhelm the present air traffic control system. Steps to develop an advanced evolutionary system must be initiated immediately. Specific areas for study and analysis have been delineated in this section of the report.

The following recommendations for action are listed in order to initiate the needed new evolutionary air traffic control system.

RECOMMENDATIONS

1. Studies should be undertaken to ascertain when and under what circumstances present navigation and other national airspace system components will become unable to handle forecast loads satisfactorily.
2. The results of these studies should be used to initiate timely development of replacement components for those reaching obsolescence.
3. The presently programmed ATC automation should be augmented before 1975 to provide advanced planning, flow control, automated sequencing and spacing, and conflict detection and resolution. These improvements must allow transition to a post-1975 system with possibly vast differences in aircraft position determination and operating rules.
4. ATC separation criteria should be analyzed to determine what reductions are possible without unduly compromising safety, directing special attention to minimums between aircraft approaching to land and taking off.
5. System performance measures need to be defined to examine effectiveness of present NAS components and for use in selecting new components.
6. System analysis and design efforts for the post-1975 period should be directed toward a system wherein pilots are enabled to assume some of the instrument flight conflict detection and resolution responsibility from the ground-based air traffic control system. Further, under this concept air traffic rules and control procedures should be amended in an evolutionary manner so that the ground ATC system is responsible for controlling groups of aircraft, but pilots within groups are responsible for separation assurance.
7. Future system design should provide for en route control service to visual flights at all altitudes. Such service would be voluntary in most low-altitude airspace but compulsory along certain high-density routes.

CONTROLLERS

Any discussion of the national airspace system in the 1975 time period must conclude that, as in the case of hardware and software, changes in the function of control personnel will involve an evolutionary process of building and modifying. With this in mind, it is necessary to start with today's problems and project these and other problems anticipated between now and the period under discussion. The principal factors discussed here regarding controllers are recruitment, advancement opportunities, work conditions, and human engineering.

RECRUITMENT

During the past several years government personnel policies plus budget restrictions on the FAA have precluded acquisition of personnel for training. The system now faces an enormous traffic growth with personnel gaps that will undoubtedly represent a major economic loss to the air transportation industry within the next few years. Controllers are not an off-the-shelf item. There is no school, university, or other privately sponsored training program that turns them out. Personnel must first be obtained and then trained. In this specialty, training requires a minimum of 18 months in a low-activity VFR tower, and as much as three to five years in a complex, high-activity facility.

To complicate the situation, the recruitment program for new personnel, which will require even greater skills and technical competence in the future, is coming to a halt as applicants begin to foresee what they are getting into. Even today, despite the fact that the average civil service grade of controllers is higher than in most echelons of government, trainee positions are going begging; the situation will worsen unless remedial action can be defined and taken.

ADVANCEMENT OPPORTUNITIES

One of the serious problems facing a young person considering an air traffic control career is the lack of opportunity for advancement. The controller is under continuous mental strain and, since shift work is involved, unnatural physical strain compounds the outlook. (For example, during bad weather and under peak traffic conditions it is impossible to eat regularly.) Consequently, a controller's productive life span is much shorter than that of any comparable government employee. Further, he is subjected to increasingly exacting medical checks of his mental and physical capability which render him vulnerable to elimination from the service early in his career. A limited few can look forward to moving from the stress and strain of the controller job into administrative positions, but the sheer population of controllers (in excess of 12,000) indicates that any one individual has little chance of entering the administrative or supervisory area.

The exacting skills required of the controller are not directly applicable in other areas of the air transport complex. Consequently, he is in a dead-end occupation and must strive to make it a lifetime career, with the odds against him. Many controllers with pilot skills, who occupy positions at Grade 12 and above, are leaving the service to take positions as pilots at lower salaries, knowing that within a year or so their compensation will be well above what they can expect by remaining in the service under the conditions described. It is thus apparent that personnel, the most important element of the NAS, cannot be effective without long-range planning to correct the existing situation.

WORK CONDITIONS

The air traffic control system today relies heavily on radar as a control and monitoring tool. Radar is used extensively by the controller as a navigation device to lead the pilot from takeoff to landing. This procedure is necessitated by the inadequacies of the navigation system itself and, in consequence, requires that the controller population increase out of proportion to the traffic demands, a costly and wasteful process. The systems approach supports the necessity of returning the navigation responsibility to the cockpit to free the controller to perform his basic function.

The extreme variations in pilot skills also place stress on the controller. Airspace rules permit pilots of all skills, operating by Visual Flight Rules (VFR), to fly at will almost anywhere in controlled airspace at the lower altitudes. Aircraft not under control mingle with those being controlled. Although not required to do so, a controller who sees on his radar an unknown, uncontrolled aircraft on a course leading toward an aircraft for which he is responsible faces a moral obligation to at least advise the controlled aircraft of the other. He does this even though his radar picture is now only two-dimensional and he therefore has no knowledge of whether the two aircraft are at the same altitude.

One of the principal complaints on the part of the controller is the inadequacy of his tools. Inadequate display devices and manually operated communications facilities plague his existence, and in some cases he must still resort to shouting in order to convey a command or agreement to a co-worker across the room.

The principal display still used for nonradar control and for record-keeping with radar control is the flight progress strip, a device developed during the 1930's. Although highly efficient for use by an individual controller, it binds him to fully manual procedures and hinders attempts to simplify and streamline the clerical and controller-to-controller communications functions. It will eventually impede development of automated controller-to-pilot communications, as well as other automation aids for the controller.

The need for continual increase in the controller population beyond what is called for by increasing traffic demands is attributable in large measure to communications problems. An individual's capacity is regulated largely by two factors, the number of aircraft he can reasonably maintain surveillance of and the number of communications he must effect with pilots and other controllers. As traffic increases, the workload must be divided among more and more controllers. Greater division of workload means more communications between controllers as flights progress from controller to controller. The more controllers and communications involved, the greater the risk of human error and the greater the stress on the controller.

HUMAN ENGINEERING

The need for effective human engineering is one of the greatest challenges facing developers of future air traffic control tools. Without a doubt, automation is the key to greatly increasing each controller's capacity. But the man-machine relation is still the most difficult problem to solve to achieve that increase.

Like other people, the controller communicates best either through the spoken word, handwritten notes, or distinctive hand motions. Push buttons require new habit patterns. The management of a few push buttons is not insurmountable, but many push buttons take too much attention away from the paramount decision-making and control tasks. They also aggravate training requirements out of proportion to the gains expected from the introduction of new tools.

The human engineer's goal in designing better computer entry and output devices must be to make new tasks simpler than the old tasks they supplant. Requiring the controller to make a computer entry in addition to a handwritten flight progress strip entry is a step backward. Automation of controller-to-controller communication must result in an action simpler than speaking three or four words over an intercommunications channel. Digital communication offers a partial solution.

The system design must consider human engineering factors for electronic maintenance technicians as well as for controllers. The design of components must allow for ease of maintenance.

Achievement of the goals discussed here holds the promise of greatly increasing controller capacity with significant lessening of stress. Increased capacity will make the ATC system more efficient, while easing of stress will alleviate many of the human problems involved.

CONCLUSIONS

1. It is evident that most job aspects of the ATC controllers need immediate attention.
2. Criteria for defining the evolutionary ATC system must incorporate more consideration of human factors.
3. Some specific studies are required, especially
   - To define the remedial measures needed for recruitment of high caliber trainees.
   - To investigate means of introducing automation in air traffic control that will allow development of skills usable in industry so that the controller may avoid a future dead end.
   - To define tools and procedures that will facilitate transfer of navigation from controller to pilot.

RECOMMENDATIONS

1. It must be recognized that the controller is the key element of the system and that decision-making must remain in his hands, with minimum distractions from his basic responsibility. Therefore he must be relieved of administrative and clerical duties, and clear lines of responsibility must be maintained.
2. It must be recognized that the controller's useful life span is limited. Some provision must be made to compensate, such as early retirement under a living wage or a guarantee of continuing employment in an administrative capacity without loss of income.
3. The entire spectrum of controller responsibilities, working conditions, and compensation must be reviewed to attract the best possible talent now and for the system of the future. The Bureau of the Budget, the Congress, the Federal Aviation Administration, the Civil Service Commission, and the industry as a whole must recognize that present efforts are inadequate.
4. Future ATC system designs should incorporate provisions for three-dimensional position information on all aircraft of concern to the controller.
5. Unique input devices should be developed to supplant push-button computer entry devices to the extent feasible.

AIRPORTS

The future demand for the movement of passengers and cargo indicates greatly increased traffic at the major airports. For traffic to flow properly, even under peak and all-weather conditions, developments for air traffic control and expansion of airports must be closely coordinated on a continuing basis. This section reviews the terminal area situation from the standpoint of air traffic and air traffic control. The terminal area includes the airport complex, terminal buildings, ILS approaches, and control tower radar coverage of the airspace out to the interface with the Air Route Traffic Control Centers.

The importance of improved terminal area operations was underscored at IATA's 17th Technical Conference, held in October 1967, on "Major Airport and Terminal Area Problems." Also related to this subject was ICAO's Fifth Air Navigation Conference, held in 1967, whose theme was "The further development of specifications aimed at improving the safety and efficiency of international air operations in the approach, landing, and takeoff phases."

Each airport has its own unique set of problems in such areas as air traffic, airport access, noise regulations, terrain, and meteorological conditions. A few examples will be discussed in this section to provide guidelines for attention and implementation.

LOCATION OF AERONAUTICAL AIDS

In order that proper evaluations can be made of major air traffic hubs, it will be necessary to make a thorough systems analysis of all forecast air and ground traffic movements. Traffic simulation studies should be carried out to determine what aeronautical aids are required to handle the expected growth. The use of both existing and new aids should be studied to ascertain if an outer ring of such facilities, possibly on a 100-mile radius around our major cities, could be utilized to set up predetermined sloping flight corridors directly into each of the runway systems. By relocating these facilities farther out than in the past, the periphery could be broadened to provide more omnidirectional "tracks" in and out of the airports. Where safety requires, radar vectoring could be provided at determined points of convergence.

AIRPORT COMPLEXES

When regional complexes of airports, including satellite airports, are established to handle traffic growth better, new air traffic control problems will no doubt arise. The air traffic control system must take into account new concepts of airport use and locations.

Satellite Airports

In the case of Los Angeles, studies have been underway for over four years on a system of satellite airports to relieve the peaking of operations at LAX. Present air traffic estimates indicate that LAX could approach complete saturation by 1975 unless corrective action is taken. One factor that has a bearing on future considerations for this airport (and other major hubs) is the fact that estimated aeronautical capacity at LAX — airspace, runway, and taxiway acceptance rate, gate positions, etc. — is 80 million passengers, while that of its ground access and parking capabilities is 40 million passengers. An outer ring of four satellite airports located in quadrants around the central city could provide the necessary ground access and parking capability.

Use as satellites of airports already built with public funds in the Los Angeles area would eliminate costly duplication of facilities whereby more land would be taken off the public tax rolls and, most important, more areas of aircraft noise would be created. Other metropolitan areas should study the possibility of establishing similar airport satellite systems to alleviate growing air and ground congestion and the attendant noise problems.

Improved access could be achieved by establishment of an air-oriented system which will limit road usage to a minimum and minimize the time delay associated with the construction of new access highways, which would require seven to ten years for completion (in part because of political problems resulting from overlapping of jurisdictional authorities).

Metroports

To supplement the satellite airport system another system of facilities, the metroport system, is under investigation. This concept consists of an inner ring of airfields located at traffic-generating points within the metropolitan area. Each facility would be designed to handle STOL and VTOL type aircraft with runway lengths up to 2000 ft and would include appropriate terminal facilities.

In the case of Los Angeles, such facilities are envisioned for the San Fernando Valley, Los Angeles Union Station, Hollywood, Anaheim, and other areas of dense population. The metroport approach should eliminate about 30 percent of present short-haul traffic from LAX, thus permitting additional capabilities for long-haul aircraft movements.

It is anticipated that metroports could provide three basic types of air service:

1. Service to the central or satellite airports of a metropolitan area
2. Intracity service between metroports
3. Downtown-to-downtown service between adjacent metropolitan areas

By decentralizing check-in, ticketing, and baggage handling, the metroport would mean substantial savings in time for a passenger. For example, today a passenger must allow 50 minutes or more to drive to the airport from downtown Los Angeles and park his car. Another 20 minutes is needed to check in, negotiate the distance to the satellite gate position, and board the aircraft. Block-to-block time from Los Angeles to San Francisco is one hour; 20 minutes more is needed to deplane, pick up baggage, and obtain a rental car or board ground transportation. Another 30 minutes is needed to arrive in downtown San Francisco. A total of three hours or more is thus required to cover a distance of 350 air miles. With the development of VTOL and STOL aircraft and application of the metroport concept it would be possible to negotiate this trip, downtown-to-downtown, in only one hour. The merits of such a system are obvious.

Both the satellite and metroport systems must be taken into account in any study of air traffic control systems. The system must be able not only to handle this type of traffic but to integrate it with fixed-wing traffic operating in and out of the major airports.

AIRPORT AND TERMINAL LAYOUTS

In order to increase air traffic capacity with conventional aircraft, the following actions might be taken. (Feasibility studies can be considered for specific airports.)

Parallel Runways

Wherever possible more parallel runways should be constructed, so that converging runways can be eliminated.

Cross-Wind Operations

In order to improve runway-use rates under cross winds, existing runways may be widened. In addition, consideration should be given to aerodynamic improvements in aircraft design to increase cross-wind tolerances.

End-to-End Runways

Consideration should be given to lengthening existing runways wherever possible so as to permit midfield takeoffs, thus eliminating much parallel taxiing problems. In the case of LAX, the existing runways can be lengthened to 17,000 ft; this would permit takeoffs directly opposite each satellite terminal with at least 12,000 feet available (the present length). The noise problem would thus be moved one mile farther west and an equivalent amount of lateral takeoff noise nuisance would be eliminated. Longer runways also improve the chances for successful emergency landings.

Parallel Taxiways

To eliminate aircraft ground traffic congestion, additional parallel taxiways should be constructed. These can possibly be placed closer than present centerline clearances permit by utilizing them for "towing" only with an offset centerline, so that towed and taxiing aircraft have adequate safety clearance. Such an arrangement would permit aircraft to proceed to and from the hangar areas and cargo areas without interfering with takeoffs and landings.

High-Speed Turnoffs

More high-speed turnoffs should be encouraged, so as to permit clearance of the active runway as soon as possible.

Taxiway Signal System

An automatic system is desired that will eliminate voice communications as well as indicate routings for pilots unfamiliar with the area.

Decentralized Terminals

Consideration should be given to decentralized terminals in somewhat remote portions of the airport, to be utilized for automobile parking and check-in only. There would be no need for aircraft gate positions or connecting taxiways. Such terminals could be connected to the aircraft by a high-speed tram system over an internal service roadway network inside the landing field area. This system is in essence an extension of the mobile lounge concept being utilized to eliminate congestion in a centralized terminal area.

V/STOL OPERATIONS

Since the previously described metroport concept is dependent upon V/STOL aircraft, separate operating corridors will be required for these aircraft, together with adequate instrumentation and navigational aids. With all-weather capabilities, V/STOL aircraft might be able to operate under a local control concept.

JOINT USAGE OF AIRPORTS

Unless certain operating criteria are met, consideration should be given to the separation of general aviation aircraft from major air carrier airports. The complexities of mixing slower and faster aircraft in the same flight approaches and on the same runways results in air traffic control delays. All major air carrier terminal areas should be under positive control, and only those aircraft that can maintain the speed controls that are FAA-determined for the best spacing should be permitted in the area. The electronic-equipment and pilot-proficiency standards required by the system must likewise be met by such aircraft.

ALL-WEATHER OPERATIONS

If Category IIIA landing operations are to be possible by 1975, the following problems must be resolved.

Snow and Ice Removal

Snow and slush removal, although a continuing problem, can generally be accomplished mechanically. However, mechanical removal of ice is difficult. Ice may be removed by heating, followed by draining, brushing, or sweeping the thawed surface. Heating may be accomplished by means of buried electric cables, heated fluids in pipes, flame throwers, or by chemical application to the surface. Regardless of the removal method, adequate drainage must be provided.

Airport Surfaces

Grooving or improved surface textures are needed for runways and taxiways to eliminate hydroplaning of aircraft tires on wet surfaces so that better braking can be obtained. It is obvious that improved stopping capability will have a noticeable effect on runway acceptance rates.

Underground Terminals

Underground terminals provide protection for passengers and parking for ground vehicles regardless of the weather. Passengers and cargo would be loaded onto the aircraft by way of the roof.

Fog Dispersal

In the post-1975 period major airports will be operating under Category IIIA minimums (700 ft RVR). At most locations dense fogs that will reduce runway visual range below the 700-ft minimum are infrequent, and when they occur, visibility can be restored in most instances by fog dispersal techniques. Obviously, the problem is more serious in the case of airports with higher minimum visibilities.

It is feasible to improve visibility in supercooled fog by fog dispersal methods. Although the warm-fog problem is much more difficult, there are indications that real progress can be made in this area also. Both chemical and mechanical methods are being investigated. Considerable research and development will be necessary for both types of fog dispersal to bring about acceptable operating techniques. Results to date point toward ground dispersing devices as the ultimate systems.

Low-Visibility Ground Operations

Aircraft and ground-vehicle movement along taxiways and on ramps under reduced visibility conditions also poses problems. Possible solutions may include self-contained navigation aids, buried leader cables, high-intensity lights, fog-dispersal techniques, and/or radar ground control. Tests of such techniques should be a part of any live on-site tests of airport operations and traffic control.

METEOROLOGICAL FACILITIES

The location of meteorological facilities might well be centralized, with on-line connections to both major and satellite airports. At metroports within the metropolitan area, vertical visibility can be reported from measurements made by the rotating beam ceilometer. This should provide adequate information for the pilot to carry out safe landings and takeoffs, since vertical visibility is generally better than horizontal visibility and the decision time for the pilot of VTOL aircraft is not as critical as for conventional aircraft.

NOISE CONSIDERATIONS

Noise has been discussed in other parts of this book, but some trends now observable call for consideration from the standpoint of air traffic and control.

First, joint civil/military use of airports is a possibility, as a result of prior public acceptance of military operations and to minimize the need for new airport construction. Second, V/STOL aircraft will be operating into city center metroports and flying at low altitudes between adjacent airports. Third, some of the next generation aircraft will have problems with both engine noise and sonic boom. If such aircraft are relegated to remote locations, an added air shuttle will be necessary. If they use close-in airports, the fact that they also have high lateral noise propagation may make it necessary to purchase a large number of homes adjacent to the airports.

In determining air traffic control needs and equipment for close-in airports, it must be borne in mind that a negative decision on the part of the airport policy group would divert this type of aircraft to remote fields.

As an aid in selecting runway locations, noise profiles for each contemplated aircraft can be overlaid to check the magnitude of the possible community noise problem.

CONCLUSIONS

Air traffic demands, coupled with the forthcoming new generations of aircraft, are resulting in new concepts concerning type and location of airports. This in turn will affect air traffic control systems. In particular, the planned dispersal of airports in metropolitan areas tied together with V/STOL aircraft will primarily guide ATC planning.

RECOMMENDATIONS

1. Conduct and periodically update systems studies for anticipated air and ground traffic movements for each metropolitan area, and determine the aeronautical aids required.
2. Conduct live field tests with various aircraft to determine acceptable closer minimum spacing for parallel runways.
3. Investigate methods of increasing runway operations under cross-wind conditions.
4. Establish aircraft equipment and operating standards for utilization of the large metropolitan airports.
5. Conduct field tests for improved snow, slush, and ice removal; particular attention should be devoted to chemical removal methods.
6. Continue investigations of safer aircraft operations on wet runways.
7. Conduct further fog dispersal field tests, particularly in relation to warm fogs.

8. Conduct cost benefit studies to select superior methods for operating on the ground during conditions of low visibility. The candidate systems should be subjected to live on-site tests.

9. Continue studies and tests of public acceptance of various noise phenomena.

10. Continue development that will lead to Category III landing operations.

11. Explore conditions permitting joint military/commercial airport jet operations.

CONCLUSIONS

The yearly reporting of lost airline revenues and inconvenience to passengers because of delays attributable to ATC (and weather) dramatically highlights the need for improved air traffic control. It is recognized that numerous factors directly affect the development of a responsive ATC system; safety, technology, regulations, and financing are four important ones. Advanced technology alone does not influence the system. Quite often concurrent updating of Federal Air Regulations (e.g., relative to such factors as speed control, separation standards, and avionics aids) becomes the key.

SYSTEMS ANALYSIS

The continuing application of systems analysis techniques is necessary in order to properly develop the needed evolutionary system. In addition, advances in technology must be incorporated in a timely and orderly manner. As an example, ATC systems have utilized radio frequency links to perform the functions of communications, navigation, and identification. These functions have traditionally been performed independently of each other. If maximum use is to be made of the electromagnetic spectrum and of the equipment on board the aircraft, every effort must be made to integrate these functions to the maximum possible extent. In theory at least, the use of properly designed digital data communications links holds promise of accomplishing these functions.

SYSTEM CAPACITY

It is generally accepted that the capacity of the present ATC system is insufficient to handle the expanding traffic requirements. Specifically, the present manual control system, even if supported by automation for controllers, will not handle post-1975 traffic. Furthermore, there is doubt that surveillance radar alone can handle the anticipated traffic.

AIRSPACE UTILIZATION

Positive control of airspace and aircraft in the major metropolitan areas appears inevitable.

FUNDING/ORGANIZATION

Adequate funding from the public sector is obviously necessary to implement ATC improvements. Private funds have not been a consideration except for equipment necessary for use by the airline operators and general aviation owners. A revised system of user charges is a partial source of revenue for ATC operations. A review of the federal interstate highway program should be informative.

Perhaps considerations of a public/private organization like the Comsat Corporation should be reviewed for some or all portions of ATC operations and functions. The shared funding of the SST is another approach that might be of value. Timely utilization of advanced technology, which often cuts across existing organizational structures, is a necessity. It is understood that ATC in Peru is operated by a private company but with some public funds. Motivation through tax relief is a possible means of securing action by the private sector.

TECHNOLOGY

Continuing review and application of advances in technology to improve ATC operations must apply to both airborne and ground equipment.

TRAINING

Courses to continue the education of personnel associated with ATC will be required in order that new developments and new systems can be smoothly integrated into the existing ATC network. Particular attention should be given to training programs for air traffic controllers.

COORDINATION

It is hoped that other countries might follow the lead of the United States in having a single agency monitor military and commercial flight operations, with obvious improvements in safety and efficiency.

Also, the increased use of computers and digital communications points toward improved coordination and transfer of information between ATC organizations, airlines, and airport authorities. In particular, the ability to forecast traffic loads should result in a reduction of traffic delays.

SUMMARY

Regardless of funding sources and organizational implementation, continued modernization and further development of air traffic control are an absolute necessity. However, owing to various lead time requirements, improvements through 1975 will be limited to currently accepted techniques. To achieve the post-1975 evolutionary system, allowing sufficient time for transitional steps, immediate planning is necessary.

It is obvious that the public and their elected representatives will not condone collisions or even traffic confusion and delays.

RECOMMENDATIONS

In addition to the recommendations listed in the preceding subsections, consideration must be given to certain major factors affecting the overall total system.

PLANNING

1. Compile basic information relative to traffic demand.
2. Develop long-range plans and establish interim goals to minimize duplication of spending.
3. Outline organizational approaches that might simplify implementation of advanced technology in air traffic control systems.
4. Initiate a technical plan for the next-generation evolutionary air traffic control system.

DEVELOPMENT

The post-1975 evolutionary system takes into account

• Air vehicles with new performance standards
• Growing numbers of aircraft, particularly in general aviation
• New concepts in types and location of airports

With these basic concepts in mind, the following recommendations are made:

1. Improve ATC in the terminal area.
2. Initiate immediate long-term evolutionary development of a new,

more responsive ATC for both en route and terminal areas. The system must adopt advanced technologies, since new types of aircraft will be in service in the coming decades, including the SST (supersonic transport), ASST (advanced supersonic transport), HST (hypersonic transport), and VTOL (vertical takeoff and landing). Complicating the introduction of these aircraft will be the large numbers of all types of aircraft that will be in operation. Forecasts indicate a continuing increase in quantities of both passenger and cargo aircraft through 1990.

3. Live on-site test programs should be undertaken by DOT/FAA so that improvements can be verified prior to integrating the new system throughout the ATC network. Such programs should include

- Test operations of VTOL aircraft in the ATC terminal area environment.
- Experiments with systems permitting expedited movement of equipment at the airport complex, particularly under poor visibility conditions.
- Experiments with noise-abatement revisions so that increased air traffic can be measured.

4. The measurement and short-period prediction of weather in the terminal area and the communication of real-time weather information between the weather system and the ATC system should be improved.

FUNDING

Future funding criteria and policy for ATC and meteorological facilities should be established.

TECHNOLOGY

Mechanisms should be developed to introduce advances in technology into the ATC system in an orderly fashion.

STANDARDIZATION

Further ATC standardization of codes, abbreviations, and system interfaces should be developed and accepted by all countries. Continued ATA, ICAO, and IATA activities in this area are encouraged. It is recommended that one United States government agency be responsible for standardization in the United States. Strong support must be given to accelerate time-consuming standardization activities in order that equipment developments can proceed.

TRAINING

Planning for ATC training programs in the United States should be a joint effort of FAA and ATCA.

SUMMARY

Policies and organizational arrangements should be established that will provide a means for continuous systems studies, reviews, and recommendations; a dynamic evolutionary air traffic control system will result.

5. AIRPORTS AND TERMINALS

INTRODUCTION

At the inception of the Air Transportation Workshop, the Airports and Terminals Panel was chartered as follows:

The Airports and Terminals Panel will identify, analyze, and evaluate the factors affecting the design of airports and terminals, multiple or single use of facilities to handle international, transcontinental, regional, and private aviation, passenger circulation, cargo and baggage handling, automated passenger schemes, and airport location.

In carrying out this charter, the panel has benefited from contributions of recognized authorities in operation, facilitation, regulation, and service to the air transportation industry. From these contributions have come the following general conclusions:

- The airport and terminal complex is a key element of the air transportation system upon which the traveler, ground environment, air space, and the airborne system all pivot each time the system is exercised. Attention given to treatment of anticipated needs and problems of airports and terminals has been insufficient considering the importance of this vital link in the air transportation system.
- The principal problem facing adequate development of the total national system of airports is one of financing. A great expansion of airport and terminal facilities is forecast today in an environment of rapidly rising costs for land and construction. Sources of money necessary to develop the facilities required to keep pace with forecast air carrier and general aviation demand are not presently identified.

337

- A brute-force approach to facility expansion, in direct proportion to the increase in aviation activity, does not seem feasible. New methods and techniques must be evolved for accomplishing the required functions, with proportionately less investment and land area devoted to facilities. Similarly, every opportunity to trade off facilities requirements with other elements of the total system must be exploited to achieve maximum total system effectiveness at minimum overall cost. For example, improved air traffic control techniques to increase utilization of runways during IFR conditions will reduce runway needs.

- Great harm can come to the image of the commercial air transportation industry if immediate planning steps are not taken to relieve the existing bottlenecks resulting from greatly increased flows of people and goods at our major hub areas.

- International air travel, now expected to grow 450 percent between 1965 and 1980 (from 5 million to 27 million passengers), will make extreme demands on customs facilities that are overloaded at present. Immediate steps to alleviate slow, archaic customs practices are mandatory. The development of sensors to "sniff" foodstuffs and dangerous drugs (narcotics) and the speedup of other customs functions are essential if acceptable service is to be provided international travelers.

- Airport and terminal problems facing the general-aviation segment of the air transportation system are great simply because of the projected rapid rise in general aviation activity. However, technology demands appear to be less than for other segments of the air transportation system. Individual problems of general aviation are not great, but the overall problem is significant because individual problems are multiplied many times.

- One of the most pressing problems facing the air transportation industry in this country is that of aircraft engine noise. This noise becomes a true system liability when exposed to the urban environment in the vicinity of the airport. Certification of aircraft and appropriate aircraft operating standards to ensure noise reduction as well as safe operation should be considered. A federally sponsored program of research and incentives to aircraft manufacturers and airlines is a necessary prerequisite to such actions. The problem involved in siting airports remotely from traffic sources or local zoning needs extensive and careful study before responsible recommendations can be offered on use of these methods for resolving any part of the aircraft noise problem. Economic considerations become vital when the airport is placed away from traffic sources, while various constraining political, legal, and social considerations must be evaluated in connection with zoning.

These and other problems, including special technical problems, are discussed in more detail in the following sections. Following brief discussions of background, scope, and assessment of the situation, various approaches to meeting the challenge at airports and terminals are presented. Once these approaches are developed, alternative regional concepts integrating various airport and terminal configurations are considered. The report closes with a discussion of specific recommendations for a program of action toward achieving meaningful progress in utilization of the air transportation system as a national resource.

RECENT HISTORY AND PERSPECTIVE

In commercial aviation the airport is the interface or exchange center where travelers change mode of transportation from ground to air. Passengers require or desire certain services, as do the carriers and airport operators.

Prior to World War II, this list of requirements and desires was modest, and services were minimal. The traveling public was a relatively small group, and carriers or operators needed to offer little more than basic, available transportation. In many ways, the very smallness of the air traveling group hid the potential problems that would multiply with increased traffic in later years to plague operations of our major airports today. Further, equipment was not complex or sophisticated, and a tolerant public was not particularly unhappy with services they did not have or did not know about.

After World War II, air travel burst upon the scene with new equipment, with a limited all-weather capability, and with much greater public awareness of air transportation need and potential (see Figure 5.1). Similarly, general aviation, incorporating the recreational flier and nonscheduled commercial aviation, experienced a greatly increased growth rate as shown in Figure 5.2.

Airports were built to serve our urban centers, and the more modern and elaborate terminals now provide the facilities to serve nearly every conceivable need of the traveler and shipper: expansive vehicle parking areas; freeway routes from civic centers; feeding, housing, and medical services; passenger processing operations; facilities for the handling of freight and cargo; elaborate maintenance and overhaul facilities for the aircraft; an endless list of special-purpose equipment and vehicles for ground services; sophisticated weather/air traffic con-

trol; safety and fire protection operations; and administrative functions for the staff of the airport operator, the government agencies
involved, and the carriers' requirements.

A more complete listing of the functions now performed at our
major air terminals is shown in Table 5.1. All combine to make the
major airport a tremendously complex industrial community with up

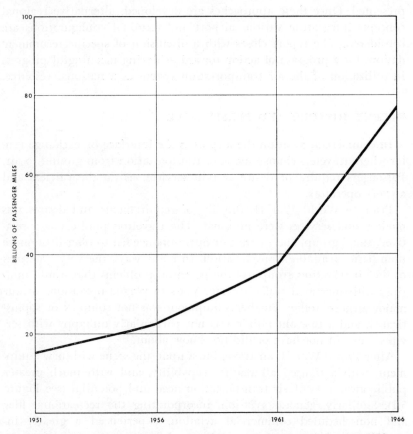

Figure 5.1. Growth of passenger traffic on U.S. scheduled airlines, 1951–1966.
SOURCE: *Air Transport Association Facts and Figures,* 1967.

to 50,000 permanent employees at our major hubs. Such a working
population demands a significant diversity of services just to take care
of the workers, e.g., vehicle parking and cafeterias for employees.

This industrial complex, when combined with the increased number of greatly extended runway and taxiway systems and huge areas
of pavement for aircraft parking, has established requirements for
land areas of up to 20,000 acres for some of our major airports.

At many airports, aircraft companies and related industries have located on adjoining properties in order to benefit from the services available in the airport operation. These industries (or others attracted to the airport industrial zoning) employ thousands of workers whose movements to and from the plants, unhappily, usually coincide with the rush-hour passenger traffic, so that arterial routes serving the area are heavily congested.

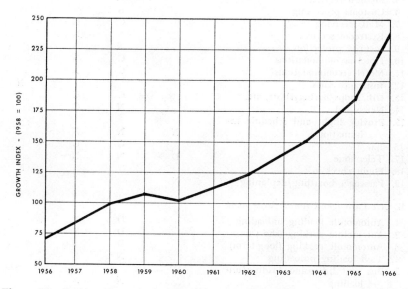

Figure 5.2. Comparative growth index of general aviation aircraft operations at airports having FAA control services, 1956–1966.

SOURCE: *FAA Air Traffic Activity, Calendar Year 1966.* Figure 4A, page 25, February 1966.

The functions listed in Table 5.1 have been designated as necessary, desirable, or convenient. These designations have been assigned to specific zones of activity. The column headed "at A/C" indicates those functions performed immediately adjacent to or in physical contact with the aircraft, no matter where it may be parked (usually at the loading gate). The "on airport" functions are those performed in the immediate vicinity of the airfield, runways, and taxiways. The "off airport" functions are those that may be performed in facilities normally dedicated to the air transportation system but not necessarily on the airfield property, e.g., at a downtown air terminal.

Allocation of the various functions to categories is necessarily a matter of judgment and subject to variances between different air

TABLE 5.1   TYPICAL AIR TERMINAL FUNCTIONS

	At A/C	On airport	Off airport	Optional on-off airport
N = Necessary Function				
D = Desirable Function				
C = Convenience Function				

A. Air Passenger Service

	At A/C	On airport	Off airport	Optional on-off airport
1. Ticketing				N
2. Baggage checking/claiming				N
3. Restaurant services		N	D	
4. Recreational services		C		
5. Medical services		N		
6. Customs processing		N		
7. Mail receiving		C	C	
8. Restroom services		N	N	
9. Security protection		N	N	
10. Hotel accommodations		C	N	
11. Motel accommodations		C	N	
12. Insurance sales				N
13. Gift shops/barber/shine, etc.		C	C	
14. Newsstand		N	C	
15. Provide flight and schedule information	N	N	N	
16. Bar		C	C	
17. Telephone	D	N	N	
18. Flight check-in				N
19. Passenger boarding/deplaning	N			

B. Air Passenger Ground Movement

	At A/C	On airport	Off airport	Optional on-off airport
1. Automobile loading/unloading		D	N	
2. Automobile parking (short-term)		D	N	
3. Automobile parking (long-term)		D	N	
4. Taxi loading/unloading		N	N	
5. Bus and limousine loading/unloading		N	N	
6. Helicopter–V/STOL, loading/unloading		N	N	
7. High-speed rail loading/unloading, if provided to airport		N	N	
8. Intraterminal transit	D	N		
9. Auto rental terminals access				N
car storage and preparation			N	

C. Auxiliary Passenger Service

	At A/C	On airport	Off airport	Optional on-off airport
1. Provide baggage handling	N	N	N	
2. Provide baggage loading/unloading	N			
3. Flight meal catering				N
4. Flight meal loading	N			

D. Air Cargo Processing and Handling

	At A/C	On airport	Off airport	Optional on-off airport
1. Receive small lots and individual packages				
from shipper				N
from forwarder				N

TABLE 5.1 (CONTINUED)

	At A/C	On airport	Off airport	Optional on-off airport
N = Necessary Function				
D = Desirable Function				
C = Convenience Function				
from pick-up and delivery service				N
2. Receive outsize, special shipments	D			N
3. Receive pallets/containers				
from shipper				N
from forwarder				N
from pick-up and delivery service				N
4. Receive intermodal shipments				
truck				N
sea			N	
rail				N
5. Prepare documentation (air bill)				N
6. Consolidation/containerization/ palletizing of cargo into lots				N
7. Label and identify shipments				N
8. Provide in-process storage warehousing		N	N	
9. Provide bonded storage (international terminal)				N
10. Provide customs, health, or agricultural inspection facilities		N		
11. Provide transportation to and from aircraft	N	N		
12. Provide storage and handling for special categories				
refrigerated		N	N	
livestock		N	N	
restricted, classified, or hazardous		N	N	
13. Provide aircraft loading/unloading	N			
14. Provide intercarrier transfer		D		N
15. Breakdown containers, pallets				N
16. Tender small lots and individual shipments to consignee				N
17. Tender containers and pallets to				
large lot receiver				N
other modes		D		N
forwarders				N
18. Provide administration facilities				
tracing				N
rating of shipments				N
routing of shipments				N
personnel administration				N
19. Provide communication	N	N	N	
20. Provide access to automated records, schedules status, etc.	D	D	D	
21. Provide maintenance support to facilities and cargo-handling equipment		N		

TABLE 5.1 (CONTINUED)

N = Necessary Function		On	Off	*Optional* on-off
D = Desirable Function		On	Off	on-off
C = Convenience Function	At A/C	airport	airport	airport

E. *Airport Operations*

	At A/C	On airport	Off airport	Optional on-off airport
1. Airport administration facilities		N		
2. Customs, FAA, other government agency administration facilities		N		
3. Nonpassenger service concessions				
employee cafeterias		N		
vending services		N		
4. Automobile parking				
passengers				N
visitors				N
employees		N		
5. Intraterminal transit		N		
6. Fire protection				
crash/fire	N			
buildings and structures		N		
7. Security and police		N		
8. Provision for service vehicle traffic		N		
9. Provide utilities and communications		N		
10. Provide air traffic control facilities		N		
11. Provide ground traffic control facilities		N		
13. Provide airport maintenance facilities and equipment, i.e., snow removal, runway maintenance		N		
14. Provide facilities for related industries		D		
15. Provide refuse collection and disposal		N		
16. Provide common P.O.L. facilities	D	D		
17. Provide aircraft storage parking	N			

F. *Aircraft Servicing*

	At A/C	On airport	Off airport	Optional on-off airport
1. Fueling	N			
2. Cleaning/service lavatories	N			
3. Food servicing, potable water	N			
4. Aircraft washing	N			
5. Provide aircraft utilities (power, air)	N			
6. Checkout, minor repair, remove and replace	N			
7. Major overhaul of components				N
8. Major overhaul of airframe	N			
9. Store spare parts and supplies		D	N	

G. *Air Carrier Operations*

	At A/C	On airport	Off airport	Optional on-off airport
1. Flight operations/crew dispatch		N		
2. Ground crew ready rooms	N			
3. Air crew ready rooms		N		

TABLE 5.1 (CONTINUED)

N = Necessary Function D = Desirable Function C = Convenience Function	At A/C	On airport	Off airport	Optional on-off airport
4. Communications center		N		
5. Ground crew and air crew intra-terminal movement		N		
H. General Aviation				
1. Flight filing		N		
2. Transient parking/tie-down	N			
3. Weather forecaster access		N		
4. Parking to operations transportation for passengers, crew, and luggage	D			
5. Additional strips		N		
6. Additional (satellite) airports			N	

terminal concepts. However, the structure of functions as listed represents generally acceptable distribution within a typical urban hub area and is included here to establish a basis for subsequent discussion of airport and terminal problems related to the introduction of larger aircraft into a rapidly expanding future market. This sort of approach to identification and classification of functions is essential in future airport planning efforts in order to ensure objective evaluation of requirements and alternative solutions.

ASSESSMENT

Some of the important observations and conclusions relating to airport and terminal requirements present and future are listed here. They provide an assessment of the challenge facing air transportation.

1. *Many airports are marginal, or even submarginal,* in terms of their ability to support the present level of operations for both passengers and freight. Some are already overtaxed. The resulting "holding" delays last year cost the airline industry $41 million in crew time and fuel expended alone. Of no less importance, these delays cost the traveling businessmen $50 million worth of work hours.

2. *Figure 5.3 indicates that passenger traffic will double between 1966 and 1971 and double again by 1976.* Similar indications are that total freight movement will increase by a factor of 10 in the same period. Growing population, increased vacation time, reduced travel costs, and expanding business needs all point to sharply rising traffic demands.

These gross predictions of passenger and freight movement become more meaningful to the future problems of airports and terminals if broken down into types of activity within different hub locations.

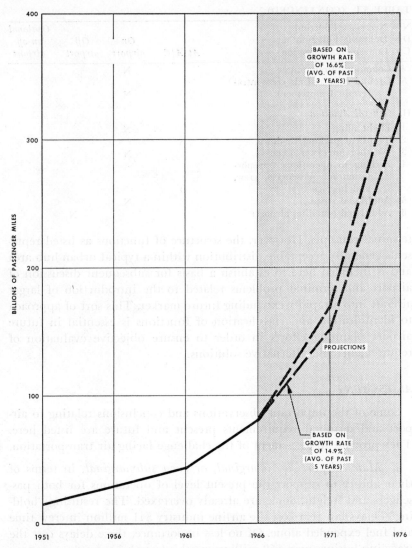

Figure 5.3. Projections of passenger traffic on U.S. scheduled airlines, 1951–1976. SOURCE: *Air Transport Association Facts and Figures*, 1967.

Figures 5.4 to 5.8 show comparative growth projections for selected air transportation activities having the greatest impact on airport and terminal facilities. The baseline for comparison is 1970, assuming that all planning and commitments for facilities to meet these 1970 demands must now be complete. Projections for the same activities are shown for 1980. The data represent activities for all airports within the major urban complex. In the case of Los Angeles, for example, 15 individual airports are represented.

Figure 5.4 indicates a fairly uniform growth in scheduled air carrier operations for the typical hub areas shown. Even more spectacular is the growth in large transport (over 200-seat capacity) operations by 1980. This, of course, is to be expected since there will be very few supersized transports in service by 1970.

Uniform increases in large transport operations are forecast for all areas, from very active hubs to less active hubs. This is particularly significant considering the fact that this increase in operational activity will occur with aircraft of the largest capacity. The stresses that such operations will place on the handling of passengers into, through, and away from the airport are of major importance to the facility planner.

Figure 5.5 shows even more spectacular growth for general aviation operations in the same typical hub areas. It should be noted that general aviation does not necessarily follow the same trends, by hub, as scheduled air carrier operations.

The spectacular rise in general aviation activity for the Los Angeles and Miami hubs indicates that extra effort will be needed in these areas to integrate effectively the general aviation activity into the urban environment while at the same time making these operations as compatible as possible with the rapid growth in scheduled carrier operations.

Figure 5.6 shows busiest-hour operations for both scheduled air carrier and general aviation (not necessarily coincidental). The great increases will put considerable stress on the capability of terminal, airport, runway, and airport egress and access facilities to handle these peak loads.

Figure 5.7 shows spectacular growth in enplaning passengers, indicative of the challenge facing the industry to devise new and more efficient methods of processing passengers onto the aircraft.

Likewise, Figure 5.8, showing the great increase in cargo tonnage predicted at the major hubs between 1970 and 1980, indicates the strong incentive for improved handling as well as the need for more efficient and larger facilities.

Volumes of passengers and cargo higher than projected norms shown in Figures 5.7 and 5.8 must be accommodated for short peak periods, owing to variations in the amount of cargo for shipment, adverse flying weather, and breakdowns in equipment. Sustained overload capability must be provided for unusual circumstances, such as strikes to other modes of transportation which would cause diversion to airlift.

3. *To function properly, air transportation must operate as an integrated system.* This means that passenger access to (and processing in) the terminal area, the handling of freight and cargo, the operation

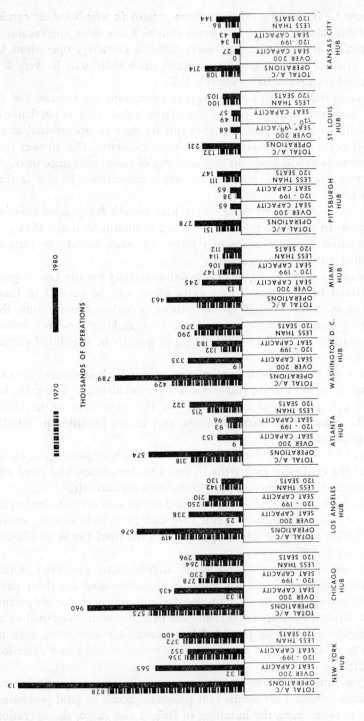

Figure 5.4. Forecast increase in annual air carrier scheduled operations, 1970–1980, at selected U.S. hubs.

SOURCE: FAA Advisory Circular No. 150/5040, 1967.

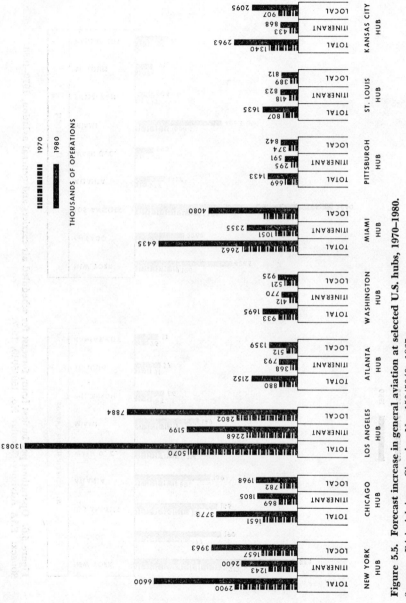

Figure 5.5. Forecast increase in general aviation at selected U.S. hubs, 1970–1980.
SOURCE: FAA Advisory Circular No. 150/5040, 1967.

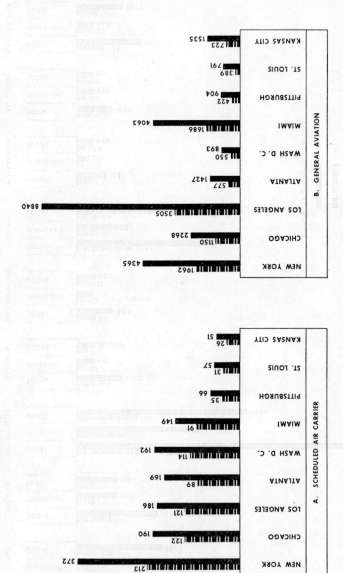

Figure 5.6. Operations per busiest hour, forecast for scheduled air carriers and general aviation, 1970–1980. SOURCE: FAA Advisory Circular No. 150/5040, 1967.

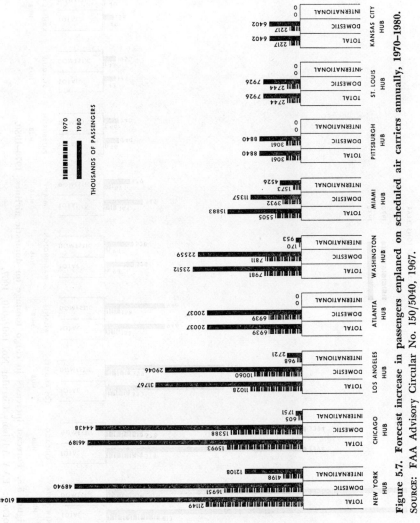

Figure 5.7. Forecast increase in passengers enplaned on scheduled air carriers annually, 1970–1980.
SOURCE: FAA Advisory Circular No. 150/5040, 1967.

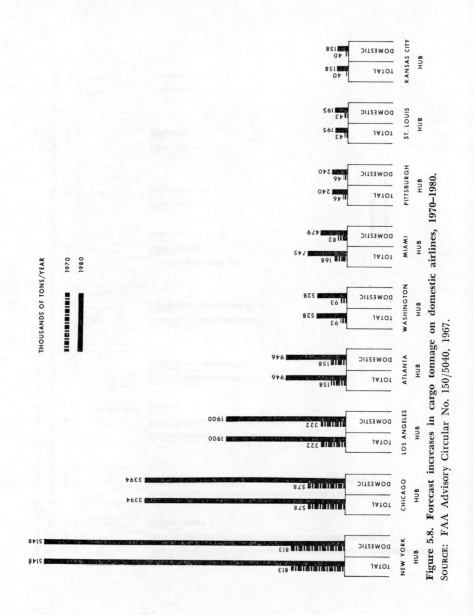

Figure 5.8. Forecast increases in cargo tonnage on domestic airlines, 1970–1980.
SOURCE: FAA Advisory Circular No. 150/5040, 1967.

and servicing of the air fleet, must all be systematized and carefully planned and programmed together. A breakdown or delay at one terminal creates a disturbance along the entire carrier network.

The air transportation system must interface efficiently and systematically with ground transportation modes if high volumes of passenger and freight traffic are to be accommodated during peak periods. This systematic integration with surface modes of transportation in turn suggests correlated planning of air transportation with commodity distribution systems and with urban development programs.

The airport and terminal elements should be considered economic benefits to the community. The airport produces many jobs, provides transportation to attract other jobs and industries to the area, and adds business revenue to the regional tax base.

The present noise level near our major airports is probably the maximum allowable from the standpoint of local tolerances. Particularly in the large hub areas, the airport is a revenue-producing asset to the community as a whole, but is often viewed as a liability by residents in the immediate vicinity of the airport. Economic or political pressure from such groups may stress the need to reduce greatly the decibels per pound of thrust, or to relocate airports in sparsely populated areas, e.g., over water or in regions remote from the urban centers served.

Most of our airports can accommodate the expected freight and passenger growth by the expedient of expanding existing facilities or by adoption of layouts currently utilized by our large terminals. Of course, unique servicing and handling requirements introduced with the new-generation aircraft must be recognized. Existing capacities may also be increased by application of new technology to arresting or retarding gear on runways and takeoff assists such as catapult and rocket, coupled with advancements in aircraft control procedures, especially all-weather landing and holding procedures.

Major urban centers such as New York, Chicago, and Los Angeles may be required to take a completely fresh look at the problems facing them in the next five years and to devise solutions peculiar to their individual needs from among the concepts suggested later in this report.

Passengers and shippers are interested in total travel time — portal-to-portal — not just air travel time or curb-to-curb at the terminal. Accordingly, all modes of transportation must be carefully examined, and the combination that best meets the criteria of convenience, cost, speed, and safety must be employed.

The air transportation industry has recognized that time is an irreplaceable natural resource and has made great strides in reducing air travel time from airport to airport. As a percentage of total travel time, further reduction in air travel time is rapidly approaching the point of diminishing returns on domestic travel. The other slices of the total trip-time spectrum, i.e., the time from point of origin to curbside at the airport and the time through the airport or terminal process to departure of the aircraft and vice versa at destination, have not kept pace with major reductions in en route time during the last decade. Consequently, the wrath of the frequent and experienced air traveler is directed toward the ground elements of the air transportation system. However, such criticism inherently reflects on all elements of the system.

The rapid rise of general aviation has and will continue to create major challenges for the air transportation industry. FAA forecasts growth in general aviation aircraft from 95,000 in 1965 to 172,000 in 1975. DMS has extended this projection to 300,000 aircraft by 1985. FAA figures extending the operational data of Figures 5.4 to 5.8 show that, for example, requirements for apron space to handle and tie down general aviation aircraft within the Los Angeles hub area will be over 16 million sq yd by 1980, as compared to 1.6 million sq yd required for air carrier terminal operations.

The preceding discussion has been primarily concerned with large hub areas and major U.S. air terminals and airports. Of equal importance to the air transportation system, however, are the thousands of small-town airports serving both general aviation and feeder-line carriers throughout the country.

Many of these airports, with runways designed for nothing larger than a DC-3 (or, if fortunate, B-17 or B-24 flying training missions during World War II) are now faced with operation of modern turbo-prop or turbojet feeder-line aircraft. The operators of these small airports are finding their runways breaking up under the increased weight of modern aircraft. They face the prospect of undertaking urgently needed modernization and expansion programs without any reasonable, available method of financing.

MEETING THE CHALLENGE: BY EVOLUTION

Since each airport must be adapted to its own environment, this report can achieve no specific solutions to the general airport and terminal problems discussed in the previous section. However, certain alternative approaches to the solution of these problems have been developed as a means of identifying future courses of action.

Projected growth of the air transportation system demands a spectacular increase in airport and terminal capability throughout the country over the next 10 years. This expansion must occur at all levels within the airport industry, ranging from large national and international hubs to small, exclusively general-aviation airports. This insistent expansion of airport capabilities must take place in the face of numerous constraints opposed to this growth:

- Limited and undefined sources of financing.
- Rising land costs.
- Social pressures to exclude airports from metropolitan environments.
- Increasing bureaucratic influence and regulation at all levels of government.
- Local interests in conflict with regional benefits.
- External influences on airport functional capabilities, such as overcrowded air space.
- Special interest groups opposing developments required to achieve national and economic transportation goals.
- Inertia and tradition.
- Weak local governmental authority.

It can be concluded that the solution to achieving increased airport functional capability will inevitably take one of two forms, depending upon the specific situation and extent of the problem.

One solution will be an evolutionary process in which existing airports, terminals, and facilities will gradually increase their functional capability through continuous modification and addition to existing facilities.

The second type of solution will be forced upon some locales by the sheer magnitude of the problem. Essentially, this solution will consist of abandoning existing complexes and starting over with completely new facilities and airport concepts.

Los Angeles International Airport and its proposed ring of satellite terminals on existing airfields might be considered an example of the former solution, whereas the new Dallas/Fort Worth development might be considered an example of the latter. There will, of course, be areas that adopt a combination of the two, in which existing facilities will be expanded for certain purposes, while at the same time totally new developments serve other purposes.

Municipalities and transport carriers have a tremendous investment in the existing inventory of airport and terminal facilities. The location of these airports has molded patterns of community growth and influenced existing ground transportation routes. It will not be easy to abandon these airports, and in most cases it may not be necessary.

New airport sites would necessarily be located even farther away from urban centers and would thus be expected to create a need for new access routes, to disturb deeply the existing air traffic patterns, and to raise serious questions of acceptability in the new neighborhoods. The new sites, huge and complex, would also cost vast sums of money.

The present section will discuss some of the many options available to local authorities for expansion of existing operations at existing municipal and regional airports.

AIRPORT GROUND ACCESS, VEHICLE MOVEMENT, AND PARKING

One of the most exasperating problems faced by today's air traveler is increasing vehicular congestion in the airport terminal area. To the airport operator, vehicle congestion represents both a management problem and a strangulation of essential operations. At the same time, vehicle parking fees are an important source of airport revenue. In 1966 an average of 52,000 vehicles per day passed through the main entrance to Los Angeles International Airport. At least a 25-cent parking fee was collected from most of these vehicles. In the face of rising traffic forecasts, airport operators and authorities will be forced to re-examine theories of private vehicle access to airport areas. Increasing use of taxis and automobiles, delivering only two to five passengers each to an airport, will create chaotic problems when flows of 20,000 passengers per hour are reached. Steps are now being taken at many airports to minimize the problems, but congestion is generally increasing at a much faster rate than relief offered by corrective actions.

There are two general approaches to solution of this problem:

1. Reduce the number of vehicles that enter and leave airport areas.
2. Improve movement and parking of vehicles in the airport area.

Options to consider under these approaches are briefly outlined here. Some of these options can be readily effected by airport management; others involve advance planning and funding. Applicability of the various options will vary with the configuration and use of each airport.

Reduce the Number of Ground Vehicles Entering and Leaving the Airport Area

Vehicles entering and leaving the airport area include those transporting airline passengers and crews, airport employees, visitors and sightseers, or freight and cargo. Options for reducing the number of vehicles required (of all four types) should be considered. Two of the options are these:

1. *Limit types of aircraft using the airport.* By limiting the number and type of commercial flights, the number of passengers and volume of freight are also reduced. This solution, of course, is not feasible unless the area is served by additional airports operating at less than capacity. However, general aviation craft might be excluded from major airports. This would be particularly useful in the case of recreation and training craft, which have great impact on major airport operations.

2. *Reduce number of employees working in the airport area.* The number of employees arriving at and departing from John F. Kennedy Airport each day is over 35,000. Los Angeles International has over 33,000 employees, and Paris-Nord expects to have about 50,000. With increasing passenger and cargo movements, reduction in the number of airport employees will be difficult; however, overall reduction may be possible by streamlining and mechanizing some activities and by relocating some functions away from the airport. Activities that could be considered for remote locations are processing and consolidation of passengers and baggage, some concessions, equipment maintenance and overhaul, cargo consolidation, overnight accommodations, airport administration and service support functions, communication and data centers, and training facilities.

Decrease Peak Loads of Ground Vehicle Traffic

Closely related to any effort to reduce the number of ground vehicles entering and leaving airport areas is the desirability of decreasing flow during peak-load periods. Two primary options for accomplishing this purpose are

• Reschedule airport employee working hours.
• Reschedule aircraft arrival and departure.

Rescheduling working hours can be more readily accomplished than rescheduling aircraft timetables. However, aircraft speeds, routes, and numbers are now so varied as to permit some flexibility in scheduling to avoid delays because of ground and air traffic congestion. In particular, peak demands for individual airport access can be lowered by scheduling simultaneous "golden hour" departures from two or more satellite airports serving the same hub area. Similarly, simultaneous arrivals could be scheduled into different airports at the destination hub to relieve individual peak-hour congestion.

When aircraft are delayed, it is difficult or impossible for an individual picking up a passenger to determine that the aircraft has been delayed and the approximate delay time. For the FAA to obtain a broadcast frequency and constantly report arrivals, departures, and delays at major airports would be a possible method of alleviating peak loads of ground traffic. Persons going to an airport to pick up a passenger could more effectively plan their arrival time by tuning into the radio broadcast station for specific data on delay and arrival and departure times.

Improve Ground Access to Airport

Too many airport locations make vehicle access to the airport unduly difficult, dangerous, and congested. As a result, the harried traveler is stalled, frustrated, and under tension from the time he approaches the airport until he has left it far behind. Some of the options that should be considered for improving this situation are

- *Provide more than one route of vehicular access.* This alternative may be difficult at some existing airports but should be carefully examined, especially where the existing airport area road net would support multiple access routes. Access from opposite sides of the airport, for example, is being planned for the new Dallas–Fort Worth complex, and ultimate four-directional roadway access is being planned for Los Angeles International.
- *Separate the various types of vehicular traffic in the airport area.* Closely related to multiple access routes is the desirability of separating various types of traffic to the greatest possible extent as they enter the airport/terminal area. Separate areas and access thereto could be provided for passengers using public transportation, those using taxis and limousines, passengers parking and leaving their cars, passengers being picked up or dropped by private car, visitors or sightseers, and cargo trucks. Separate levels of access and departure, including underground levels, would normally be required, depending on existing airport configurations.
- *Provide for smooth flow of traffic on and off access roads.* Many present airports have poor connections with adjacent highways, resulting in congestion and accidents. Separation of flow through use of cloverleafs and other designs is desirable. A well-designed system of lights and signs backed by effective policing is essential to minimize congestion. Such planning and controls must be effective not only at the airport boundary but also within the surrounding area of traffic dispersal. For example, the present limiting factor in Los Angeles International expansion capability is the

capacity of existing or planned public highways to handle incoming or departing passengers. Air traffic and gate capacity is ultimately forecast at 80 million passengers per year. Ground access and parking capacity is forecast as being adequate to support only 40 million passengers per year.

- *Increase the use of public transportation to and from the airport.* Such an increase would result from a combination of better facilities, better scheduling, better pricing and better promotion. It may also involve discouragement of private vehicles through increased parking charges and airport tolls. Rapid-transit type, high-speed rail has high potential in this area if vehicles are designed and dedicated to the needs of the air traveler rather than the daily urban commuter.

As air commerce continues to grow and urban population density increases, land demand for airports will be further affected by demands for rights-of-way to and from the airport. In many communities, especially large metropolitan hubs, rail right-of-way may be used as a network for interconnecting airports as well as various satellite locations throughout the metropolitan region.

- *Eliminate visitors and sightseers from congested areas.* This may require increased traffic control during certain periods, increased charges for parking, or perhaps some provision of observation areas adjacent to the airport but outside the flow of airport traffic.
- *Increased use of V/STOL aircraft for arrival and departure of passengers.* At present little use is made of V/STOL service with the result that this mode has not provided significant relief to ground transportation. However, the potential involved is great, and as appropriate aircraft reach operational status, they should aid considerably in the movement of passengers and air cargo to and from the airport. Increased emphasis should be placed on V/STOL research development and demonstration to hurry the date when this important element of the transportation system becomes available for use.

Improve Vehicle Movement in Airport/Terminal Area[1]

Actions available to improve vehicle movement in the airport/terminal area are similar to those for consideration in improving ac-

[1] The reader interested in a detailed report may refer to Research Report No. 44, *Vehicular Traffic Patterns at an Airport in Relation to Airline Passenger Volumes,* prepared by the Institute of Transportation and Traffic Engineering, University of California, May 1967.

cess to and departure from the airport. The basic principle should normally be division of traffic by destination at the earliest possible point and, insofar as practicable, the design of vehicle movement to facilitate handling of passengers and baggage.

Grade intersections should be avoided, and visitors or sightseers should be routed away from passenger-handling areas. After a desirable pattern of vehicle movement has been provided for, it should be enforced with traffic control (lights, signs, police, grade separation). Interference of pedestrian traffic with the flow of vehicles must be avoided by use of overhead or tunnel crossings.

Make Appropriate Provision for Vehicle Parking

Problems of parking vehicles in the airport/terminal area can be expected to increase as air travel increases, regardless of public transportation provided. Facilities for parking should give primary consideration to passenger- and baggage-handling. Some options to be considered in handling parking problems are

- *Provide separate parking areas, according to purpose for which vehicle is brought to the airport.* Access to terminal and gates should not be the same for passengers, employees, and visitors. Employees and visitors can be required to walk or to ride shuttle buses to and from parking areas.
- *Provide multilevel parking facilities.* This choice will decrease land area requirements and shorten walking distances for individuals arriving in private vehicles. Priority for multilevel parking should go to meeting the needs of air passengers. While height will be a limiting factor, seven-story facilities are already planned or under construction at existing airports.
- *Improve traffic control procedures related to parking.* This will be difficult, especially in relation to passengers vis-à-vis visitors or sightseers, but ways can be developed to improve existing controls. Parking space reservations for travelers who store their autos at the airport while away might be sold with the advance purchase ticket, thereby giving improved service through guaranteed parking and improved management information for parking facilities and traffic control.
- *Limit private vehicle parking through premium parking charges.* This will have the combined effect of decreasing parking area requirements, decreasing traffic congestion (both personnel and vehicle), and increasing the utilization of public transportation. Such steps will require the close attention of airport operators to assess the net effect on airport parking revenues.

GROUND MOVEMENT OF AIRCRAFT AND SERVICE VEHICLES ON THE AIRPORT

Figures 5.4 and 5.6 clearly indicate that ground movement and circulation of aircraft and related servicing vehicles will grow in direct proportion to the forecast air movement of the aircraft. This growth, imposed upon the existing system of runways, taxiways, and parking aprons at small and large major hub airports, will create confusion, inefficiencies, delays, and potential accident situations, unless methods are found to utilize more efficiently the existing or expanded facilities.

Some possible approaches to more efficient use of airport facilities for ground handling of aircraft are now discussed.

Restrict or Control Mix of General Aviation Aircraft with Scheduled Carriers at Specific Terminals

Figures 5.4, 5.5, and 5.6 show a substantial growth in both general aviation activity and operation of large supersized transports occurring within the same areas. The problem of better ground movement is compounded by the introduction of large transports, which require more ground space to operate and maneuver safely.

Although general aviation aircraft are considerably smaller, the forecast increase in the number of their operations will collectively demand more airspace and surface area at our airports than will the scheduled carrier operations. Furthermore, the size disparity between these two classes of aviation will of itself create additional problems, primarily with regard to visibility during ground movement.

For these reasons, the air transportation system must give consideration to reclassifying into more meaningful categories and to selectively restricting the use of certain terminal airspace and groundspace, particularly during peak traffic periods. For example, recreation and training aircraft might be prohibited from certain areas during periods of high commercial traffic. At these times, however, the operation of properly certified air taxis and/or high-performance executive jets might be allowed to continue.

This restriction of certain types of general aviation from over-crowded terminals might be accomplished either by strict legislation or by selective fee structure for landing and operating. It should be noted that national precedence has been established for the selective exclusion of certain types of vehicles on the public highways. For example, trucks are not allowed on the Pasadena Freeway in the Los Angeles area, on the George Washington Parkway in Washington, or on the Dulles Airport access highway. In some situations, certain types of traffic are excluded from highways during specified periods.

Develop Balanced Metropolitan Airport Systems

There can be no doubt that the volume of aviation activity forecast for all the nation's major metropolitan areas during the next decade requires development of multiple airports to serve each such area. As presently in evidence at New York, Chicago, and Los Angeles, two or more major airports are (or will be) required just to accommodate scheduled carrier activity. When coupled with the demands of general aviation, needed airport capacity translates to a dozen or more facilities. The wisdom of planning and developing a system of metropolitan airports has long been recognized. The Federal Aid to Airports Program, for example, dedicates a portion of the annually available federal financial assistance exclusively to development of general-aviation airports, which tend to relieve operational congestion at nearby major airports.

The objective is clear. By providing less costly facilities meeting the operational needs of general aviation, and which are appropriately located for metropolitan access, aeronautical users will tend to be drawn away from the major congested airport. In turn, this reaction enhances the major airport's capacity to serve the increasing growth of scheduled carrier activity. Thus the benefits of metropolitan airport systems appear in both operational safety and public cost.

For these reasons, pursuit of metropolitan airport system planning and implementation by each local government appears advisable. Specifically, the multiple-jurisdiction problem posed by hundreds of separate and distinct political jurisdictions comprising such areas, each possessing the individual ability to hinder comprehensive metropolitan area planning and its implementation, would appear to be at least partially solved by creation of a jurisdictional umbrella. This jurisdictional entity could be charged with, responsible for, and authorized under proper controls to work toward, metro-wide and systematic development of a balanced airport network.

Increase Runways and Taxiways at Existing Airports

The obvious way to increase capabilities for ground movement and near-airspace movement of aircraft at terminals and airports is to add more runways and taxiways. Many of our airports can be expanded in this way, but others cannot. U.S. airlines now operate approximately 1500 airplanes and in 1976 are predicted to operate approximately 3500, many of which will be the jumbo-sized jets. Expansion of runway/taxiway capacity will be required both to accommodate larger aircraft and to handle much higher traffic, including great increases in general aviation. Since an airport's capacity is limited in the worst case to its IFR capability, the greatest gains to functional capability will accrue from the addition of IFR runways. Real constraints upon the addition of runways and taxiways are availability and cost of land, topography of the area, and prevailing winds.

Reduce Ground Movement Time for Aircraft

One means of achieving more effective runway and taxiway capability is to reduce the time that each individual aircraft operation requires for use of these facilities. Improved taxiway utilization could be achieved by increasing the safe taxiing and ground maneuvering speed of aircraft, by improving ground control and surveillance over individual pilot-guided ground movements, or by providing positive controls over the aircraft, to move it within the ground complex either under automatic control or by a conveyance such as a movable platform.

Increased utilization rate of apron and parking facilities for commercial operations can be achieved by reducing turnaround time of aircraft at the gates. Reduced turnaround time here will require improved methods of maintenance, servicing, and checkout through the application of automated techniques, capsule replenishment, high-speed refueling, and efficient passenger and freight loading and unloading.

Similarly, the use of permanently installed servicing equipment (either underground or within terminal facilities) can reduce turnaround time by avoiding confusion or time-consuming operations in moving mobile equipment to and from aircraft.

Runway utilization efficiency can be increased by improving air traffic control procedures, especially by providing positive control in the airspace serving the airport for holding patterns and in landing approaches. This improved control would allow less separation of individual operations, particularly during IFR conditions, and would significantly improve the utilization of runway facilities.

It should be noted that if traffic rates require control of minimum-approach speed in airport areas, general aviation aircraft lacking the required flight speed and electronic equipment would be denied access to a particular airport when under such positive control. Further, improvement in runway utilization might be achieved through use of launching aids for takeoff and appropriate arresting gear for landings.

Additional investigation would be required to determine if actual time savings due to reduced takeoff distance or landing rollout would be greater than time consumed in engaging the catapult or disengaging the arresting gear. If these types of takeoff or landing aids come into use at all, it will probably be as a result of noise abatement programs, rather than because of time savings or positive-control improvements.

Improve Reliability and Accuracy of Information

Additional safety and operational confidence in terminal aircraft movement can be achieved by improving the accuracy and quality of environmental information available to controllers and pilots. Improved information about the weather in the immediate area can allow safe, confident operations of aircraft at more frequent intervals than is now possible.

Additionally, accurate information about the ground environment and vehicle and aircraft movements can improve utilization of taxiways and aprons. To achieve additional benefits in this area beyond safety minimums now in force will require development of new techniques for real-time gathering and processing of such information. These new techniques must be more efficient, less costly, and more accurate than present ground-movement surveillance radars and weather radar systems.

However, as was pointed out previously, the limiting factor on operations is the IFR capacity of the terminal complex. Technology is rapidly developing a capability for all-weather landings and takeoffs, but this increased IFR capacity cannot be utilized unless a corresponding all-weather capability can be applied to the ground movement of aircraft from runway to terminal, and to the movement of surface vehicles that must support each aircraft operation. Increased IFR landing and takeoff capacity is meaningless if the airport is still capacity-limited at the runway boundary by taxiway and ground traffic capacity.

Improve Flow Patterns of Ground Movement

Utilization of taxiways and runways at some airports appears amenable to possible significant improvements by minor flow-pattern modifications to make ground flow of aircraft and service vehicles more efficient. Savings can be particularly substantial in serving through flights and turnaround flights. If ground movement functions can be arranged so that aircraft move off the runway to the terminal and back to the runway with a minimum of doubling back, changing direction, or crossing other traffic flow, less time will be consumed in these operations.

Similarly, structures and aircraft parking areas interfering with this smooth flow might be critically examined to determine if the function of the interfering item can be performed elsewhere. In this regard, gate assignments might be made so that different flow patterns are established for aircraft terminating, passing through, or connecting with other flights, to minimize ground movement of vehicles and aircraft.

A less restricted flow of aircraft on the ground might be achieved at many airports by removing surface structures from the terminal area entirely and placing most terminal functions underground. This expedient not only offers opportunities to improve ground movement flow, but can add a significant area for passenger processing and support services to the terminal without sacrificing parking space for aircraft or increasing overall land area of the airport.

Reduce Peak Operations

Ultimate capacity of airport, runways, taxiways, and parking aprons must be geared to expected peak-hour operations. This results in relatively low utilization of these facilities over a 24-hour period. Although air transportation must serve demands, and demands are difficult to control, still it is possible for scheduled carriers to influence passenger demand through promotion and incentive fare reductions during off-peak hours and reschedule operations so that delays during the peak operations do not become "scheduled delays." Also, simultaneous departures or arrivals at different airports serving the same hub area can reduce individual airport peaks, particularly when multiple carriers serve the same basic route at the same time.

Regulatory actions applied to general aviation could lower peak-hour operations for this segment of the aviation system.

PASSENGER PROCESSING IN TERMINAL AREAS

Taken by itself, the sheer growth of passenger traffic projected in Figure 5.3 will create major problems for the carrier and the airport operator in processing passengers through terminals to aircraft. This problem will be further complicated by the fact that this passenger throughput will tend to bunch because of greatly increased use of large-capacity transports.

Since our terminal processing systems must be designed for peak loads, it is apparent that the passenger-processing capability of our existing airports and terminals must increase. Figure 5.9 is representative of forecasts that show space requirements for facilities as a function of passenger peak-hour volume.

Indicative of these problems of terminal growth are the following facts about the Boeing 747, from *The Boeing Company* Document D6-13440 dated May 1967. This aircraft can be loaded through various door combinations from ground ramps, from enclosed mobile bridges and walkways, or from mobile passenger lounges.

For 180 ticketed passengers loading through one door, Boeing calculations indicate that 2700 sq ft holding area will be required if passenger loading starts 18 minutes prior to departure. With three-door loading of 240 passengers, 3600 sq ft holding area will be required if passenger loading starts 7 minutes prior to departure. These loading

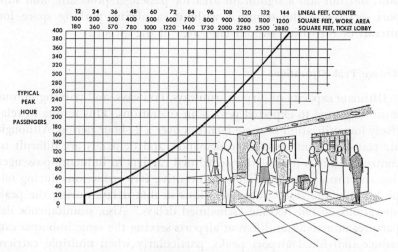

Figure 5.9. Space needs for passenger-serving facilities increase greatly as passenger numbers increase.
Source: U.S. Dept. of Commerce, CAA.

times are minimums for one- and three-door loading, respectively, and will in practice heavily influence holding-area requirements, particularly if actual loading is delayed to the last possible minute. Under these conditions, sure to prevail in many instances, the holding area must accommodate the greatest number of arrivals possible before loading begins.

There are several methods whereby passenger-processing capabilities of existing airports can be increased. The first method is the brute-force approach, in which terminal buildings and processing facilities are greatly increased in size and capacity to perform the traditional passenger-processing functions. This approach must compete for land with other necessary airport functions. It also expands required intra-terminal travel distances, and if deployed vertically, results in either higher underground construction costs or competition for airspace within the vicinity of runways and approach patterns.

A second approach would be to streamline passenger flow within the terminal by altering the basic layouts within the buildings and planning future additions to these buildings. Although some improvements can be achieved by this method at many terminals, the improvement in efficiency cannot possibly be more than stopgap; it cannot keep pace with long-term growth in passenger travel.

The third and most promising solution is to develop totally new concepts and techniques assisted by automated methods. Present functional designs of the nation's major air terminal buildings are based on decentralization and duplication of all passenger services within such structures. If designers are to have any liberty to depart from today's conventional air terminal building design, new conceptual disciplines must be applied to the two primary functions of the air terminal buildings. These functions are passenger baggage service and passenger ticketing.

If these two prime functions can be standardized and effectively centralized through real-time on-line computer systems, designers will be free to create designs of terminal buildings as efficient interfaces to the total air transportation system.

Baggage System in the Air Terminal Area

A new system concept of expediting passenger baggage must be created to solve the time-consuming, inefficient baggage system presently in operation at commercial airports. The airline industry anticipates it will handle some 320 million bags per year by the time jumbo jet aircraft are placed in service in 1969.

The functions of a "typical" new system are described in the paragraphs that follow. If present services to the traveler are continued, a system must be devised that will accomplish at least the same objectives.

- A passenger must be able to turn his luggage over to the airline at one of several terminal or satellite check-in areas — parking lots, sidewalks, or ticket counters. Luggage would be placed on an automated baggage conveyance, and the conveyance's memory unit would be programmed with the flight number and destination of the passenger. The control unit in the conveyance would next be activated and the luggage would be dispatched.
- The conveyance must automatically proceed to a collection area in the terminal where other units containing baggage for that

flight are accumulated and held in storage until the departing
flight is ready to be loaded.

- When the flight departure gate is ready, an airline employee acti-
  vates the memory units on the conveyance to summon all luggage
  collected for that flight. The luggage automatically travels from
  storage to the departure gates where bags are removed from the
  carts and placed in the airliner's luggage compartment.

Delivery of luggage from the aircraft to passengers or to connecting
airlines might be accomplished as follows:

- Baggage is removed from the aircraft and placed in conveyance
  units programmed for delivery to the airport terminal claim area
  or holding area.
- Baggage-receiving units are located in airport parking areas, at
  curbside where ground transportation is available, and in several
  other airport claim areas.
- Passengers, upon reaching a convenient claim area may insert
  claim stubs into a self-service unit which will scan baggage data
  on the stub and electronically select the correct luggage units from
  the incoming group. The controller then orders luggage delivered
  to the passenger wherever he is located at the airport, thus saving
  him the necessity of going to the central claim area.
- Luggage transfer to other flights should be possible, either at the
  discretion of the transferring traveler through reclaiming luggage
  at the most convenient location for rechecking, or by the airline
  using the same system to transfer checked-through luggage.

This concept of baggage handling is typical of several that could be
implemented within today's state-of-the-art. That the described functions be performed rapidly and reliably is more important than the
exact method of execution. Cost will certainly be a major factor in
the implementation of any such system and will undoubtedly require
investment pooling by the scheduled carriers or installation by the
airport operator with appropriate service charges to carriers. Under
either condition full potential of the system will be gained only
through standardization by all carriers.

Another major factor in the planning of such automated baggage-
handling systems would be the movement of luggage throughout the
terminal complex. This requires cleared right-of-way for movement
by cart, conveyor, or some other method between terminals and terminal support facilities such as parking lots, bus boarding areas, and
transit boarding areas. Although the conveyances will be automatically controlled, they will operate in an environment of uncontrolled

human beings, so physical segregation such as grade separation will probably be mandatory. This will further increase installation costs.

An alternative approach to the highly automated system just described would require a wholly new concept of baggage-handling services. For example, future aircraft could be equipped to encourage carry-on luggage, with checking on board the aircraft or with adequate space provided at the passenger seating location for the safe storage of a reasonable amount of luggage, as has been the practice for many years on the railroads. In the days of small-cross-section-fuselage aircraft, such practice was impossible or impractical. However, modern aircraft with their large cross section allow much more opportunity for new, flexible concepts in seating arrangements and in mixing passengers and luggage. Also, simple on-board conveyors might be provided to transfer passenger luggage from the separation point at the aircraft entry door to the luggage bay, for storage in a location corresponding to the assigned seat number. It would then be recalled by seat number sequence at the destination.

Ticketing in the Terminal Area

The present passenger ticketing process in the terminal area is a highly decentralized function performed by each airline. This approach inflicts severe penalties of time and inconvenience on the air passenger. This rigid system is fast becoming inadequate to serve even the present surge of air travelers through terminal buildings, much less the anticipated growth over the next few years.

Employment of a standard computerized airline-ticketing process that permits a single document to serve the air passenger from the time of initial issuance to destination appears to be a basic requirement. Such a system can memorize and record date, time, fare, and reservation of space, and provide an instant account of the services rendered, such as reconfirmation.

Any new standardized ticketing concept should accomplish the following desired objectives:

- Display and quote fares for an established itinerary or flight, based on class of service, length of stay, and appropriate discounts.
- Extract necessary information from a computer-stored reservations record.
- Permit passengers to obtain tickets at downtown terminals, airport parking lots, curbside, or terminal entrances.
- Reject invalid or used tickets and boarding passes.
- Permit passengers to perform self-ticketing or check-in.

- Provide continuous information on the number of passengers boarded according to destination, class of service, and class of travel.
- Direct passengers to airline employees for assistance when necessary.
- Reroute boarded passengers in case of flight cancellation or other altered circumstances.
- Keep track of standby passengers according to priority.
- Simultaneously process no-show information.
- Update revenue records by transferring the amount represented by the ticket from "unearned" to "earned" account.
- Produce an automatic schedule-retrieval system, virtually eliminating the need for reference guides and manuals either for on-line or selected off-line schedules and fares.
- Permit airline reservations agents to determine instantaneously schedules for approximately 95 percent of their inquiries.
- Provide for automated baggage claim checks similar to travel tickets.
- Provide access to a common reservations computer for travel agencies and carriers.
- Provide documentation required by U.S. Customs, Public Health, and Immigration Service, to streamline considerably entry/exit requirements for international passengers.

Success of such a system will require an industry-approved format, probably magnetically encoded for mechanized reading. Compatibility with credit cards will also be desirable for an airline industry format so that tickets and cards also can be processed by credit agencies. "Black-listed" credit cards will be detected by the system.

A common interpretation of tariff and interline settlement rules is a major prerequisite for successful system development. Development of standard fares and interline settlement values will result in considerable accounting-operations savings in addition to reservations and ticketing benefits.

This concept of centralized automatic ticketing and passenger movement information is technically possible today. Unlike the automated baggage system, it can probably be implemented with little additional investment and with exploitation of existing physical plants at airports and terminals. Present obstacles to early implementation of such a system include lack of standardization between methods of participating carriers, competitive promotion by individual carriers of unique customer services, and lack of standardization or compatibility between existing reservation and management information-system computers of various carriers. All major airlines now have a large investment in automated reservation and communications systems, which should be preserved if possible.

Implementation of automatic ticketing systems will not only improve service reliability but will also significantly reduce relative terminal facility and furnishing requirements, thereby reducing facility costs.

Passenger Movement in the Airport Area

Effective baggage handling and ticketing will ease the frustrations and decrease the distances over which the passengers must move in the terminal area but will not eliminate the necessity for passengers to move, or to be moved, to and from the aircraft. The smoothness of such movement is important.

Airport configuration will generally be the determining factor of distances over which passengers must move. The contemporary radial layout normally requires passenger movement over greater distances than the linear design, which brings the surface mode and the aircraft into near proximity. However, the many variations of these two types, plus the frequent necessity for passengers to move between two airlines in a terminal, make distance a problem in any configuration. Table 5.2 indicates the variations in distances at existing airports.

There are several means of aiding passenger movement within the airport. Moving belts and sidewalks have been installed in a number of airports. Buses and small cars are frequently used for interline movement of passengers and for general circulation in the airport/ terminal area.

TABLE 5.2. WALKING DISTANCES TO AND FROM AIRCRAFT

| | Originating passengers | | Interline passengers |
| | Maximum walking distance to nearest gate (feet) | Minimum walking distance to farthest gate (feet) | Maximum walking distance (feet) |
Airport			
Chicago, O'Hare	580	1,735	4,720
New York, John F. Kennedy	200	1,130	7,780
Los Angeles International	836	1,020	6,640
Atlanta	630	1,730	2,680
San Francisco International	555	1,300	3,500
Dallas	730	1,650	1,990
Miami International	510	1,120	3,290
Philadelphia International	480	1,240	1,940
Detroit Metropolitan	560	1,150	4,280
Dulles International (mobile lounges used)	160	600	600

An aircraft access system is being developed at the new airport for Tampa, Florida, based on the use of a skybus operating on fixed rails between the center terminal and satellite terminals. Other means of intra-airport transportation are being considered to speed and simplify passenger movement. Such movement will become more important as larger aircraft, such as the B-747, are placed in service and numbers of air passengers increase. Increased attention should be given to a means of moving passengers in discrete groups, rather than individually, to the boarding area. Provisions for underground movement should also be fully considered. This method would permit movement directly to aircraft, avoiding such problems as noise, inclement weather, and surface traffic congestion.

Reduction of On-Airport Service

An additional approach to increasing the efficiency of present airports for necessary functions may be the reduction or elimination of nonessential functions. A review of the airport functions (Table 5.1) indicates that a large proportion can be performed on or off the airport. Some could be located on land under the aircraft flight pattern (land excluded from other uses because of noise). The possibility of relocating freight terminal functions to off-airport consolidation terminals will be discussed in the next section.

Relocation of some passenger-processing functions has already occurred in some cities, where passengers may report into a downtown terminal and check baggage prior to a surface or helicopter ride to the airport. Other services that might be relocated to relieve overcrowding of available airport facilities include the following.

Concessions

Many concessions such as barbershops, gift shops, and restaurants now found at airport terminal facilities are more for passenger convenience than a necessary adjunct to air travel. Attempts to relocate these concessions selectively must be approached objectively, however, since the experienced air traveler has become dependent upon them. Furthermore, they provide a significant source of revenue to the airport and a substantial base of community business.

Relocation of these concessions should probably be attempted only in conjunction with relocation of major passenger-processing functions off the airport. If most passengers can be brought to the airport so as to arrive only minutes before flight time and then proceed smoothly and continuously onto the aircraft, the concessions would not be missed. However, if passengers are subjected to significant waits at the terminal or if the terminal is used extensively for interplane or inter-carrier transfers, then retention of the concessions would be essential.

Private Vehicle Parking

Several major-hub airports are now offering reduced parking rates to encourage long-term parkers to store their cars farther from the terminal building. Off-airport parking both relieves congestion around the terminal and makes additional parking available to satisfy the increasing demand.

This approach can be extended further by using off-airport consolidated passenger-marshalling points, connected to the airport by efficient, high-capacity vehicles. However, if the concept of such satellite points is developed primarily to relieve airport parking congestion, the economic advantages will probably not be sufficient to justify relocation. The cost of off-airport land, structures, and interconnecting transportation systems would have to be sufficiently less than the cost of horizontal or vertical expansion of airport parking facilities and increased access-route capability, or than the cost of developing other "reliever" airports.

A secondary consideration would be loss of significant revenues from higher on-airport parking fees, since it would be unlikely that the rates charged for parking away from the airport could be as high as those charged for parking at a convenient walking distance from aircraft.

Aviation-Related Business

Many businesses that serve the aviation industry (e.g., suppliers of parts and operating materials) are today located on or immediately adjacent to airport properties. Again location is a matter of convenience, since these businesses do not directly impinge on day-to-day aircraft operation. Relocation of these activities can be expected to be almost a direct function of land values, which in turn can be greatly influenced by the airport operator and competing demands upon him for land and facilities.

Much like aviation-related businesses, many airline support functions that do not directly interface with aircraft can be relocated to off-airport locations. Examples of such functions are engine overhaul shops, avionics repair shops, and air crew–training simulators. The small advantage in transportation and management control offered by the location of these functions at the airport can be easily offset by the reduced capital investment, particularly if two or more airlines pool supervision and transportation to maintain a single consolidated off-base maintenance facility.

AIR CARGO PROCESSING AND HANDLING

The over fivefold increase expected in domestic air cargo tonnage between 1970 and 1980 will heavily influence planning of airport and terminal facilities as carriers act to meet this growth (Figures 5.10

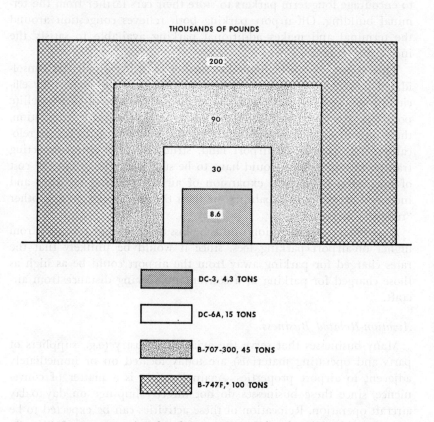

THOUSANDS OF POUNDS

200

90

30

8.6

DC-3, 4.3 TONS

DC-6A, 15 TONS

B-707-300, 45 TONS

B-747F,* 100 TONS

Figure 5.10. How cargo capacity of some representative aircraft has been increasing.
* Scheduled for service by 1970.
SOURCE: Manufacturers' specifications.

through 5.12). As in the case of increased passenger-processing requirements, a number of alternate approaches are available to the industry to relieve these pressures. The magnitude of the problem will undoubtedly require exploitation of all possible approaches. Facility expansion, improved methods, more efficient techniques, and new concepts of distribution and intermodal integration will all be required in combination.

Air Cargo Terminal Expansion

The evolution of air cargo terminals, based on normal growth patterns experienced before the present air cargo boom, is shown in Figure 5.11. Blocks 1 and 2 show a normal historic growth pattern in

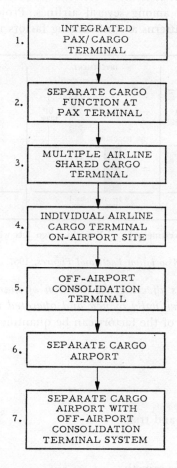

Figure 5.11. Growth progression of cargo terminals.

which passenger (PAX) terminals share space with air cargo operations. At the end of block 2, the air cargo operation is forced to depart from the passenger facility as a result of passenger traffic growth, air cargo traffic growth, or a combination that exceeds available space.

This decision to separate air cargo operations from the passenger terminal is a major milestone in an airline's history. Cost factors at this point begin to weigh heavily.

Historically, a large airline that has experienced rapid passenger and cargo growth may elect to bypass block 3 and go it alone. Other airlines may find that it is more economical to enter into a "shared terminal" agreement among several airlines. Projected growth, economics, and route patterns are influencing factors in the decision.

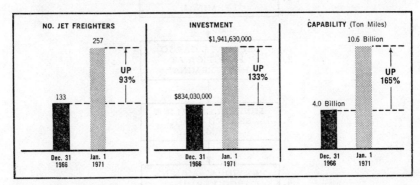

Figure 5.12. Planned investment by airlines in cargo jets will pay off in ton-miles capability.
SOURCE: *Air Transport Association Facts and Figures,* 1967.

Some of·the factors affecting the decision of shared cargo terminals (block 3) versus individually owned and operated terminals (block 4) are listed here. Each of the factors can be quantified for a specific airline case.

Economic factors
  • Building
  • Equipment
  • Manning
Routes, schedules, and traffic
  • Frequency
  • Volume
  • Anticipated traffic growth
  • Domestic or foreign location

The factors listed suggest that a case can probably be made for a shared air cargo terminal when

  • Cargo traffic is low.
  • The airline is small, or if large has extensive routes which include some small-volume stops.

- Utilization of facility, equipment, and manpower would be low if maintained as a wholly owned system.
- Total cargo-processing cost would be lower than with a separate facility.

A comparative cost analysis can readily be accomplished through systems-analysis cost models capable of cycling alternative terminal-system concepts and comparing costs with output. It is anticipated that when air cargo traffic exceeds a specific volume it will be at least as economical and probably more convenient for the carrier to consider a separate facility of his own.

In connection with this, there are a number of cities serviced by more than one airport. Under such circumstances, one of the airports may well have exhausted land sites available for construction of a new cargo terminal, while another airport may have sites available. However, the fact that large volumes of cargo may be already flowing in and out of the airport with no expansion sites available may prove to be a deterrent to moving to another airport. Under such circumstances the carrier may consider establishment of a receiving facility at the more active airport rather than risk fall-off in business. Then accumulated cargo can be transferred to the other airport for processing and loading.

The possible requirement for one or more off-airport consolidation terminals (block 5 of Figure 5.11) is another major milestone in an airline's history. Analysis of this concept appears to be somewhat more complex than that of the previous case. However, with proper analysis of design and cost inputs, the same cost model can be applied to the problem. Among factors to consider in the analysis are

- Cargo volume (flow rate projection)
- On-airport land cost
- On-airport land availability
- Passenger system land needs
- High-rise restrictions
- Surface traffic congestion affecting scheduling of outbound freight into the terminal
- Shipment size (affects surface vehicle count)
- Communication system between the airport loading complex and the consolidation terminal
- Transportation link between the two areas
- Industrial complex compactness
- Consignor-to-terminal surface link cost
- Terminal-to-consignee surface link cost

Summarization of the listed factors indicates that a case can be made for off-terminal consolidation terminals when combination of the factors results in a higher total-system cost for an on-airport complex than for an off-airport one. Some of the factors could force consideration of an off-airport complex for reasons other than economic, e.g., complete unavailability of land or heavily congested surface transport links.

In general, cost of an off-airport consolidation terminal (excluding land cost) would be similar to an equal capacity on-airport facility, less the aircraft loading system, and less surface vehicle loading systems (for transfer of unitized loads to and from the airport). Total cost for a combination of on-airport aircraft-loading facility and off-airport consolidation terminal may prove slightly higher than that of a single on-airport terminal. Despite this, other factors may force the cargo terminal off the airport.

The shipper-to-terminal link may be improved by a centrally located consolidation terminal and could conceivably attract a considerable amount of business because of location convenient to shippers or consignees.

In evaluating blocks 6 and 7 (separate cargo airports) analysis progressively becomes more complex and may require slight modifications expanding the cost analysis. The basic model, however, is generally adequate to handle these cases, provided sufficient data are developed. Certain localities with heavy community support in attracting air cargo business are promoting all-cargo airports. During the next 20 years all-cargo airport concepts are expected to become increasingly popular at high-volume locations, with some form of interest from the community, state, or federal officials.

The Separate All-Cargo Airport

Because of the good possibility that the concept of the separate all-cargo airport will be followed in certain localities, it becomes worthwhile to consider alternate ways of accomplishing this and some constraints affecting operation of an integrated cargo system.

First, if an all-cargo airport is to be developed, the decision must be made whether to start from scratch or to develop gradually a mixed operation into an all-cargo function at an existing airport. Problems of developing an entirely new airport are discussed in detail later in this report. The more likely approach will be to convert airports gradually from passenger service to freight service — particularly those near metropolitan shipping points that have reached practical expansion limits for passenger service.

Second, the decision to build or convert for a separate cargo airport must be considered in light of the large "belly loads" of cargo possible with passenger-carrying aircraft, such as the Boeing 747. Possible mixed configurations for cargo and passengers have been proposed for the same aircraft. Examples are shown in Figures 5.13 and 5.14).

These mixed configurations and larger belly loads will provide a considerably greater cargo capacity than today's passenger flights. Moreover, this cargo capacity must be filled at the passenger terminal.

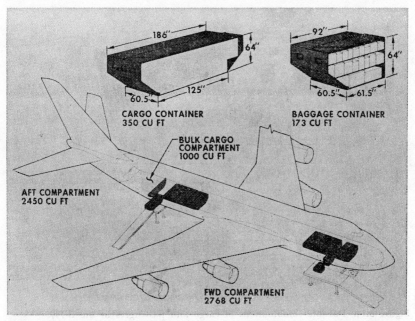

Figure 5.13. One design for efficient accommodation of cargo in lower compartments of a passenger-cargo plane, the B-747.

SOURCE: The Boeing Company.

Operational economies of these large aircraft cannot be realized if the aircraft must make multiple stops for cargo and passenger loading. As a result, these craft will require that a significant amount of cargo still be handled at the passenger terminal complexes and will generally limit the all-cargo airport to loading and processing of air cargo consigned to freighters or to quick-change aircraft configured for all-freight operations.

Various studies have shown that cargo revenues should exceed passenger revenues by sometime between 1976 and 1980. In other transportation modes, such as the railroad industry, a downgrading of passenger service has resulted when cargo-carrying revenues exceeded passenger revenues. Solutions to the competitive demands for service between cargo and passenger, especially as a result of the large belly-load capabilities of jumbo aircraft, must be carefully reviewed to expose the inherent problems. Indeed, the air transport system must render continuously improved service both to the passenger and to cargo. Demurrage and "in bond" cargo problems should be studied. Also, air transportation's seven-day week is a problem, since in many instances bondsmen, customs agents, and interfacing transportation

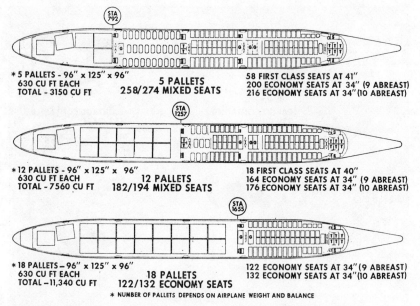

Figure 5.14. Possible combinations of cargo and passengers in the B-747.
Source: The Boeing Company.

modes function on a five-day week. This disparity helps create demands for additional storage space and acts as another inhibitor to the free flow of goods.

Improved Cargo-Handling Procedures and Equipment

In addition to the expansion of facilities, it will be important for air-cargo operators to develop and install more efficient equipment and procedures for handling of cargo and attendant paperwork.

The airlines' present investment in mobile and fixed cargo-handling equipment and loaders at air-cargo terminals is high. For the most part, this equipment is especially designed to move air-shipment pallets and containers in and out of aircraft that have been designed primarily as passenger-carrying transports. Thus this expensive special-purpose equipment is tied closely to the characteristics of the aircraft that it serves. Many airlines own equipment used with their aircraft. In the future, carriers may consider pooling equipment to increase utilization, reduce costs, and permit wider distribution to airports lacking such equipment.

Alternatively, if a method can be found to handle containerized and palletized cargo from both short- and long-haul freighter aircraft, using primarily general-purpose conventional equipment such as flat-bed trailers and pickup trucks, then the investment in material-handling equipment will be greatly reduced at major terminals. Just as important, low-volume containerized shipping will be brought within the reach of the small but steady shipper located in the vicinity of many feeder-line or nonhub terminals.

The use of rail transportation for freight deliveries would relieve surface roadway traffic in and out of airports. Many airports have rail lines leading directly to the airport property or terminating nearby that could be extended to individually owned or collectively operated air-freight terminals on the airport. Special high-speed, diesel-powered or electric trains could be employed to handle both loose bulk cargo and palletized or containerized cargo from and to off-airport locations.

In the case of loose cargo, airline collection trucks or individual shippers could deliver cargo to one of several convenient marshalling points throughout the urban area. In the simplest form, the marshalling points could consist of merely a railway siding at the proper level for easy transfer of the cargo from the truck to the railcar, and a small office or shelter for use by the agent. In more sophisticated form, the marshalling point could include loading docks to allow some presorting of cargo prior to its arrival at the airport terminal, and to allow receipt of cargo without the necessity of having a car always present at the siding during "business hours."

Containerized freight could be handled by specially equipped rail-cars shuttling directly from the off-airport consolidation terminals to the plane-loading location, where cargo could be transferred directly to and from the aircraft using a minimum of real estate, equipment, and terminal facilities.

Effective capacity of existing terminals can be increased by increasing the processing rate through these terminals and onto aircraft. This can be achieved by a combination of improved material-handling equipment within the terminal and warehouses, improved equipment for safe, faster loading of large-capacity aircraft at major hubs, and initiation of new control and paperwork procedures. Computer-controlled material-handling and sorting systems, similar in function to those described previously for baggage handling, can improve air-cargo flow rates.

More significantly, high-speed transmission coupled with data processing will eliminate time-consuming paperwork at the shipment source so that paper processing can be completed while shipments are in transit. The various inefficiencies that now occur in documentation and communications in such areas as shipment tracing, routing, and rate information can be eliminated. Greater use of data systems can also enable carriers to provide customs brokers with advance data on imported shipments, thus facilitating earlier customs release. The systems can also provide real-time information on availability of space on all scheduled flights and make automatic invoicing a reality.

Figure 5.15 depicts a conceptual distribution system for air cargo, utilizing electronic data-processing systems for collection and distribution of information on cargo movements within the United States

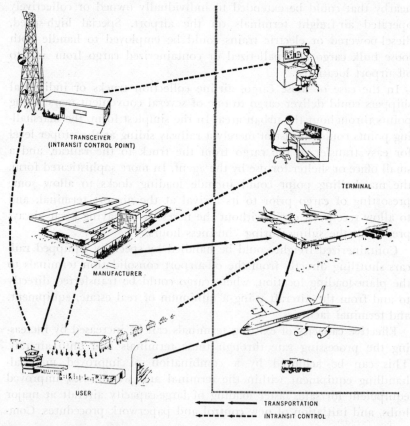

Figure 5.15. Electronic data-processing systems may control cargo distribution.

and overseas. Heavy block lines indicate the flow of goods. Dashed
lines show information flow on cargo movements.

Improved Intermodal Compatibility

Processing capacity of air-cargo facilities can be improved by greater
compatibility between different modes of transportation — aircraft,
ship, truck, and rail. This will require joint industry efforts to standardize containers and container-handling equipment as is shown in
Figures 5.16 and 5.17. When this has been done, shippers will have

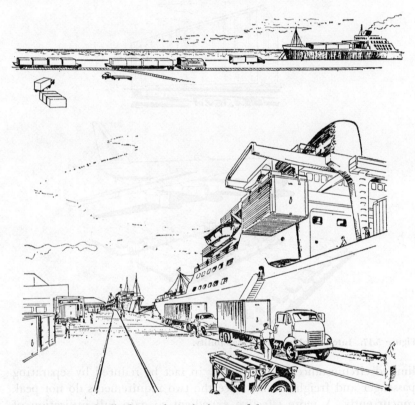

Figure 5.16. Standardized containers in intermodal use.

new incentives to containerize their own shipments where intermodal
distribution is required, thus removing this function from the time-
sensitive air freight system.

Improved Airport Access of Cargo Vehicles

Although movement of cargo in and out of airports has been discussed in previous sections of this report, it must be emphasized that

monumental traffic jams will occur if the future volumes of cargo and passengers attempt to arrive or depart from the airport over existing roadways at anticipated vehicle densities.

At some airports, it is already too late to start planning and constructing new roadways in time to relieve the traffic situation. Although it would be functionally desirable to separate incoming passenger vehicle traffic from incoming truck traffic, the increased capacity achieved by this expedient would probably be slight. Under

Figure 5.17. Intermodal container capability.

limited circumstances, capacity may in fact be reduced by separating passenger and freight traffic, since the two requirements do not peak concurrently. A more effective expedient to gain full utilization of existing access and egress routes may be the implementation of skillful real-time traffic management and controls, to optimize the traffic flow according to the specific situation existing at the moment.

Other means of moving freight to and from the airport should be considered in the event that access to the airport with existing means becomes a limiting factor on terminal capacity. Flying-crane helicopters, similar to those being used for military transport (and proposed for moving the Los Angeles skybus passenger vans to and from the airport) could be used to transport cargo containers from off-airport sites. The economics of this approach will require further investigation and study.

MEETING THE CHALLENGE: BY DEVELOPING NEW AIRPORTS

The preceding section on change by evolution applies in cities where introduction of new aircraft in the next 10 years will bring about gradual, manageable changes in local airport operations. At some hubs, however, conditions will become critical in five years or less and will require the development of totally new or redesigned airports.

Some of the planning factors for a major new airport are the following:

- The location of the airport site must meet airport needs conveniently and economically for the community it serves if it is to realize the full benefits of a modern air terminal. In general, a suitable location for a major airport must meet traffic demands at the time it goes into operation and for at least 20 years thereafter.
- Planning of a new facility must also involve all affected parties — urban development authorities, architects and engineers, FAA officials, civil authorities on all levels of city and state, land-transportation officials, and representatives of the airlines and other related industries. Once formulated, plans must be continually updated and modified as better data become available and usage conditions evolve.
- Primary technical criteria for the selection of an appropriate airport site include the extent of present and future demand, airspace requirements, acreage requirements and reserve land, proximity of alternate sites to the traffic-generating area to be served, and the acceptability of noise levels.
- Access routes (highways, transit, rail, etc.) can be channeled into a transportation corridor by lining them up with the runway under the flight path. A highly desirable plan would border this corridor with industrial development up to a mile wide in which many off-airport services may be located.

To these primary criteria must be added the important physical, economic, and social considerations bearing on site selection. These include the geological and climatographical characteristics of various sites, general engineering, and cost criteria such as utility requirements and access, along with the environmental and economic impact a new airport may have on the community.

Ideally, the new airport should also enhance or advance urban development. The proximity of the site to railroads, pipelines, highways, and rivers must be evaluated for access of bulk fuel as well as passengers and freight. Topography, including natural or man-made obstructions, drainage, soil qualities, and other features, is a further essential consideration.

In actual practice, any airport site under consideration will be evaluated by the executive and legislative branches of the government bodies responsible and by other representatives of the people. These evaluations will go beyond technical and engineering criteria and include considerations of governmental and social policy outside the scope of the prospective airport operator's responsibility.

FACTORS IN PLANNING OF NEW AIRPORTS

The following sections discuss these planning factors in more detail. This discussion is not intended as a specific guide to airport planning but rather as a digest of various well-documented methodologies which reviews the many interacting factors that must be considered to ensure that the new airport becomes an optimum element of the air transportation system.

Air Traffic Demand

The first basic criterion to be developed in planning new airport facilities is the determination of the extent of present and future air traffic demand. The fact that five to seven years are required to build a major airport must be taken into account. The planner must estimate how many people will be traveling by air and how much cargo will be shipped by air in order to "size" airports capable of handling the volume.

Air traffic demand consists of three components: commercial passenger demand, cargo service demand, and general aviation demand. Each of these components is generated by distinct and independent factors, with individual characteristics that must be separately evaluated and projected to estimate total future air traffic demand. Estimated passenger and cargo levels must then be translated into the number of plane movements needed to accommodate the demand.

By analyzing present fleets of the airlines operating at each of the airports in a region, and then phasing into the present fleets the subsonic and supersonic aircraft on order, estimates of average-seats-per-aircraft at each airport can be computed. By developing estimated future load factors (percentage of available seats occupied), the number of plane movements required to accommodate average peak-hour passenger demand can be computed. To this total must be added the number of plane movements required to accommodate average peak-hour cargo and the general aviation demand to be served.

The controlling factor in determining an airport's ability to accommodate traffic is the number of aircraft movements that can be handled in an average peak hour when Instrument Flight Rules (IFR) are in effect. When forecast peak-hour IFR demand is matched to expected peak-hour IFR capacity, the suitability of new facilities planned to meet future air traffic demand can be judged.

Airspace Requirements

For this report, air traffic is considered to be IFR traffic, which requires more airspace per aircraft than Visual Flight Rules (VFR) traffic and is the more demanding of the two.

Airspace requirements may be based on the highest standards required by the most demanding user aircraft. Such aircraft operating under IFR consume enormous segments of airspace, and airports must be located so that one in no way impedes another. Consequently, airports must be separated by certain minimum distances that depend upon the type of operations conducted under IFR conditions.

A poorly located airport will not reach full potential if traffic from other airports interferes with its operation. Existing airport capability can also be reduced if new air traffic interferes with established routes and patterns. Considering established procedures for IFR traffic and underlying fundamentals, certain basic criteria can be established to rate a proposed location:

- Runway alignment relative to other runways in the area
- Major air traffic directions
- Holding airspace
- Local control airspace
- Navigational aids and other facilities

The effect of a new airport upon navigable airspace depends upon present airspace use and proposed use of the new airport. In a highly developed area the airport should obtain an advance airspace review by the FAA to identify possible problems that may be associated with a proposed site.

Safety, an urgent consideration, is partially dependent upon the quantity and type of user aircraft. Current airspace criteria on separation of airports, runway structures, effects of navigational aids, and other matters are made available by the FAA.

Airport Size and Design Considerations

The basic design requirements for a new major airport should be based not only upon future traffic volume but must also reflect operating characteristics of future aircraft as well as airspace and desired airport capacity. Design should also incorporate FAA safety standards and planning guide principles. As with location, the types of aircraft using the airport — commercial, private, military, or general — must be considered in the layout and design. Mail and cargo volume are other critical factors.

In determining airport size, a primary consideration is the amount and type of anticipated usage the airport is to accommodate. The specific aircraft type or class expected to be the heaviest user, and that requiring the longest runway length, should be analyzed first. A simple schematic layout plan, identifying aircraft movement and major land use areas, is desirable initially. Provisions for internal and freight traffic are more simply visualized on such a plan. Other factors influencing runway length are elevation of airport site, temperature, and longitudinal gradient. FAA Publication AC 150/5060, *Airport Capacity Criteria Used in Preparing the National Airport Plan* is a useful guide in relating airfield pavement requirements to airport operating capacity.

For airports to be used only by general aviation aircraft, the recommended FAA standards are less stringent than those discussed in this report. FAA publications AC 150/5325-5, *Runway Length Requirements for Airport Design* and AC 150/5100-1, *Information on Federal Aid to Airports Program (FAAP),* contain detailed information on air-carrier and utility-airport runway length dimensions and other details.

Other factors bearing on airport size — such as terminal and cargo building space, hangars, maintenance facilities, and other building developments, access roads, parking facilities, and buffer zones for airport noise — are discussed in subsequent sections of this report.

Airport Layout

Two basic configurations for airport layout have been considered for comparison purposes. First is the contemporary radial layout with all terminal activities centered in a "hub." Figure 5.18 is typical of this type of layout. Taxiways emanate from the hub area to the rim or runway area. In this design, airport terminal activities (i.e., passenger processing) are generally centralized. Airline support activities such as maintenance are usually decentralized.

The second basic configuration is the linear or parallel offset design. Here, the basic emphasis is on a process that moves the payload from surface to air in the simplest fashion along the shortest route with minimum recirculation or backtracking.

In the hub design, taxiway lengths exceeding runway lengths by ratios of as much as seven to one interlace the surface of the airport, joining runways with maintenance areas, loading and unloading ramps, and servicing facilities. One runway normally is designated the IFR runway, and this runway actually determines peak or near-peak demand capability of the airport in terms of flights per hour.

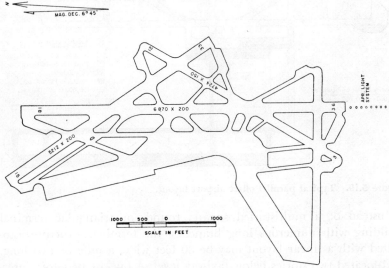

Figure 5.18. Typical radial airport layout.

At many airports congestion at this IFR runway has already become unacceptable because of the cost of delays. New airport planning should critically examine methods to reduce this nonproductive ground time.

The parallel offset layout illustrated in Figure 5.19 offers significant economies in ground traffic flow and ground time, and is highly recommended where suitable land space is available. The concept complies with FAA instrument flying rules for separation requirements, allowing aircraft to progress in a generally uninterrupted flow from the exit end of a landing runway to the terminal and then on to a takeoff runway and thus minimizing taxi distances (no doubling back) and the necessity for crossing taxiway or active runway traffic.

Variations upon this general layout provide for efficient incorporation of crosswind runways when required by local conditions and allow for addition of other parallel runways for expansion. Also, if appropriately shaped plots of ground are not available to allow implementation of the full offset configuration, the amount of offset can be varied to incorporate more overlap without seriously affecting efficiency of aircraft ground movement. A recently introduced true linear concept[2] with the takeoff runway a linear extension of the landing runway is appropriate to certain site configurations and worthy of further evaluation.

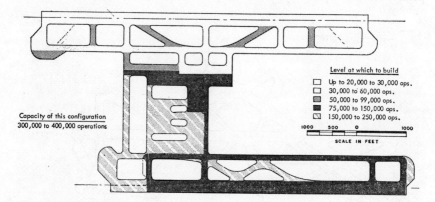

Figure 5.19. Typical parallel offset airport layout.

Instead of a multistoried square, round, or triangular terminal building with numerous long branches, the terminal structure associated with a linear layout may be 80 feet wide, a mile or two long, and located two stories below taxiway level. A one- or two-story intermittent or continuous structure could be atop the lower structure for aircraft loading and unloading. If the terminal building is long and narrow, extensive parking areas could be available closer to passenger check-in and loading lounge areas would be adjacent to the apron.

The long, narrow terminal building along a service road or other ground transportation system can provide easy, short access routes to departure and arrival areas. A considerable monetary saving may lie in eliminating the need for a complex mechanical handling system for extensive movement of passengers and baggage. In this layout one side of the aircraft fuselage might be moved adjacent to the face of

2 Steele, W. S., *A New Concept for Airports and Airport Terminals.* Tracey, Brunstrom and Dudley, Inc., 1967.

the terminal itself using a transfer table and thus further minimize the time and distance factors involving passenger movements.

Aircraft maintenance structures, mail and freight distribution centers, ground transportation terminals, and employee parking areas could be positioned along additional aprons located adjacent to runway extensions.

Airport Accessibility

Airport access time, distance, and cost are vital considerations in site selection, closely related and interacting with demand. Airport accessibility is essential to full realization of a region's air commerce potential and to the development of sufficient traffic to make an airport economically feasible.

The location must be as close as possible to developed areas that provide the travel demand the airport is to serve. In this connection, population and employment must be projected well into the future to determine those areas of the region likely to grow most rapidly in population and employment, and to generate increased air travel demand.

Projections of the need for various types of ground access at a new major airport will be accurate only if they are based on estimates of the number of each category of persons to use an airport at each site. The origin and destination of each user within the region must also be taken into account. A further distinction must be made between air trips originating or ending in the central air-traffic generating center and trips that originate or end at other points in the region.

Each category of user is an important segment of total airport traffic, and employees and visitors must be considered too. However, required and possible airport access services are quite different for each. The travel modes of each group (e.g., highway transportation, public transportation, rail, or helicopter service) should be analyzed in depth.

Geological Considerations

Physical characteristics of the soil of proposed sites play an important part in layout, design, construction, and costs. A thorough knowledge of soil types and physical properties to be encountered is essential to proper selection of a major airport site. Soils information can be obtained from state geologists and highway departments, consulting engineers, private contractors, industrial building owners, and other sources. It may be neither practical nor necessary to take borings at all sites under consideration, but enough information should be obtained to estimate types of soils likely to be encountered, and how the characteristics of each would affect construction.

Compounding this problem is the lack of standard methods for calculating pavement stress. Two basic methods are presently used, flexible pavement analysis (by the FAA method, the Corps of Engineers CBR [California Bearing Ratio] method, or the U.S. Air Force SESL method), and rigid pavement analysis (by Westergaard analysis, the Influence Charts method, the FAA method, the Portland Cement Association method, or the Load Classification Number methods).

Although similarities exist between the various methods, different tests conducted at different times by separate individuals often cannot be equated. For example, tests recently made at Los Angeles International resulted in an FAA soil classification of Fa and a CBR rating of 10. These data specify pavement thickness for a DC 8-55 of 11.5 in. if the FAA method is used and 32.5 in. if the Corps of Engineers method is used. There is currently no correlation among the pavement analysis methods, as this example indicates. A single method for calculating stress is required.

Climatographical Considerations

Because of the close relationship of weather and flying, a survey of the climatographical features of the area should be undertaken to give the airport operator a climatological planning guide. A general climatographical survey of land area within an 80-mile radius of the proposed site should be made for a major airport. Topographical features should be assessed and existing weather patterns evaluated, along with observational data analyzing climatographical features of the area. The survey should define important meteorological experience in approaches, landings, and departures at airports in the local area (i.e., fog, stratus clouds, precipitation, severe storms, wind and turbulence) and relate them climatologically to the area within the 80-mile radius.

Fundamental weather and climatological characteristics of the region should be determined on the basis of weather systems, as reflected in historical weather maps and studies of weather conditions at major airports in the area. These data can be prepared by the meteorology departments of major airlines and can be found in records of weather observations taken by the Weather Bureau or Armed Forces units at important area airports.

Obstructions to safe use of the airport site are an integral part of the airspace and climatological study. The number and type of obstructions should be tabulated for each site, and the cost of eliminating obstructions must be analyzed in each site evaluation. Enactment of local zoning to protect airport approaches and other related surfaces is highly desirable.[3]

The United States, the Soviet Union, and other nations have done preliminary research in weather mitigation and control. Even with category III airports such control would be beneficial. Some recent experimentation in this field has employed mercuric iodide and ice shavings to disperse heavy fog. Feeder aircraft such as air taxis or small domestic lines would not otherwise be in an economic position to take full advantage of these class III airports on an all-weather basis, owing to the prohibitive cost of enabling avionics. An extra safety factor will also be afforded if weather can be mitigated and controlled. The cost effectiveness of weather mitigation and control must, however, be assessed in relationship to climatographical considerations of airport location and selection.

Ecological Considerations

Bird strikes and bird ingestion into turbine engines are serious flight safety problems that must be considered by the planner in locating a new airport, and by the designer in developing detailed plans. Natural habitat and surroundings such as natural preserves and feeding grounds that would attract fowl are important in evaluating potential sites. Once the site is chosen, the designer must be careful not to create a more favorable ecological climate for wildlife by creating ponds that in turn attract waterfowl or insects that would attract other birds. Ground cover and treatment should be such that the number of rodents or of seeds and berries does not increase, since these attract both predatory and nonpredatory birds.

If a site with a dangerous bird population cannot be avoided, then the airport planner must devise and specify appropriate bird controls such as repellent ground cover, warning devices, and repellent audio or RF signals.

Noise Considerations

A major social consideration in selection of an airport site is the community's response to aircraft noise. An airport should be acceptable to its neighbors in this respect. Consequently, existing and pro-

---

[3] See FAA Regulation Part 77 on "Objects Affecting Navigable Airspace" for current criteria on this factor of airport location and operation.

posed development of property surrounding a potential site is extremely important in the determination of a proper location for an airport. The site should not be in close proximity to established schools, churches, and residential areas.

Special attention should be paid to runway orientation so that adjacent buildings are not in immediate approach-departure paths. Ideally, airports should be located in relatively undeveloped areas and land-use zoning legislation then should be enacted to prevent or minimize future problems.

One of the troublesome aspects of coping with the airport noise problem is the inability of regional authorities to control land use beyond the confines of the airport. In most cases the regional airport body has no control over adjacent land use, and even where the neighboring land is undeveloped the zoning power resides in local jurisdictions. For the most part, in the vicinity of developed major airports, zoning and existing land use are predetermined, and all too often the area is zoned for residential occupancy.

To sum up, planners should take all possible measures to encourage land use in the vicinity of airports in ways compatible with expected noise levels.

General Engineering and Construction Costs Criteria

General engineering criteria common to all major airport sites under consideration would include those involved in design and construction of runway and taxiway pavement, hanger and terminal apron pavement, interior and terminal roads, buildings, utilities such as heating and air conditioning, high and low pressure water, power, communication and fuel, sanitary and drainage collection systems, blast and security fencing, and landscaping.

Utilizing preliminary layout plans for selected locations, other factors include standards for landing aids, approach and clear zones, overrun areas, runway configuration and orientation, expected traffic loads, and aircraft ground-handling efficiency.

Wide variations in total construction costs will result from varying conditions at each site. The cost of basic site preparation is dependent upon site topography, geological conditions, and requirements for clearing, grading, and accommodation of proper drainage. Relocation of existing buildings, utilities, highways, railroads, or streams will also be required in some sites. Geological conditions can affect foundation costs of structures to be built. Cost of access highways to a site depend upon proximity of existing or proposed major roadway networks. Other major variables include a potable water supply and sanitary disposal facilities.

The Economic Effect of a New Major Airport

In addition to total development costs, the possible economic effects resulting from development of a major new area airport must be considered. In the past a new airport has often proved a positive force in creating new growth and stimulating further expansion of the economy of the communities in the immediate vicinity.

Four factors best measure the economic effects of a new major airport on a community:

- Wages and salaries earned by employees in the primary aviation activities connected with a new major airport.
- Purchases of goods and services by establishments in the primary aviation group.
- Expenditures by out-of-town business travelers, tourists, convention delegates, and other visitors at the travel-serving businesses within the region.
- Sales transacted by area manufacturing and distribution establishments with out-of-town business visitors arriving at the airport.

Selection of Heliport and V/STOL-Port Sites

Commercial heliport design is much more complex than it seems initially. Careful site selection and proper attention to approach-zone clearance are essential if the heliport is to be operated safely and efficiently in an urban environment. Although many criteria established for heliport site selection are similar to those for airport site selection, these criteria must be applied in terms of the unique operational characteristics of present and future helicopters and proposed V/STOL aircraft.

A heliport built today, based on overly optimistic prediction of future helicopter performance, might prove entirely useless if helicopters fail to meet projected performance standards. On the other hand, a heliport built on the basis of an underestimate of future performance may prove slightly larger than necessary but would still be a safe, usable installation.

Major factors to be considered in the selection of commercial heliport sites may be summarized as follows:

- Proximity to traffic-generating centers.
- Accessibility to cars and availability of public transportation.
- Sufficient site area and proper elevation. Elevation ranging from ground level to that of a relatively low building seems preferable. Space needed for the landing area, combined with the necessary

parking facilities, will require a sizable area—possibly unobtainable in downtown sections.

• Location such that the using aircraft will be able to operate in conjunction with other helicopter and V/STOL traffic in the area without detrimental effect on fixed-wing traffic.

• Clearance of existing obstructions. Possibilities of permanent approach protection by zoning or through natural means should be explored.

• An approach area that permits emergency landings in case of engine failure without serious damage to the aircraft, occupants, or property owners. This requirement may be reduced by improvements in one-engine-out performance of future helicopter and V/STOL designs.

• Cost of site development.

• Effects on neighboring property use due to helicopter operations, noise, air pollution, and air blast effects.

• Practicability of providing refueling facilities and bulk storage. Storage of large amounts of fuel in residential or business areas must be evaluated from the standpoint of safety and fire codes.

ALTERNATIVE REGIONAL APPROACHES

Previous sections of this report have discussed alternative approaches by which individual airports and accompanying facilities might meet the air-transportation problem. Whether individual airports meet this challenge by evolutionary growth, or whether completely new airports are designed and planned to relieve the problems at existing airports, many regions of the United States will require that individual airports be knit together into an overall regional system.

Regional systems of airports have already been formulated in our largest hub areas such as New York, Los Angeles, and Washington, D.C. Within these areas it has become an absolute necessity to disperse certain elements of commercial aviation as well as large segments of general aviation.

Two principal prerequisites to the development of an efficient system of airports are

• A defined set of objectives during both initiation and execution of total-system planning.

• Formation of a regional authority with sufficient political power, regional influence, and financing capability to effectively execute systematic planning.

Within the latter prerequisite are many facets of the social, economic, political, and regulatory influences in the urban environment. The various levels and tiers of government agencies and regulatory agencies with which a large regional airport authority must maintain relationships can create major problems for the planner.

The following subsections describe some typical regional approaches to integrated airport systems, along with some advantages and disadvantages of each. No particular solution is recommended; instead, these typical approaches are presented as a discussion platform through which a better understanding of the problems of regional airport planning may be obtained.

DESIGNATION OF SINGLE-PURPOSE AIRPORTS

One of the options available to the planner confronted with the problems of most effective utilization of multiple landing fields in a large metropolitan area is the designation of certain or all fields as single-purpose airports; i.e., one type of operation or mission (cargo, general aviation, military, long-haul passenger, short-haul passenger, etc.) is to be carried out at that field. Arguments for and against such an approach to handling the growing number of flights and the increasing demand for air transportation of passengers and cargo could fill several volumes.

The parameters of the problem will differ for each metropolitan area because of differences in weather, geography, size, and type of ground transportation network, and demand. However, many factors pertaining to the future growth of air transportation suggest that a "divide and conquer" approach will be necessary if we are to avoid chaos at our major airports. FAA predicts that within ten years private corporations and individuals will be flying 8,000 jet aircraft while domestic airlines will have only 3,500. Increasing size and speed of commercial planes along with higher utilization emphasize the need for minimum delays to these aircraft while on and near airfields.

Changing technology and procedures relative to safety, fuels, maintenance, cargo handling, passenger processing, and air traffic control indicate the need for segregating various types of air operations wherever practical. Even though new and larger airports will be built to meet the needs of 1975 and beyond, the realities of geography, cost, airspace and other factors will still dictate that improvement (and improved utilization) of existing airfields be the primary approach to meeting future airport needs. An article entitled "Tomorrow's Solution to Today's Air Traffic Jam" (*Esquire*, August 1967), outlines a future specialized airport system for the New York City area, tied to a modern ground rapid-transit system and a system of depots and interchanges supplemented by V/STOL aircraft. Specialized airports are visualized for a variety of flights: international, long-haul domestic, short-haul domestic, general aviation, cargo and major maintenance, and military aviation. Emphasis is placed on a ground transportation system which would be used to tie the airport system together. Total cost is conservatively estimated to be $50 billion, most of which would be for the ground transportation network.

A general summary of the advantages and disadvantages of the single-purpose or specialized airport approach in a major metropolitan area is presented here. A more accurate general delineation of the pros and cons of this approach should be evaluated in relation to each metropolitan area to provide a true assessment of the value of this approach.

Advantages of Specialized Airport System

- Improved air traffic control and safety. Approach and takeoff routes can be more clearly delineated and operating zones of certain types of aircraft more readily prescribed.
- Better location of airfields in relation to problems of noise, height limitation, climatic conditions, and ground transportation network.
- Better design. Runways, taxiways, parking, fueling, and terminal facilities can be specifically designed for specialized needs.
- Better handling of passengers. Passenger services and service facilities may concentrate on the effective handling and processing of a particular kind of traveler.
- Improved ground transportation and air feeder-system planning. Needs for rapid transit, freeways, and V/STOL can be more accurately determined and concentrated to meet specialized needs at each location; i.e., short-haul high-density commuter flights may be profitably served by urban commuter-type rapid-transit systems.
- Decreased cost of airport facilities. Facility requirements of the various airports can also be specialized to meet a specific need.
- Better handling of air cargo. Concentration of air cargo at one airport will improve utilization and efficiency of specialized cargo processing and handling equipment.

Disadvantages of Specialized Airport System

- Decreased flexibility to meet unusual requirements. Unexpected limitations on use of a specialized field due to weather, peak loads, or other causes could not be readily overcome by shifting to other local fields, which would have other specialties.

- Inconvenience to passengers. The average travel distance of passenger to airport would be increased. Also, interchange between flights of different types would be more difficult and time-consuming.
- Inconvenience to general aviation. The average individual in general aviation might be forced to live and work farther from his plane, and opportunities to use his private plane to make direct connections with commercial flights would be less frequent.
- Increased cost to general aviation. Airport support costs now shared with commercial aviation would have to be carried by general aviation alone at exclusive general aviation airports.
- Difficulty of balancing passenger and cargo loads. The concentration of cargo at one airport would probably complicate scheduling of balanced loads at passenger airports.

DIRECTIONAL ASSIGNMENT OF AIRPORTS

An option available to the regional planner for the dispersal of activity to major airports within a megalopolis area is that of designating individual airfields in terms of the origin or destination of flights using the airfield.

For example, if a traveler from the Los Angeles area wished to embark on an eastbound flight, he might board the aircraft at Ontario Air Terminal, approximately 40 miles east of the city center. A passenger bound for the northwest quadrant of the country might depart from Van Nuys or from Palmdale airports, in the northern part of the Los Angeles metropolitan area. An overseas-bound passenger to Hawaii or points west might depart from Los Angeles International or from Oxnard air terminal. (Both of these terminals are in the westerly portions of the Southern California megalopolis; Oxnard is approximately 50 miles northwest of downtown Los Angeles.) Finally, southbound passengers might be boarded at one of several airports in the southeastern quadrant of the Los Angeles metropolitan area.

In such a scheme an effective feeder system would be required to move passengers from collection points to point of departure. This collection system could involve the use of feeder aircraft operating from existing limited-capacity airports such as Burbank, Long Beach, Santa Monica, and the Riverside/San Bernardino area. V/STOL aircraft could also be used to collect passengers from even more widely distributed metroports. Although this concept of airport specialization would probably increase travel distances to the airport for most travelers, the direction of travel would always be the same, and total travel time would therefore tend to be equalized.

The Los Angeles area probably lends itself more readily to this approach than most areas of the country; however, actual planning for this type of specialization is not implied in this discussion. The geographical location and travel patterns of Los Angeles encourage a moderately rigid directional flow, and a higher than normal percentage of 500-mile or greater flights. In addition, a relatively large percentage of scheduled flights either terminate or originate there.

Advantages of Directional Specialization

- Improved air traffic control and safety. Less mixing of aircraft from different airways into and out of the approach zones of the airport can be expected. Approach control can be more effectively coordinated with en route control.
- Less crowding of passenger service facilities. The directional concept, combined with the CAB route-allocation structure, could significantly reduce the number of different carriers processing passengers at any one airport and thereby reduce duplication of facilities.
- Improved collection and distribution of passengers. Feeder routes to the airport would always be in the same general direction of travel, with less convergence and mixing of local travel patterns.
- Possible reduction in total travel time. Passengers would always be traveling in the same general direction, and consequently would not "lose" time spent in doubling back in a different transportation mode on the route of travel to the airport.

Disadvantages of Directional Specialization

- Decreased flexibility to meet unusual requirements (as in the case of functional specialization discussed previously).
- Inflexibility caused by arrival/departure at different locations. A passenger, for example, who departs from an airport located on the *west* side of the city would conceivably park his car at the west terminal. If he then returned to the city through the *east* side airport he might find himself 50 miles from his parked car.
- Inconvenience to passengers. Some passengers would have to travel considerably greater distances across a metropolitan complex to reach departing aircraft, depending on point of origin and intended direction of travel.
- Difficulty of interline or interdirectional transfer if a mode change were required.

- Interline scheduling inflexibility. Scheduling between major trunk routes and feeder routes would be more difficult.
- Through-flight stops. To preserve the purity of the directional arrival and departure concept, it would be necessary for through flights to make two stops — one at the inbound direction arrival terminal and one at the outbound direction departure terminal.

The two concepts, of single-purpose or single-direction, represent extremes of possible multiple airport designations. A similar, more easily implemented (but probably less efficient) concept would involve the dispersal of various scheduled departures *by time* to different airports.

SATELLITE COLLECTION CONCEPT

The preceding discussion of problems and alternate solutions to both on-airport and regional airport problems, has indicated that certain functions traditionally found at the airport (see Table 5.1) might better be distributed throughout the large areas served by our major hubs. This implies the need for satellite points. These might also provide a shuttle service to get passengers across large metropolitan areas efficiently, to take advantage of the specialized (in function or direction) airport.

There seems to be no question but that hubs serving large metropolitan regions, many of which are already at the point of crisis with respect to intra-urban surface transportation, will have to meet the problems of air transportation through some sort of collective airport system to serve the scheduled air traveler properly. It is impossible to foresee a solution that would allow a single airport such as New York's Kennedy International, Chicago's O'Hare International, or Los Angeles International to handle adequately the air traffic necessary to meet the forecast passenger demand. The dispersal of airports, coupled with the increasing problems of any surface traveler, demands that careful attention be paid to integration of the air transportation system into the urban environment, and particularly the urban transportation system.

Users of air transportation are becoming more concerned with total door-to-door travel time. Door-to-door travel time can be broken into five discrete time slices:

1. Time from office or home to airport
2. Processing time from curb to enplaning
3. In-flight time

4. Deplaning and processing time to curb

5. Time from terminal to destination

Continued improvements in flight time will have only a marginal effect on the air transport system's performance. Time slices 1, 2, 4, and 5, however, will be greatly affected by the large increase in the number of travelers during the 1970 to 1980 period, regardless of improvements in aircraft. To remain viable, the air transport industry must maintain an image of comfort, service, newness, and speed not just in the third time slice but in all five segments. Processing of baggage and passengers must be improved to reduce the delays, waits, and queues that will occur with the predicted growth in air travel and the increase in aircraft carrying capacity. A basic consideration for the future is that passengers, cargo, and baggage should move to the point of maximum congestion, the aircraft boarding area, as discrete groups rather than individually. This concept affords more control in passenger processing and also permits early separation of the passenger from "bon voyage" wishers.

One way to achieve the grouping of passengers and to gain better control over movement and behavior is to capture the passenger in the air transportation system as early as possible in time slice 1 and to release him as far downstream as possible in time slice 5. An approach to this goal would be establishment of satellite collection terminals throughout the major metropolitan hub area, in a manner similar to that discussed previously for air cargo collection and distribution. Into these collection satellites would be distributed all processing functions that need not be performed at the airport site.

Location of these satellites may be within the downtown business district with distribution throughout suburban areas where air travelers are concentrated. The satellite collection centers should have complete facilities to maintain the image and amenities that the air traveler has grown to expect. These will include concessions of all types, food and drink, car rental, and other personal services. Basic functions of satellite collection centers are to process both passengers and baggage away from the airport proper and to organize controlled movement of groups of passengers as directly as possible to aircraft boarding positions.

Satellite Collection Terminals

Design and configuration of the satellite collection terminals would depend greatly upon their location in the urban environment and their interface with other modes of urban transportation. For example, a terminal located in suburban or predominantly residential areas in an automobile-oriented community should provide adequate, convenient, and secure parking for those passengers who would customarily drive their cars to the airport and leave them there.

A satellite terminal serving a denser residential area, such as a heavy concentration of apartment houses, would probably have less need for long-term parking but would want to give stronger emphasis to the interface with urban transportation systems and taxicab loading and unloading. A city center satellite collection terminal might well be integrated into a high-rise commercial building, such as the Pan American Building in New York; parking would normally not be required at such a facility.

Two major technological advances will be required at the satellite collection centers: automated handling of baggage and fast, reliable passenger ticketing. With these advances, centers at various locations in a community could preprocess both baggage and passenger for the complete trip and insert them into a coordinated collection and distribution transportation subsystem.

Various modes of surface and air transportation for collecting and distributing passengers and cargo are under consideration. Each mode has advantages and disadvantages in specific situations. It is extremely important, however, that the planner recognize that when airport and terminal functions are distributed as described here, the mode of transportation must become an integral part of the satellite. Passengers must be made to feel that they are in the system from the minute they enter satellite terminals until the trip is completed — with the hope that they will find an equivalent level of service in some distant city. The system design applies not only to function but to imagery and esthetics. Certain thematic identities should be sustained throughout, from main airport terminals and boarding areas through collection and distribution-transportation media to satellite terminals. At the same time, satellite terminals should esthetically blend into the local community.

Transportation Between Satellite and Main Terminals

Economics, prevailing climatic conditions, and reliability of equipment are factors that will influence decisions on use of ground transportation, air transportation, or combinations of both to link satellite collection terminals to major airports. If a ground system is chosen, the total time considerations of the air traveler will emphasize the need for high speed.

If a high-speed rail (rapid-transit) system is chosen, vehicles working in this system must be dedicated to the needs of the air traveler, which

are considerably different than those of the urban commuter. The ultimate in this regard would be a combination rail-transportation vehicle
and boarding lounge, similar to the Dulles concept, that would speed
travelers from off-airport satellite collection terminals directly to the
aircraft boarding location at the airport. There the lounge would join
a compatible enclosed loading-ramp system. Automatically controlled
and dispatched vehicles with high operational reliability could be
scheduled so that they arrive punctually for sequential boarding of
passengers for one flight from several collection centers. Such precision
is entirely feasible, as demonstrated by modern automatically controlled rapid-transit systems.

Figure 5.20 shows one of many possible concepts for collection of

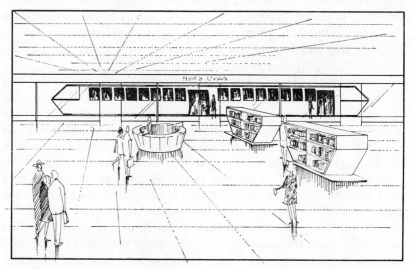

Figure 5.20. A passenger-processing terminal, with high-speed rail link to airport.
SOURCE: Ralph M. Parsons Company.

air passengers into a surface transportation system that has been fully
integrated with the air travel mode. In this case, a number of the facilities normally found within the passenger terminal (check-in coun-
ter, baggage checking, passenger-holding area, etc.) have been included
at the loading platform or in the special-purpose high-speed rail car.

Each car would be individually destined for a particular flight and
could perform many of the check-in and passenger information functions en route. The car would be designed to carry standardized baggage containers, allowing baggage to be checked directly into the container for its particular satellite destination, i.e., a particular satellite

terminal at the destination hub. Passenger and baggage-container capacity of the cars would be determined from the observed and predicted travel characteristics of the population served by the hub. Partial or split containers might be provided for low-traffic destinations.

Figure 5.21 shows a possible approach for the interface of the rail car and the airplane. Here, as in the case of satellite collection terminals, a minimum of facilities is required. A highly functional structure is provided to support the loading fingers, terminate the rail system, and provide for handling of baggage and freight and comfortable, rapid transition of passengers from the rail car to the aircraft. This concept, patterned around the Boeing 747, also shows the simul-

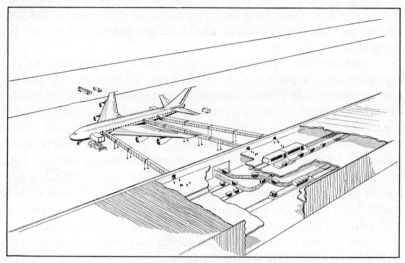

Figure 5.21. Design of terminal facility where passengers are enplaned from rapid-transit cars.
SOURCE: Ralph M. Parsons Company.

taneous arrival of a special carload of freight containers from an off-airport freight terminal. This freight, along with the baggage containers, would be processed through the lower level and out through under-ramp tunnels via conveyor systems to loading elevators at the aircraft. Containers would be automatically checked for weight and balance and would be given other final inspection as required. Some capability would be provided for repacking and consolidation of baggage within the containers, but this would be kept to a minimum and done quickly in order not to compromise the rapid transfer of preprocessed passengers into the air.

Problems of integration into an urban environment

Concepts like these are described not as recommended solutions to specific problems but rather to encourage critical appraisal of the problem of air transportation integration into a complex urban environment. Actually, there are many reasons that preclude the immediate introduction of concepts such as these into the urban and air transportation system. If such an integrated system is to be achieved at all, it will undoubtedly be through a process of evolution rather than revolution. For example, baggage containers are not sufficiently standardized among carriers or among aircraft to allow the design of an efficient universal system. Also, passenger-handling, check-in, or recording procedures are not standard among carriers. Lastly, the system is geared to the long-haul, large-capacity type transport. A high volume of this type of traffic would be needed to accrue the full advantages of the concept.

Nevertheless, such problems are not beyond solution, and the concept does illustrate some of the advantages of integrated air and surface transportation. It also illustrates the necessity for the integration of such functions as ticketing, reservations, aircraft status, and schedule deviations into an industry-wide information system — a system that would also allow efficient control of the ground transportation system as an operational extension of each individual carrier's flight operations. Since it is unlikely that each carrier could profitably operate his own satellite collection system, it is probable that such a system would have to be operated jointly by the various carriers served.

A critically important planning factor in high-speed ground transportation systems is the cost of acquiring and constructing exclusive right-of-way with grade separation from routine urban vehicular and pedestrian traffic. Because the cost is great, it is extremely doubtful that an exclusive-use high-speed ground transportation system of the type described above will be economically feasible within the foreseeable future. Therefore, air transportation-system planners should join urban transit-system planners in attempting to evolve common plans for routing and right-of-way that will allow joint use of this expensive right-of-way. This does not suggest that rolling stock would be common to both air and urban systems, but rolling stock is not the major cost item in the total system.

Such an effort does presuppose, however, that urban air transportation collection terminals be within short spur-line access to rapid-transit right-of-way; that control and scheduling of urban and airport traffic on rights-of-way be coordinated and integrated; and that minimum feasible distances between collection terminals and airports be considered in overall routing and interchange provisions of the rapid-transit right-of-way.

Where urban rapid-transit systems are not planned, or integration of the two systems is otherwise not feasible, collection and distribution travel loads will undoubtedly be relegated to some other form of transportation. Many of the concepts discussed above can be effectively applied to other types of transportation, such as the skybus currently under study for Los Angeles, in which the passenger lounge is airlifted from collection satellites to airport by a "flying crane" type of helicopter. In this case, the same principles of identification with the system, convenience of boarding, and interfacing with terminals should be applied.

Two concepts for terminals to serve V/STOL collection media are shown in Figures 5.22 and 5.23. Except for the psychological effect, it should make relatively little difference to the traveler whether he is in a high-speed ground transportation vehicle or a high-speed air transportation vehicle such as the skybus. Although point-to-point speeds would undoubtedly be higher for the skybus, maneuvering and interface time at the destination may be somewhat more complex and scheduling may be less precise, thereby equalizing the overall time. Of course, overall time would be greatly dependent upon the trip length. As a result, it is quite possible that a combination of air-plus-surface connecting systems may be employed in larger hub areas.

Pooled Operation of Satellite Facilities

Costs of facilities and maintenance within satellite terminals will depend greatly upon carrier policies. The very fact that passenger reception functions have been distributed away from the central terminal to reduce congestion implies that processing density over a 24-hour period would be less at the satellite locations than at the central locations.

In some cases, a less-than-optimum work load for each satellite agent for each individual carrier may result. Likewise, density of processing may be reduced below the level where each individual airline is justified in having its own unshared processing desk. For these low-density collection terminals, carriers should evaluate the possibility of pooling passenger agent manpower, along with employment of the maximum automation feasible. This approach would not only reduce direct costs to the individual carriers but in many cases would reduce costs of structures and fixtures too. Further, it is entirely feasible to consider a completely unattended satellite station with automated ticketing

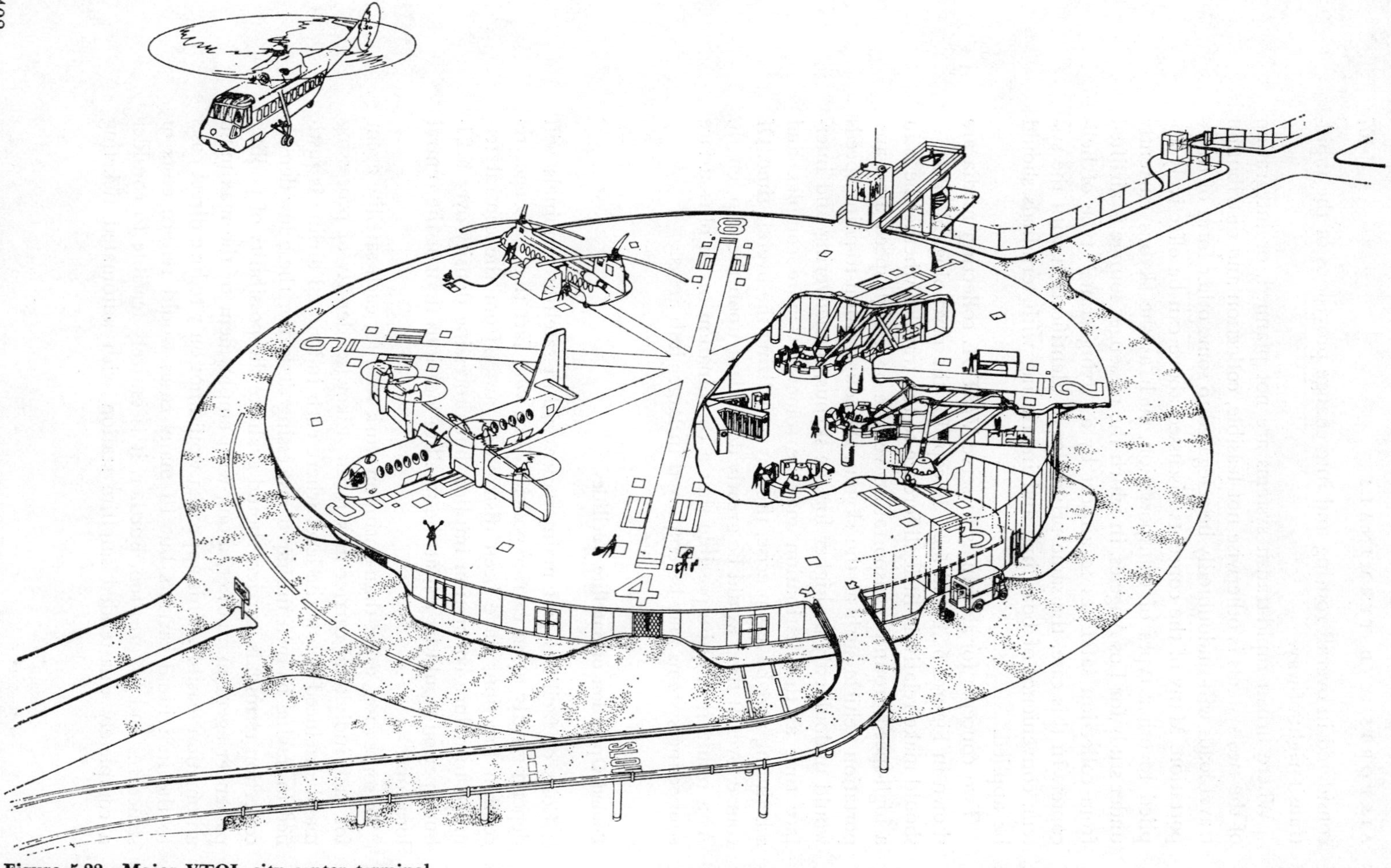

Figure 5.22. Major VTOL city center terminal. Airports and Terminals, M. M. et al., Tata McGraw-Hill Publishing Co., Massachusetts Institute of Tech.

Figure 5.23. V/STOL transport operating from freeway interchange terminal. SOURCE: LTV Aerospace Corporation.

and closed-circuit television monitoring by one agent serving a number of satellite terminals.

Integration of Satellite Collection Systems of Passengers and Cargo

In previous discussions of air cargo handling and processing, a similar concept of satellite collection or consolidation points was discussed. It is important that any analysis of modes of transportation between satellite collection terminals and airports consider air cargo problems as well as air passenger problems. Careful consideration should be given to the design of multipurpose satellite collection terminals with contiguous but physically separated areas for handling cargo and processing passengers. For cargo handling, planning between urban transit systems and airport collection systems would require coordination of standards for container sizes and tunnel cross sections (of underground rapid-transit systems).

Advantages and disadvantages of the regional satellite terminal approach are summarized as follows.

Advantages of distributed terminal functions
  • Decentralization. Functions not essential at the airport area are removed from the airport.
  • Increased convenience and peace of mind to the traveler. Travelers

may enter the system at points closer to their true point of origin and then relax, knowing they are shielded from obstacles beyond their control such as traffic jams.

- Improved reservation status. The earlier capturing of individual passengers will allow improved advance notice of shows and no-shows.
- Improved handling of passengers under adverse conditions. Precise scheduling of the collection mode will allow holding passengers away from the airport during delays due to mechanical difficulties or weather, as well as efficient transfer of passengers to alternate departure points on flights.
- Reduced travel time. Overall travel time from point of origin to ultimate point of destination will be reduced.

Disadvantages of distributed terminal functions

- High cost. The investment required, primarily for transportation media between satellite collection terminals and airports, may be greater than can be extracted from the traveler in additional fares. Also, total facility cost for a given passenger-processing capability will probably be higher with distributed facilities than would be the case for centralized facilities.
- Higher operating costs. Individual carriers will experience higher operating costs unless pooling and automation are employed.
- Urban integration. Much coordination between urban planners, air carriers, local and federal regulatory agencies, and other modes of transportation would be required. Experience has shown that such fully integrated planning and development are difficult to achieve.

Single-purpose airports, single-direction airports, and satellite collection points have been discussed. These three concepts of regional airport systems are only a few of many possible variations. For example, it is quite possible that in major hub areas such as New York or Los Angeles a specialized airport might eventually be combined with the satellite terminal. It should be emphasized that the systems presented have been singled out for discussion merely to emphasize and amplify some major planning problems facing the air transportation industry, and not as recommended solutions to specific problems.

STOL/VTOL AIRPORTS AND TERMINALS[4]

Design and layout of the STOL/VTOL port buildings and apron should aim at achieving minimum apron-occupancy time, minimum

4 Portions of this section have been extracted from Volume 2 of the study *Technical and Economic Evaluation of Aircraft for Intercity Short-Haul Transportation*, FAA Report ADS-74, II, April 1966.

time for processing passengers, baggage, and cargo, and maximum turnaround efficiency consistent with airline operational requirements. Terminal parking, passenger processing, and aircraft apron areas should be designed to provide passengers with increasingly effective service and facilities.

STOL/VTOL Terminal Requirements

The airport designer must generally satisfy the diverse objectives and desires of many interested groups, and STOL/VTOL terminal design is no exception. Such interested parties include the municipality, the airport operator, passengers, officials of airlines and equipment representatives, airport neighbors, and regulating government agencies. Each can be expected to be concerned with such key items as location, size, appearance, technical requirements, initial costs, noise and air pollution, and operating costs.

Special STOL/VTOL terminals may be established for city center service (if noise and pollution conditions are acceptable), or they might be developed at existing general aviation or air carrier airports convenient to city centers. Terminal requirements for STOL/VTOL operations are listed here. These indicate the more important considerations in establishing STOL/VTOL facilities, but are not listed in order of priority. What applies to one location may not apply to another.

- Proximity to traffic-generating centers, convenience to central business district
- Vehicular accessibility (in downtown areas, taxicab traffic primarily)
- Availability of site
- Adequacy of size (STOL will require more space than VTOL)
- Proper elevation (ground level or elevated)
- Operational safety
- Obstruction clearance
- Permanence of obstruction clearances (preservation possible by zoning or through natural means, with approaches over water, parks, or highways)
- Relative insensitivity of area to noise (industrial or nonresidential locations preferable; sites near schools and hospitals to be avoided)
- Compatibility with normal air traffic patterns and helicopter traffic
- Cost of acquiring and developing site
- Compatibility with neighboring property uses
- Accessibility to utilities (water, gas, electric power, A/C fuel, sewage disposal)

• Connection convenience with other transport modes
• Aircraft physical and operational characteristics

Design of STOL/VTOL Terminals

STOL and VTOL terminals might be located in the central business district or "downtown," in outlying or suburban areas, or in conventional airports. The central business district location is visualized as a multilevel structure, with lower levels for parking and passenger processing and upper levels for loading and unloading travelers and for aircraft operations. The STOL/VTOL facility at a conventional airport might possibly be situated at ground level. It may include a terminal, to separate the short-haul traveler from the conventional air traveler, and specially constructed short runways or pads for efficient STOL/VTOL operations. At major hubs these should be located so as not to interfere with conventional carrier operations.

The outlying or suburban facility location may permit the use of more land (instead of multilevel vertical structures) and will require more overnight automobile parking than central business district locations.

STOL/VTOL airport design must be in accord with anticipated operating requirements of future STOL/VTOL aircraft and with other facilities in the system. Required terminal facilities depend upon traffic potential and airline operational methods and requirements to ensure efficient and safe air service operation.

Detailed criteria used in developing the required facilities involve

1. Aircraft types and physical characteristics.
2. Aircraft capacities with respect to passengers and cargo.
3. Passenger traffic.
4. Movement rate (including peaking).
5. Gate control and passenger-cargo handling techniques.

Design of passenger and aircraft areas must take into account noise, fumes, and heat. A primary consideration is minimization of aircraft ground-stop times, which can be achieved by efficient traffic flow and simplification of interposed formalities. Also, safe passenger movement to and from aircraft without engine shutdown is a consideration in reduced ground time. Primary considerations in passenger processing are space relationships and area requirements, which contribute to construction and operation costs.

The size and number of gate positions will of course affect apron design, and consideration must be given to fixed installations for ground service to reduce apron congestion and servicing times. Building costs should be held to the minimum appropriate to the architectural motif of the surrounding area and future planned developments. Each terminal in the system will differ in size and configuration because of passenger volume and location, but in general the linear-type layouts are more easily expanded if original terminal capacity is exceeded.

Figure 5.24 summarizes the estimated area requirements for elevated or ground-level STOL or VTOL ports. Major areas required are

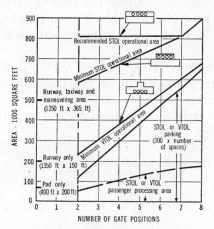

Figure 5.24. How area requirements for STOL and VTOL ports vary with number of gates.

those for aircraft operations, passenger processing, and vehicle parking. In an elevated configuration, passenger-processing parking areas can be efficiently decked or situated below aircraft operational areas. For conventional designs at ground level, passenger processing and parking areas must be added to the port's minimum operational area. The total area required for a four-gate ground-level STOL or VTOL port is about twice that required for an equivalent elevated configuration. This difference in area requirements diminishes as gate positions are added, owing to the fact that, while requirements for runways and taxiways are fixed, variation with number of gate positions is fairly constant for STOL ports but increases rapidly as gate positions are added to VTOL ports.

As the number of gates for the STOL port increases beyond seven, the planform must be lengthened to maintain clearances when all positions are in use. A family of curves for different gate position sizes could be generated. Operational areas can in some designs be utilized for off-line parking and maintenance of STOL aircraft, with lower levels providing additional parking area.

A two-gate terminal is considered the minimum practical size. Terminal area requirements for vehicle parking, servicing and fueling of aircraft, and processing of passengers are similar for STOL and VTOL handling equal traffic volumes. The major differences are in the take-off and landing areas.

Airfield area

A principal design element of STOL/VTOL terminals is the aircraft operational area (comprising the landing facilities and apron areas). The size of the airfield is based upon (1) physical and operational characteristics of the aircraft, and (2) the size and number of gate positions.

Evaluations of various STOL port and VTOL port planforms have shown rectangular planforms to be the most efficient, based upon STOL/VTOL aircraft operational requirements and future expansion possibilities inherent in these designs. Airfield area requirements are summarized in Figure 5.25.

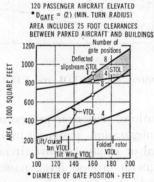

Figure 5.25. How STOL and VTOL airfield area requirements vary with diameter of gate position.

Terminal area

The STOL/VTOL terminal is essentially the service center for transferring passengers and their property, as well as mail, express, fuel, and cargo, between surface carriers and air carriers. Passenger area space requirements (Figure 5.26) are based upon FAA airport terminal building design data. Space allocation should be coordinated with carriers to promote efficiency, reliability, and speed of airport and airline operations.

The space relationships developed by the FAA are based on the functional disposition of facilities for airlines, the public, and concessions, allocated on the basis of passenger volume. Floor space required

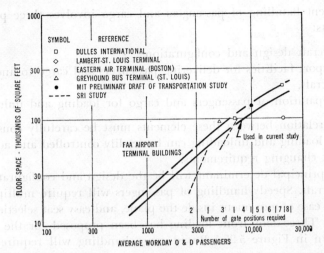

Figure 5.26. Passenger-processing space requirements in the STOL/VTOL airport.

for STOL/VTOL operation is taken as 80 percent of the FAA design
curve for conventional terminal facilities, for airlines operations, waiting area, and restaurants.

SPECIAL TECHNICAL PROBLEMS OF FUTURE AIRPORT, TERMINAL, AND FACILITY PLANNING

Regardless of the nature of the airport or regional concept adopted,
insertion of technically sophisticated and expensive aircraft into the
system will create certain technical problems for the facility planner
and designer. In many instances, this interface between the facility
and the aircraft will exert a much greater influence upon profitable
aircraft operation in a commercial environment than is now the case.
In other cases, new facility technology must be developed in order to
serve demand adequately at a cost compatible with projected growth.
Some of these technical problems are discussed in this section of the
report.

RAPID AND CONCURRENT PASSENGER AND CARGO LOADING AND UNLOADING

As aircraft become larger and more expensive, means of decreasing
ground time will be of increasing importance. Rapid and concurrent
passenger and cargo loading or unloading will be among the most
important factors to be considered in decreasing ground time (and in
moving hundreds of passengers on and off planes with minimum frus-
tration and inconvenience).

Efficient handling of passengers and cargo involves three primary elements:

- Aircraft design and configuration.
- Airport facilities for delivering passengers and cargo to and from aircraft.
- Preparation of passengers and cargo for loading and unloading.

The relation between these elements must be carefully considered so that loading and unloading can be readily controlled and adjusted to meet changing requirements.

The principal determinant will be the design and configuration of the aircraft. Speedy handling of passengers will require multiple entrances, ease of movement inside the plane, and easy seat selection and seating. Three-door front loading has been proposed for the B-747, as shown in Figure 5.27.[5] Rapid cargo handling will require ready

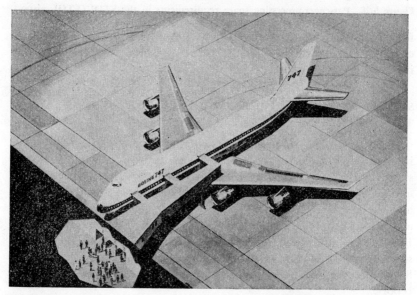

Figure 5.27. A covered multidoor loading sleeve has been proposed for nose-in parking.
SOURCE: The Boeing Company.

access to plane cargo areas, compartmented areas within the cargo area to allow for sorted loads, and equipment installed aboard the plane to facilitate rapid handling of cargo. Concurrent loading or unloading of passengers and cargo will be largely a matter of simultaneous access

[5] Boeing Aircraft Company, *Boeing 747 at Airport*, Document D6-13440, May 1967.

to the plane and adequate entrances, probably on both sides of the fuselage.

The second most important determinant of rapid loading or unloading will be adequacy of airport facilities involved in delivery of passengers and cargo to and from the aircraft. One can envision the offloading of 200 or more passengers at an alternate stop that has no covered loading finger, on a rainy night, with all of these passengers passing single file through one or two narrow doors into the terminal building.

Distance between passenger and cargo assembly areas and aircraft is also a major factor. Whether passengers reach the aircraft via mobile lounge, along a telescoped gangplank, or up a snorkel from underground, or are merely aided by moving sidewalks, skybuses, and the like, distance is a major factor in determining time required to load or unload the aircraft. Distance is also an important factor for cargo, but more significant is the avoidance of undue interference with other airport and aircraft service activities in moving cargo to and from planes.

While aircraft servicing (fuel, food, water) must be accomplished concurrently, congestion around an aircraft should be minimized for rapid, safe aircraft turnaround. Loading cargo onto an aircraft while passengers are enplaning will greatly increase the congestion.

Only very sophisticated facilities, such as the underground type originally conceived for the proposed Burlington County, New Jersey, Jet Global Airport, can be expected to provide rapid turnaround without congestion. This type of facility may be justified in a few high-volume traffic generation areas (New York, Chicago, Los Angeles) or when cargo and passengers must be loaded concurrently.

CARRIER OPERATIONAL DATA SYSTEMS

Basic to all preparation of passengers and cargo for loading must be an effective system of control, computerized as necessary, to ensure that airline and airport employees involved have up-to-the-minute information on passenger and cargo movement and timing. The need for data systems in handling, storage, and transfer of air cargo at the present time is confirmed by experience with both commercial and military data systems currently used to provide inventory control and processing management information. The enormous forecast increase in air cargo volume and tonnage will certainly not simplify inventory management and processing control problems in the 1975 time frame.

An effective data management system is also required for planning of air cargo flow, inventory control, and tracing of lost cargo. Present technology can be applied in developing the data systems required, using available equipment or future product improvement. Paramount in any data system application is the ability to communicate with other data systems in use; a finite evaluation of the specific tasks it must perform should be made in advance. Accordingly, the facility designer must not only accommodate the data system hardware but must be fully aware of its function, since it influences operations and process flow within the facility.

STANDARDIZATION OF EQUIPMENT AND FIXTURES

In a rapidly growing field such as the air transportation industry, in which changing technology has many profound effects on primary system elements, standardization of equipment and fixtures is difficult to obtain. Nevertheless, maximum standardization is essential in a volume operation of this nature, where time is vitally important and the interfaces between airplane and airport terminals are crucial to successful operation of the system.

Many different areas should be continuously considered for standardization of equipment and fixtures. Following are some of the more important:

- Cargo handling on the airport and in aircraft cargo compartments.
- Passenger loading, especially within each airport.
- Baggage handing, especially within each airport.
- Plane servicing (fueling, air conditioning, waste disposal, aircraft cleaning, food servicing).

Equipment involved in transfer of cargo from one airline to another must be a primary target for standardization. Pallets, containers, restraint systems, data interface-billing, and tracing and cargo identification fall within this area. The SAE Subcommittee AGE-2A, Passenger and Cargo Handling, has established pallet standards for the most part, and interchangeability of pallets between aircraft and airlines has been achieved. Small containers (types A, B, C, and D) are now sized to fit standard pallets.

Large van-type containers (8 ft × 8 ft in cross section, and 10, 20, 30, or 40 ft in the long dimension) have been recommended by industry. Containers of this type are designed and sized for maximum intermodal compatibility among railroads, highway trucks, cargo vessels, and commercial aircraft. Jumbo jet commercial aircraft are being designed for efficient loading with 8 ft × 8 ft containers. Conversion of other cargo aircraft to this standard will be necessary to achieve true intermodal capability. As now conceived, large van containers will induce a weight penalty and a deadweight shipping charge which directly or indirectly is paid by the shipper.

FUEL HANDLING AND STORAGE

Only two new fuels appear potentially attractive for the 1980's, and both appear restricted to rather specialized use at that time.

Methane offers considerable promise for SST application because of its higher heating value, greater cooling capacity, and lower cost. Because of these qualities, it promises higher speed and substantially longer range at low cost. It also offers possibilities of reduced sonic boom by permitting flights at higher altitudes.

Disadvantages of methane include low density and the fact that it is a cryogenic fuel and therefore cannot be substituted directly for presently used jet fuels but requires new aircraft designs with larger insulated fuel tanks. Most significantly, considerable expenditures would be required to provide fueling at airports from which such aircraft would operate. However, methane may be a distinct possibility as a new fuel in the 1980's.

Nuclear fuel appears technically feasible for the 1980's, although existing data are insufficient to establish its economic competitiveness. Application would involve large capital investment but only at the few airports where maintenance and nuclear refueling would be required. It is anticipated that aircraft would be able to fly on conventional fuels to reach such bases.

Problems of the nuclear power plant derive for the most part from social pressures regarding nuclear safety in flights over populated areas and crashes — pressures which may be overcome in time.

Conventional fueling trends will continue to stress stationary hydrants and external fuel sources with hoses and nozzles that have mating connections similar to those on the using aircraft, either permanently installed at the hydrant or on mobile carts. In order to ensure minimum service time, fueling equipment should match or exceed the capability of the airplane (2,000 gpm at 50 psi for the SST).

The higher the refueling rate the better. Any means or devices developed to shorten fueling time should be pursued with vigor and imagination by the facility designer or planner.

GROUND HANDLING OF AIRCRAFT

The increased weight of future aircraft poses problems in moving to and from gate positions. If tow tugs are to be used for this purpose, they would have to be considerably larger and much heavier than at present, and would thus further encumber and congest ramps. Some alternate methods might employ the following:

- Turntables on which aircraft wheels would be positioned and the aircraft then rotated to or from the gate.
- Drag lines with subpavement driven cables (similar to the San Francisco cable car system). Arriving or departing aircraft would be connected by a simple drop-in device and towed to or from the gate.
- Driven aircraft main wheels for aircraft maneuvering. A mobile power plant of relatively small dimensions would be driven into position between the main gear wheels of the aircraft. Telescoping arms could then be attached to opposing gears and, by means of a transmission, drive the aircraft wheels to maneuver it as required.

GROUND SERVICING EQUIPMENT

One major airline operator has in proposal a fixed service system of engine starting, air conditioning, electrical power, and potable water for possible installation at Boston. This system will be used primarily for present aircraft but by extension and quantitative adjustments could be adaptable to future aircraft. It will be contained in either a pit area, a powered boom, or a combination of both at each gate position. The commodities will be fed from remote locations through the boom or pits.

Pressurized and heated air will be regulated at the gate position to meet requirements of a particular aircraft. Chilled brine will be pumped to each service area and, by means of a compressor and blower, will provide suitable cooled air to the aircraft. Reversing the system will make warmed air available.

Electrical power will be supplied by an auxiliary power unit at each gate position. Potable water will be available. Toilet servicing added to this complex would involve extensive additions to the sewage disposal system of the terminal but should pay benefits through further reduction in the number of ramp vehicles. The importance of reducing servicing equipment on the ramp must be carefully considered by the terminal designer and the aircraft operator.

ULTRA-EFFECTIVE SAFETY AND FIRE PROTECTION SYSTEMS

Many present safety and fire protection deficiencies in terminals and airports may be the result of insufficient emphasis and failure to give adequate authority to safety and fire protection consultants. With the introduction of larger aircraft, larger fuel loads, and, possibly, exotic fuels, safety and fire protection will take on greater importance. In future expansion or new construction, consultants conversant with the latest items and methods should be given more freedom and funds for safety and fire protection systems.

Additional areas for exploration include built-in dry chemical systems at each gate position in lieu of portable extinguishers, permanently installed systems for automatically foaming a section of runway, and retractable arresting gear at runway ends. The high incidence of aircraft damage by ground vehicles could be eliminated or reduced by removing all or most ramp servicing vehicles.

PAVING STRENGTHS AND WIDTHS

Design of the new jumbo jets and SST is such that these aircraft will impose no greater runway or airfield pavement wheel loading than present aircraft (Figure 5.28) nor will they require runways of

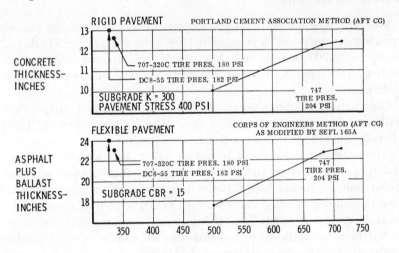

Figure 5.28. Pavement load tolerances.
SOURCE: Airport Operators Council International.

any greater length. However, the gross weight imposed on the total aircraft footprint may exceed the safe limits for culverts or tunnels beneath ramps or runways, as in the case of the highway underpass at Los Angeles International.

Pavement patterns must accommodate relationships between turning radii of the forward main gear, nose gear, and arcs described by the outboard wing tip and the nose at various nose gear steering angles. Turns of 180 degrees on a runway are not normal at most airports because runways are constructed with parallel taxiways and exit taxiways at many points. The SST can make a 180-degree turn on a 200-foot wide runway, using a maximum steering angle of 76 degrees.

Turning maneuvers for the SST are based on a 150-foot-wide runway, 75-foot wide taxiway, and typical runway and taxiway fillets recommended by the FAA. A 90-degree turn by the SST from a 75-ft taxiway to a 75-ft taxiway requires a fillet radius of 150 ft.

Dependent on parking-apron configurations and positions of adjacent aircraft, maneuvering with a tow vehicle may be necessary. Obviously, the many possibilities which exist in each particular airport must be carefully evaluated by the designer.

FACILITIES PLANNING FOR V/STOL AIRCRAFT AND HELICOPTERS

Forecasts now envision new helicopters of 50,000 to 80,000 pounds gross weight, carrying 75 people. In 1970 gross weights for STOL will be up to 70,000 pounds and those for VTOL up to 90,000 pounds, with overall lengths of about 100 feet. STOL's will require 100-ft-wide runways.

Obstruction clearance slopes of 20:1 for the last mile of the flight path and 14:1 for the preceding few miles will be required. These aircraft can follow at least a 6-degree glide slope.

The expected noise nevel is 100 to 110 PNdB within a 300-foot radius of these aircraft, and it does not appear that this will be appreciably reduced in the 1980's. Reduction may require development of new techniques of noise control at V/STOL terminals situated in a nonairport environment. The "flying crane" concept, used extensively in Vietnam for retrieval of downed aircraft, can be applied productively to containerized passengers and cargo, prepackaged in standardized containers and readily picked up by crane vehicles and transported to or from main or satellite terminals. Support of such containers when detached from the crane may require modifications in facility design.

ROUTING AND HANDLING OF U.S. MAIL

A current mail-handling problem is the necessity of reading individual mailbag tags over and over again. Good lighting is required for this operation, but at present it must frequently be conducted at the murky edge of aircraft cargo compartments. In an effort to ameliorate this problem, containers to hold larger volumes of mail are now being tried experimentally.

It is probable that within a few years all first-class mail traveling over 150 to 200 miles will go by air, and parcel post may soon be in the same category. The result of this volume increase will be an increasing need for better and faster methods of handling and loading mail. Larger containers seem to be a logical answer, with the Post Office Department possibly playing a greater role in planeside delivery and pickup of mail. Other approaches would involve an increased airport area for processing mail in much the same manner as air cargo is processed.

DATA PROCESSING IN PHYSICAL PLANT OPERATIONS

Airport and terminal operators will probably see increased use of modern computer equipment and data display devices in day-to-day and minute-to-minute operations of the physical plant of a modern terminal. The airport operators' concern with this continuous growth in application of computers and data-processing assistance in management of the airport complex may be expected to involve the following considerations.

Operation and Maintenance of Airport Utilities

Increasingly, computers are being used to collect and analyze data and to control the operation of large buildings in widely spread facilities such as college campuses and hospitals. These systems reduce the number of personnel that must be on hand to observe the operation of electric power, central air conditioning, and heating systems and to record data and make operating decisions. Telemetering of information to a central control room and the decision-making assistance offered by the computer and its rapid data retrieval all contribute to improved efficiency of operations.

Maintenance Management

A large airport and terminal complex requires considerable maintenance to keep the facility, grounds, and services in operating order. Several computer programs have recently been developed that keep track of preventive maintenance performed, required schedules, and may actually issue work orders to accomplish preventive maintenance when due. These same programs have been expanded in some cases to record and file data on all scheduled and unscheduled maintenance performed on given items of installed equipment.

Job standards may be incorporated to assist in assignment of man-hour budgets and workload controls. Automatic routines have been developed to determine and assign daily priorities for given work orders based on schedules and availability of personnel. This application of computers will undoubtedly increase at airports and terminals.

Logistics Management

As in airport maintenance, logistics or material-support management for a complex may be assisted by computers, which would handle routing of spare parts and supplies, administration, and inventory management for all items falling within the cognizance of the airport operator. Functions accomplished by computers would comprise issuance, receipting, automatic reorders, and expediting, and could also include consideration of cost data and consumption trends.

Future data systems may also control and dispense fuel from common stocks to individual carriers. In this application, computers would not only control and manage inventory or bulk transfer from offsite storage but could also control dispensing of fuel through common use hydrants upon proper authorization, plus provision of basic billing data to the operator and individual carriers. The same data could allow oil vendors to maintain a common inventory.

Facility Allocation

There have been indications of possible increased usage of common gates or loading docks by two or more carriers for different scheduled departures of future large-capacity aircraft. Under this concept of operation, on-line computers could monitor gate utilization and commitments and could continuously update the utilization plan with any necessary changes brought about by flight schedule slippage or delayed arrivals.

Servicing equipment needed for gate positions or docks might be monitored by the central computer control system to ensure that it is functioning properly and available to aircraft when required. If the gate is used by two or more carriers, computer monitoring and control would be almost essential to ensure correct prorated billing for use of the common equipment. If servicing equipment is mobile but assigned from a common pool, computer management of the pool on a real-time basis would be desirable. This would ensure high up-time for the equipment when it is needed to serve flexible schedules resulting from arrival and departure delays.

Traffic Control

Properly equipped and programmed to sense airport activity in people and aircraft, the airport operations computer could alert the airport operator to possible trouble spots such as vehicular or pedestrian congestion. This notification would allow immediate dispatch of police, standby employees, or other relief.

Similarly, the central computer could monitor airport parking lot gates and maintain a running count of available capacity in various lots. This information could in turn be displayed on signs near airport entrances, to direct incoming passengers to lots where parking was available.

Computer Interfaces with Air Traffic Control

In addition to the immediate real-time control and information availability just discussed, there are several potential applications for improved operation brought about by forecasting. However, to fully exploit this capability for forecasting traffic loads and equipment requirements, airport operations computers need to communicate with the computers used in other elements of air transport such as air traffic control and ground collection and distribution of passengers.

Reporting and forecasting capabilities of modern computer control and information network systems become especially advantageous to airport operations when applied to those functions concerned with resource allocation. For example, changes in arrival times could be passed directly by air traffic control computers to the airport-management computer with a minimum of human intervention.

Departure delays offer similar opportunities. For example, the system described earlier would permit the terminal operations computer to know immediately if aircraft departure was delayed because of maintenance or servicing problems. The terminal computer should pass this information to the air traffic control computer, advising it of the delay and forecasting a possible revised schedule. If a delay could be accurately forecast by the air traffic control computer, the airport management computer should be informed of the probable delay so that it can adjust other scheduled airport activities.

Thus, if arrival time and passenger load of a B-747 can be accurately forecast on a hot summer day, the central terminal air conditioning system can be alerted to an expected sudden influx of 350 or more passengers and can arrange sufficient cooling capacity on stream at the proper time to handle the extra heat production. The ability to anticipate such loads against a continually varying schedule could both provide improved passenger comfort and save many dollars per year in terminal operating costs.

An automated (or semiautomated) digital communication system would make it possible to telemeter data from an aircraft to the destination terminal giving the condition of the various subsystems in the aircraft. The information could be transmitted on command from the ground, without participation of the aircraft crew. The necessary facilities could thus be made ready at the terminal for servicing the aircraft as soon as it arrived, the diagnostic work having already been performed. Such a system becomes a necessity for the high-performance aircraft of the future if servicing time is to be kept to an acceptable minimum.

Interface with Ground Transportation Control

In addition to information exchange with the air traffic control mode, there is an opportunity for effective communication between computers controlling airport functions and other computer systems controlling collection, distribution, and transportation functions in an interairport or intraurban mode. Just as it would be advantageous for airport operators to know the exact arrival load of incoming air passengers, it would also be advantageous for them to know the arrival time at the airport of enplaning passengers.

It might be even more advantageous to be able to control the arrival of these enplaning passengers at the airport complex, if there is a known departure delay due to aircraft servicing or air traffic control problems. It appears that little can be done in this regard when the passenger arrives at the air terminal in a personal automobile or taxi. However, there are indications that such personal transportation cannot survive in the jumbo-transport era because of the traffic density it produces at the airport.

Mass transportation of departing passengers from several collection points remote from the airport will receive increased emphasis. These mass media, as we are seeing from current trends in rapid transit, lend themselves to enforced automatic control within their own environment and also allow controlled interactions from interfacing environments. The possibility thus exists of holding passengers in the transportation system but away from the high-density area of aircraft boarding within the air terminal.

By the same token, computer information exchange should provide a means to better manage the utilization of mass ground-transportation media. Accurate arrival time and load forecasts can move directly from the air traffic control mode to the terminal operation and then to the ground-transportation operation — allowing operators to dynamically and continually adjust ground transportation departure schedules from the airport to provide supplemental transportation equipment when needed, and to coordinate transport availability at the loading point precisely as required. If a truly effective air transport system is created, integrated information systems will be a necessity. Such systems should therefore be a vital factor in planning and consideration of the future airport and terminal complex.

RECOMMENDATIONS

Following are general recommendations for immediate action by government and industry to meet the challenges of aviation growth. Due to the inherently long lead time of airport and facility development and construction, it is imperative that remedial action be initiated now to prepare for continued growth and the introduction of the SST, the airbus, and jumbo transports.

AIRPORT AND TERMINAL FINANCING

Possibly the greatest problem facing the air transportation system is the high cost of land acquisition and construction to provide the airports, terminals, and facilities necessary to keep pace with projected air transportation growth. This applies not only to metropolitan hub areas and scheduled air-carrier operations but also to the many small municipal airports and general aviation facilities throughout the country. It is recommended that a Department of Transportation-sponsored study be initiated to

- Determine types and quantities of construction required at a variety of airport developments.
- Forecast costs of these developments by type of community and region.
- Identify and evaluate all sources of financing related to the requirements identified earlier.
- Compile, utilize, and correlate existing data in these areas to the greatest possible extent.
- Develop a National Airport Plan, including a recommended plan

for economic development, showing recommended sources and methods of financing, important milestones of national planning, and recommended development of new sources and methods of financing if required.

• Perform a benefit analysis to provide quantitative, accurate estimates of economic and social benefits to be derived nationally, regionally, and at the municipal level from the expenditure of required funds for airport and terminal development.

AIRPORT AND TERMINAL GROWTH PUBLICITY

Lack of local community support for airport development is frequently the result of inadequate presentation to the public of the economic and social benefits of the airport operation. To secure the needed support (or at least to offset the negative influences), action must be taken to educate the voting public to the problems and economic loss that will occur if required airport and terminal growth is inhibited by voter and taxpayer apathy.

This effort should be directed toward the problems of general-aviation airports as well as commercial air terminals. One of the primary objectives of the campaign should be to convey the fact that the airport is an economic asset to the community as well as the nation, and that the role of air transportation as a national resource is much too important to be restricted by minority interests.

NOISE TOLERANCE

One of the more serious problems facing aviation is the noise caused by the operation of aircraft at or in the vicinity of airports. This is a complex problem because it is not an airport problem per se. The airport does not control the source, or source design, and no feasible methods are now known to capture and dissipate noise within the confines of active airport property.

The imposed noise problem is a major factor in the planning of future airports away from urban areas and in the development of large, controlled-use areas around airports. However, the relocation of all airports is not feasible, and a way must be found to use existing airports in the face of greater traffic and increasing aircraft engine noise.

Because of the significance of the noise problem it is recommended that studies be initiated to establish acceptable standards of noise related to different urban situations such as residence areas, retailing, and light manufacturing. It is important that such standards be established on the basis of scientific and economic realism and not through arbitrary action of the courts in the absence of scientific data.

As background information is developed from the suggested studies, standards of acceptable noise levels can be legislated that would protect the public interest, protect the airport operator, and provide definitive guidance to aircraft designers and operators. This would put aircraft noise limits into the same category as highway speed limits (a government determination by legislation of what are safe speeds), acceptable levels of air pollution related to health and discomfort, etc.

In order to determine acceptable limits for legislation or adjudication, it is essential that study and research be expanded to determine a scientific basis for establishing standard levels. The medical aspects, considering temporary or permanent physiological effects, are quite well known. The controlling limit on acceptable noise will be somewhat below tolerable levels.

Much work has been done on evaluating human tolerance to noise in industrial and other environments. However, further research is required to quantify human reaction to the specifics of aircraft operation noise and to establish meaningful, feasible acceptance levels based on data collected from interviews, psychoacoustic measurements, and human behavior studies.

LAND BANKS

The continuing need for new airports and terminals is abundantly clear. When the presently land-starved urban areas are reviewed, the problem of obtaining the land required for new airports is also apparent. Studies and methods must be developed to begin systematic acquisition of land for future airports. The larger land areas to be required (20,000 acres and more, per airport) for the regional hub and national network mean that the airport land bank should be considered from a nationwide viewpoint.

Land-use plans with appropriate zoning must consider the noise problem in the development of land adjacent to the land-bank airport. For years airports have been considered islands unto themselves. Forecast data now rightly consider them as networks; certainly metropolitan hubs will be served by more than one airport. Methods of interconnecting airports by helicopter, V/STOL, ground transportation, or water transportation must be studied in relation to the entire hub, and possible solutions to these problems must be enumerated.

Air transportation can no longer be restricted by ground or interconnecting transportation interfaces. Therefore, another and equally important land bank for future airports is the right-of-way land bank.

This includes not only interconnected airports in a hub but also right-of-way requirements to move people from various locations in a metropolitan area as expeditiously as possible to the airports. The present trend of railroad mergers, in which certain railroad branch lines are being abandoned or scheduled for abandonment, may afford a national resource that will serve as the core of right-of-way land banks.

Possible approaches to accomplishment of these goals would include establishment of land reserves in the public interest by the appropriate state or regional government, providing interim, controlled use for other revenue-producing or public-benefit purposes. Land areas thus controlled would be large enough to provide both airports and all anticipated clear-zone and noise-problem areas. Controlled zoning would allow utilization of these reserved areas for activities that would be compatible with aviation. Federal participation, in the form of financing grants or indebtedness guarantees, would be useful, in exchange for incorporation of federal standards for development and coordination with a national airport plan.

A comprehensive study is recommended to determine technical and economic feasibility and methods of establishing such land banks or reservations for the future development of major airports, together with the access rights-of-way necessary to integrate efficiently the airport into the urban community it is to serve.

URBAN TRANSPORTATION AND AIR TRANSPORTATION INTEGRATION

The large growth in air transportation demands improved planning for integration of air terminals and airport complexes into the urban environment and, in particular, into a combination urban and interurban transportation system. Not only must competing ground and air modes of interurban or corridor transportation be coordinated, but the interurban modes in turn must be closely integrated into the urban transportation complex.

A possible method of achieving this improved coordinated planning would be the establishment of a standing committee at the national level, to include representatives of the Department of Transportation, the Department of Housing and Urban Development, and representatives of the air and ground transportation industry. This national committee could be duplicated at the state, regional, or municipal government level as necessary to consider the individual problems of a specific area. The purpose of the committee would be to provide overall guidance and policy relative to integration of air transportation with urban transportation systems.

OPTIMUM AIRPORT LAYOUTS

The distance factors involved in various airport layout concepts (for example, radial and linear) in relation to aircraft, passenger, and cargo handling must be further analyzed in detail.

Various existing or planned airport configurations should be studied by appropriate agencies to establish a basis for adoption of new concepts and innovation in airport/terminal layout. Additional verified information is needed as a basis for future plans. The Urban Transportation Administration of the Department of Housing and Urban Development is sponsoring a similar study by ASCE in relation to the country's future urban transportation needs. Preliminary recommendations pertaining to aircraft servicing and airport operations, if adopted and carried out, will develop some of this information, but a broader look at the airport/terminal layout parameters would be highly desirable. Federally assisted demonstration programs should be considered to encourage experimentation and data-gathering to verify optimum configurations.

FUNCTIONAL STUDIES

It has been stated that the inevitable overloading of airport and terminal facilities can be somewhat relieved by displacing certain non-essential functions from the airport property, or by improving or developing methods to achieve more efficient utilization of existing facilities. In order to achieve maximum benefits from relief of this type, it is recommended that studies be initiated to develop methods and issue optimum guidelines for the performance of total functions relative to air transportation.

For example, the concept of goods distribution as a total system from producer to consumer continues to be a major factor in air cargo development. Other functions of air transportation should be similarly evaluated, and distribution functions studied further to develop areas for improved efficiency (e.g., intermodal compatibility of air cargo containers, improved bulk cargo-handling techniques, simplified and less costly aircraft loading and unloading techniques, etc.). Every function of the process should be evaluated against the total process.

Other potential areas for study include the movement of mail from sender to receiver, the movement of livestock or produce from farm to market, and the movement of tourists (as opposed to the movement of business travelers). These studies can be assigned to major established, competent firms with full capabilities in systems engineering and facilities planning, or to teams of such firms, and sponsored by industry associations such as the Air Transport Association or by appropriate government agencies. Federal demonstration grants should be applied to assist in those areas where private financing is not practical because of complicated intermodal relationships.

SMOOTHING OF PEAK DEMANDS

As an interim measure pending expansion of capacity, it is recommended that the carriers analyze ways and means of smoothing peak airport operations in order to obtain a more uniform distribution of landings and takeoffs throughout the day.

NEW DESIGN AND CONSTRUCTION TECHNIQUES AND MATERIALS

The rapid evolution of aviation technology over the past few years has tended to force certain facilities into early obsolescence. This continuing trend, combined with the rapid rise in construction costs, dictates the need for development of new design concepts and economical construction techniques and materials for terminal buildings and facilities to meet functional requirements, allow flexibility of rearrangement and modification, and extend projected service life in a rapidly evolving technology.

New concepts of building design that provide a permanent structural frame but allow great flexibility in shell and internal working space should be studied. Increased use of esthetically pleasing, low-cost materials such as plastics and light metals should be investigated. Federally assisted demonstration projects can encourage research and testing by airport operators to determine the feasibility of new materials and techniques.

Studies of methods used to compare pavement strength and potential load to be imposed by a specific aircraft reveal considerable confusion. At least nine methods exist for determining pavement stress calculations. The lack of correlation between methods and specific differences in pavement thicknesses calculated by the various methods confirms the serious need for more basic research in methods of calculating stress and of sampling and determining soil characteristics. A single, uniform method should be established for determining pavement stress.

A quick and inexpensive means of measuring the strength of existing airfield pavements is needed immediately. With the introduction of a superclass of aircraft into the commercial inventory, and with the general aviation fleet converting to planes of larger size, airport operators need to know what limitations they must impose on the ground movement of aircraft, or the extent of pavement upgrading that may be necessary.

CONTAINERIZATION SYSTEMS FOR AIR CARGO

In order to provide information necessary for optimum facility planning, it is recommended that the entire containerization problem be examined, with specific emphasis upon filling some of the gaps that now exist in containerization planning. Specific questions to be answered by such a study are as follows:

- Who owns the containers?
- How are containers distributed to the point of need, and how is their flow controlled?
- Can rental of containers to the shipper who wishes to do his own containerization be a profitable enterprise for air carriers? For specialized rental companies?
- Will a sufficient amount of container deadheading be required in the future to justify knockdown or collapsible containers?
- Can an acceptable disposable one-way container be developed?
- To what extent can a true intermodal capability for containerized air freight be achieved?
- Can the different structural requirements imposed upon air containers be made compatible with the structural requirements (or practices) of sea, rail, and highway containers and container-handling equipment?
- What is the balance between benefits in terms of potential increased revenue to airlines and increased costs which will result from weight penalties imposed by container compatibility?
- To what extent might facilitation costs be reduced and speed of handling improved at the expense of reduced airlift efficiency? Can aircraft afford to carry some of their own material-handling equipment?
- What premiums can be paid for special-purpose short- and long-haul air freighters designed specifically to improve speed and ease of loading and unloading with minimum use of special-purpose ground handling equipment.

Although these recommendations for study areas of containerization touch on many aspects not specifically related to airports and terminals, the impact of such studies on service both at airports and at other intermodal transfer points is great. For this reason, facility planners should make major contributions to such studies.

SUPPORT EQUIPMENT AND AIRPORT SERVICES STUDIES

Several areas of equipment technology and operational concepts should be investigated in the development of future airports and terminals. The implications of new technology and concepts must be carefully evaluated in the light of specific problems at individual airports. However, government- and industry-sponsored parametric studies can provide an accurate, expanded data base from which to choose and apply individual solutions.

Such broadly based parametric studies could contribute materially to standardization of support equipment designs among aircraft manufacturers on the one hand, and among aircraft operators on the other. New technology and operational concepts should be tested through prototype development or government- and industry-funded demonstration projects, which would ultimately benefit the public in lower operating costs and proportionately reduced capital investment in public-owned airports and facilities. Some possible areas of technology and concept development for coordinated government and industry study and demonstration are discussed in this section.

Aircraft Servicing

- *Pit servicing.* Placement of all possible aircraft-serving facilities underground should be thoroughly explored to minimize surface vehicle requirements. If the size and number of surface vehicles is increased to handle the new aircraft, extreme congestion will result.
- *Aircraft servicing center standardization.* The feasibility of standardizing the location of servicing centers on the aircraft (for example, in relation to main landing-gear wheels) should be studied, with the objective of deriving a standard pit position applicable to all types of aircraft. This would permit identical pit positions at all parking locations, reducing costs and complexity.
- *Standard couplings.* Industry standardization of fuel, air conditioning, electrical connections, water, waste disposal, and other aircraft couplings should be studied to reduce costs and complexity.
- *Fuel.* Storage of fuel at airports in sufficient quantity to meet the tremendous increases in volume appears impractical (a B-747 will carry 52,000 gallons and an SST 56,000 gallons, as compared to 23,000 for today's largest aircraft), as does the transportation of

fuel by surface means. The possibility of moving directly from bulk storage to aircraft hydrants should be studied, as well as other practical alternatives.

- *Pneumatic air.* Centrally located pneumatic air facilities, with volumes and temperatures sufficient to supply starting and other needs of the 1980 generation of aircraft, must be developed to replace the expensive and inadequate sources now in use. Emphasis should be on elimination of surface vehicles in favor of a pit-supplied source. B-747 and SST starting requirements will be about double those of current aircraft.

- *Air conditioning.* Massive quantities of conditioned air will be required to make aircraft comfortable at gate positions. Elimination of surface vehicles in favor of an underground source appears desirable. Air source and transmission will require study. As some aircraft will have self-contained air conditioners, varying requirements must be anticipated.

- *Waste disposal.* Present aircraft waste-disposal methods leave much to be desired. Amounts of waste will increase proportionately with large aircraft sizes. It appears that careful analysis could produce a waste-disposal system that would automatically empty into underground facilities rather than into surface vehicles and that would comply with local sanitary standards.

- *Baggage and passenger conveyors.* The sheer volume of baggage involved in future jet aircraft makes some form of baggage-handling automation mandatory. In addition, automated means of transferring passengers between long-range aircraft, or to VTOL/STOL short-range aircraft, should be investigated to minimize uncontrolled foot traffic as much as possible.

- *Movement.* Problems of moving aircraft for servicing increase in proportion to aircraft size. Enough gate positions should be provided so that movement of aircraft for servicing is minimized or eliminated within reasonable time limits. Exposure to damage will increase with movement. Prime movers will be massive machines, and ramp design must provide ample maneuvering room.

- *Cleaning aircraft interiors.* Cleaning of the aircraft between trips within reasonable time limits presents major problems (in the case of the B-747, similar to those involved in cleaning a 400-seat theater). Underground vacuum systems with periscope-like hydraulically actuated extensions to aircraft door height would permit coupling of flexible hoses and rapid disposal of waste. This and other similar systems should be explored.

- *Food service loading.* Present surface-vehicle meal service loading would probably be totally inadequate to handle the volumes involved with larger aircraft. Loading through jetways or access by elevator might be one solution; however, all possibilities should be explored.

Maintenance and Overhaul

- *Hangars and aircraft repair locations.* Major maintenance sites for hangars and aircraft parking should be so located that access to the terminal area is not difficult. The possibility of using maintenance parking sites to relieve terminal congestion can be considered if they are reasonably close.
- *Maintenance areas.* The advantage of concentrating heavy maintenance of all airlines in a common area should be considered. Personnel access, personnel parking near the maintenance area, highway access, and employee interference with passenger movements must be taken into account.
- *Overhaul shops for engines and components.* The need for locating support shops on the airport property should be investigated. Problems of congestion, cost, transportation of units, employee parking, and other factors must be analyzed.
- *Warehousing of spare parts.* Locations for supplies and the complexities involved in moving parts rapidly between airports must be investigated. High-speed automated systems such as pneumatic tubes or conveyors might provide partial solutions. Pooling of items among airlines will necessitate high refinement of distribution systems.
- *External aircraft washing.* Common facilities, numerically programmed to match aircraft types, are being developed and may be shared by several operators. Development should be continued.

Airport Operations

- *Car rental agencies.* Use of rental cars appears to be increasing even more rapidly than airline travel. Present methods of handling rental cars in passenger baggage areas, as well as the parking of such cars, should be re-evaluated to determine if some system can be developed to minimize confusion and congestion.
- *Taxicabs.* Where required, methods should be developed to separate taxicabs from private vehicles and rental car pickups.
- *Airline food kitchens.* Although some airlines have food kitchens at airports, re-evaluation of this activity is necessary.

- *Facilities maintenance.* Rising costs of maintenance require the most efficient possible maintainance of airport and terminal facilities and equipment. New techniques and standards for maintainability should be studied. Every project should incorporate maintenance analysis and planning into the facilities design.
- *Safety and economics* will demand the development of reliable fog dispersal and ice and snow removal from runways and aircraft movement areas.
- *Weather control.* More fundamental research into weather mitigation and control is required, even if instrumentation opens category III airports in the future. Further research in this area would not only benefit airports by improving safety but would also aid the airlines through improved scheduling and control. Furthermore, land that was previously marginal owing to climatographical factors might be utilized.
- *Crash and fire protection* equipment and techniques need to be re-examined in light of new demands, and a program should be undertaken to upgrade their effectiveness in emergencies.

INTERNATIONAL PASSENGER PROCESSING

The 450-percent increase in international passenger traffic forecast between 1965 and 1980 is attributable to the higher speed and different cost characteristics of the new aircraft entering the airline inventory. The presently overloaded customs facilities in the United States will be further strained, so that air passengers will need one-half to two-thirds of a day to go through customs (the usual delay experienced by ocean travelers). A sensor that can "sniff" any explosive in baggage has been developed but needs further refinement because of its extreme sensitivity and present high cost. If it is possible to develop sensors that will be able to inspect foodstuffs and locate dangerous drugs, two major concerns of customs agents will be eliminated.

It is recommended that a study be undertaken to determine a method of randomly selecting passengers for customs inspection prior to arrival at the airport. These individuals would then go through the normal customs operations while others would be expedited.

Many functions currently being performed on the ground could possibly be performed by stewardesses or special-assignment individuals on the aircraft in flight (e.g., health certificate inspection). A comprehensive study of customs is required in order to develop procedures and sensing devices that would eliminate many of the archaic methods of processing international travelers.

JOINT PLANNING

The advantages of communication and coordinated planning by groups of experts representing different aviation interests and disciplines have been clearly demonstrated. The existing organizations and associations provide an adequate structure for such communication and coordination on a continuing basis. However, the effectiveness of joint planning will be improved by designating specific groups or committees within existing government and industry organizations to work with other interested groups and committees, with the object of achieving joint-planning solutions to specific problems such as those identified in the present report. The appointment of such groups or committees is recommended.

It has further been suggested that the federal government take effective leadership in providing a forum for coordinated planning by various industry and government groups. This leadership role should not usurp the planning and management capability of existing organizations, but rather should encourage coordination among air carriers, general aviation, airport-operating agencies, airport planners and designers, equipment suppliers, and local, state, and federal agencies, and application of their joint planning capabilities to the specific problems that demand an interdisciplinary systems approach.

As an alternative to federal leadership, the various interests within industry and government previously mentioned could voluntarily form a high-level steering group to effect coordinated systems planning between the members. To be truly effective, such a steering group would require the services of a small but capable full-time staff, funded by the members (industry and government) but at the same time protected from pressures of any one member or group of member organizations with special interests. Because of the many types of organizations and interests that have been shown to be influential in the air transportation system, such immunity will probably be difficult to achieve.

6. COLLECTION AND DISTRIBUTION OF PASSENGERS AND AIR FREIGHT

INTRODUCTION

The success of the future air transportation system in the United States will depend largely on our ability to collect and distribute passengers and freight efficiently, expeditiously, and in consonance with the advances achieved by subsonic and supersonic commercial aircraft. The total trip time door-to-door must be the criterion for determining system effectiveness. Gains achieved through the reduction of air travel time must not be offset by increases in ground travel time, a trend that will prevail if positive steps are not taken to improve ground travel time and passenger processing.

The collection and distribution system poses complex problems principally because it must operate in an uncontrolled environment. The traveler cannot be forced to travel to and from the airport by the mode that makes the system work most effectively. The best that can be done is to provide the most efficient door-to-door system possible and trust that the traveler will use it.

NEW EFFORTS TO ADVANCE GROUND TRANSPORTATION

Major new efforts to advance the technology of ground transportation systems have been inaugurated, principally through federal programs such as those initiated by the Department of Transportation's Office of High-Speed Ground Transportation (OHSGT)[1] and the studies of urban transportation[2] being carried out by the Department of Housing and Urban Development (HUD). The OHSGT project

---

1 Public Law 89-220, Sept. 30, 1965.
2 Public Law 89-562, Sept. 8, 1966.

is designed both to develop a better understanding of overall transportation in the Northeast Corridor and to initiate major advances in high-speed intercity ground transport technology. A quantum jump in technology analogous to the transition from piston-powered to jet aircraft may result from this program.

The HUD program is designed to study and prepare a program of research, development, and demonstration of new systems of urban transportation. The results of this program were to be reported to Congress in the spring of 1968, and in that year, too, HUD was to go before Congress with a major program of transportation research, development, and demonstration projects. Although these programs are not explicitly addressed to the airport access problem, the new systems that will be developed, if properly planned and executed, should have a highly beneficial effect on the quality of transportation in general and should thus represent a significant improvement in airport access.

THE IMPACT OF FEDERAL POLICY

The decision of the federal government to take an active role in accelerating the development of new technology for ground transport has led a number of large industrial and "high-technology" aerospace firms to reexamine their role in this area. Many in the transportation research community hope that the effect will be similar to that of other U.S. programs in new technology (e.g., in the atomic energy field), in that private industry will be encouraged to take an aggressive part in the impending transportation revolution. The aviation community has not generally appreciated the fact that changes in ground transport technology promise to provide a whole spectrum of advanced transport systems of superior performance and lower cost that will match and perhaps exceed the continuing advances in aircraft technology. A systems approach to air transport problems has to take these developments into account, not only in relation to airport design and location but also in developing the appropriate mix of air and ground modes to serve the traveler over both short- and long-haul trips.

AN INTEGRATED SYSTEM

The present air transportation system comprises 22 major hubs (metropolitan regions), 36 medium hubs, 23 small hubs, and some 9000 airports not presently classified as hubs. Because each hub represents an integral part of the total air transportation system, the collection and distribution problems of at least the major hubs must be solved before the air transportation network can operate as an integrated system. Metropolitan regions or cities can be described on the basis of their geography, topography, population density and distribution, economic and industrial profile, and weather. These descriptive elements may be used in defining airport access problems, as a first step in a systems approach to the problems of collecting and distributing passengers and cargo. Since the elements of the problems are similar (although the combinational differences of the elements make the problems unique for each hub), the collection and distribution problem can be cast in three major areas:

1. Collection of passengers and cargo in the central business district or in other high-demand areas (not necessarily high-population-density regions).
2. Movement to the airport by either ground or air vehicles.
3. Distribution of passengers and cargo to gate positions or directly to the aircraft.

If a set of transportation modes adaptable to each of the three transport problems just delineated were available, each hub, even though unique, could find modal solutions to fit its collection and distribution problems.

THE SYSTEMS APPROACH

Figure 6.1 depicts the analysis process required for a complete systems study of the collection and distribution system. The rectangles indicate the three basic steps: demand-requirements analysis, develop-

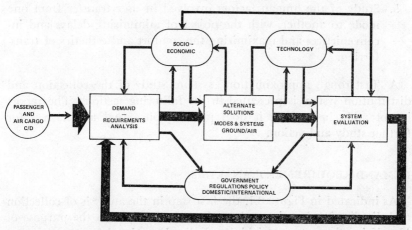

Figure 6.1. Analysis of the collection and distribution system depends upon interactions between basic steps (center) and environmental forces.

ment of alternative solutions, and the evaluation of the alternative systems postulated. The ellipses indicate the broad environmental forces. This analytical process is iterative, as shown by the many feedback loops.

SUMMARY OF RECOMMENDATIONS

1. Development of a comprehensive computer model of the total air transportation system, including but not limited to
   - Projections of future traffic demand
   - Origin and destination matrices (airport users and others)
   - Social and economic variables
   - All modes of access to and from airports
   - Weather, equipment, labor
2. Selection and structuring of live experiments to aid in evaluating the impact of airport location vis-à-vis various access transport modes such as
   - V/STOL
   - Satellite airports
   - Fixed-wing aircraft
   - High-speed ground transportation systems
3. Design of a program to integrate airport access problems into urban planning at the regional level.
4. Detailed analysis of the inadequate airport access routes at the major airport hubs and identification of specific bottlenecks relating to both passenger and cargo flow to and from specific origins and destinations.
5. Study of the human factors involved in user transfer from one mode to another, with the object of minimizing delays and inconveniences and maximizing the comfort and esthetics of transferring.

A "first rough approximation" systems study of the collection and distribution system is presented in the following sections. The report is not all-inclusive, but it does present conceptual alternatives for further study and action.

DEMAND-REQUIREMENT ANALYSIS

As indicated in Figure 6.1, the first step in the analysis of collection and distribution is a demand-requirements study with the purpose of identifying the system variables and all other related factors.

Once the variables are identified and quantified, it is then necessary to develop a computer demand model that should allow the system analyst to vary the system elements and measure the weighted effect each has on the total system.

The analysis comprises the following studies:

- System requirements
- Traveler-oriented requirements
- Freight-oriented requirements
- Socioeconomic requirements

These can be further broken down as follows:

Analysis of System Requirements

- Volume (how many travelers?)
- True origin/destination of travelers
- Time-phased loading (time of day, day of week)
- Traveler characteristics (who or what?)
- Trip time (how fast?)
- Land use (network)

Analysis of Traveler-Oriented Requirements

- Safety and reliability
- Trip time
- Trip cost (direct and indirect)
- Noise and vibration
- Convenience (transfer and waiting time)
- Aesthetics

Analysis of Freight-Oriented Requirements

- Safety and reliability
- Origin and destination of freight
- Trip time
- Trip cost
- Vibration
- Convenience

Analysis of Socioeconomic Requirements

- Land use
- Noise
- Cost of development and operational subsidy

- Air pollution
- Aesthetics
- Jurisdictional and intergovernmental regulations

These requirements, which are both interdependent and dynamic, differing for each metropolitan area, indicate the data demands for full analysis. Although some origin-and-destination studies have been conducted,[3] the paucity of data available to quantify the variables and parameters represents a major problem in the effective analysis of the collection and distribution system. Assuming that valid data can be obtained, a requirement exists for computer demand network models[4] to test the sensitivity to change of the many parameters and to predict demand and cost. Because of the complexity attendant to both the passenger and freight problem, separate demand network models should be developed. To be comprehensive, such a computer model would include intraterminal, central business district, and other high-demand areas, as well as interterminal and interzonal movements which would encompass not only the airport but other city functions and land use patterns.

The suspect nature of the limited data which now serve as the basis for major decisions concerning airport and terminal size, location, and highway needs represents a major constraint in developing and justifying feasible solutions to the collection and distribution problem.

The predicted growth in air transportation and its impact are discussed in Chapter 2. The additional factor of peak loads caused by the large passenger/air freight capacity of jumbo jets (B747, C5A) has also been considered.

AIR TRAFFIC HUBS AS INDICATIONS OF FUTURE REQUIREMENTS

One method of domestic air traffic forecasting is based on the observation that the nation's air traffic hubs account for a relatively consistent share of the nation's domestic originating passengers, as shown in Tables 6.1, 6.2, and 6.3. The term "air traffic hub," developed by the FAA, refers not to airports but to cities and Standard Metropolitan Statistical Areas requiring aviation services. These have been segre-

3 Port of New York Authority study of the New York hub region; DOT study of the Washington hub airports.
4 During the past decade many forms of computer models to study urban transportation have been developed. Network, distribution, assignment, and modal split models of varying refinement are being used. In most instances, however, the airport is considered as a terminal node rather than a generation node. These models should nonetheless contain the seeds for the models being recommended.

TABLE 6.1. U.S. ORIGINATING AIR PASSENGERS, DOMESTIC FLIGHTS, 1949 TO 1965*

(Each metropolitan area shown as percentage of U.S. total)

Major hubs (22)	1949	1950	1951	1952	1953	1954	1955	1956	1957	1958	1959	1960	1961	1962	1963	1964	1965
Atlanta	2.39	2.34	2.56	2.65	2.55	2.70	2.71	2.74	2.34	2.20	2.19	2.24	2.53	2.59	2.79	3.01	2.94
Boston	2.95	2.66	2.55	2.18	2.25	2.25	2.32	2.06	2.52	2.66	2.72	2.74	2.86	3.05	3.26	3.20	3.12
Chicago	7.93	8.49	8.44	9.02	9.46	9.62	9.68	9.73	9.16	9.32	9.19	9.48	9.14	8.99	9.26	9.42	9.39
Cincinnati	1.30	1.31	1.43	1.42	1.44	1.39	1.33	1.24	1.24	1.26	1.10	1.07	1.10	1.09	1.01	1.00	1.01
Cleveland	2.13	2.07	2.04	2.01	2.17	2.17	2.10	2.07	2.03	2.03	2.03	2.00	2.03	1.97	1.93	1.88	1.87
Dallas	2.80	2.61	2.79	2.90	2.23	2.18	2.29	2.40	2.24	2.35	2.39	2.60	2.55	2.67	2.76	2.71	2.76
Denver	1.54	1.44	1.38	1.51	1.45	1.52	1.51	1.50	1.52	1.56	1.60	1.79	1.85	1.81	1.80	1.76	1.80
Detroit	2.78	2.86	2.84	2.30	2.94	2.82	2.80	2.80	2.84	2.69	2.62	2.59	2.55	2.52	2.36	2.34	2.31
Houston	1.36	1.35	1.35	1.39	1.28	1.31	1.33	1.42	1.40	1.32	1.25	1.25	1.37	1.40	1.42	1.43	1.49
Kansas City, Mo.	1.83	1.70	1.64	1.57	1.43	1.46	1.41	1.41	1.40	1.43	1.42	1.40	1.47	1.41	1.42	1.42	1.40
Los Angeles	4.32	4.91	4.62	4.92	4.93	4.67	4.87	5.02	5.11	5.15	5.41	5.71	5.54	5.67	5.73	5.83	5.83
Miami/Ft. Lauderdale	1.82	2.18	2.12	2.32	2.59	2.80	2.85	3.07	3.25	3.10	3.25	3.10	2.94	2.95	2.73	2.64	2.79
Minneapolis	1.85	1.74	1.32	1.42	1.45	1.48	1.45	1.38	1.41	1.46	1.51	1.55	1.47	1.00	1.55	1.55	1.59
New Orleans	1.17	1.19	1.27	1.33	1.30	1.31	1.40	1.44	1.36	1.38	1.28	1.26	1.20	1.16	1.23	1.19	1.23
Newark } New York	12.24	12.14	12.38	11.40	12.00	12.12	11.88	11.98	11.88	11.83	11.98	11.86	11.78	11.88	11.85	11.90	11.70
Philadelphia	1.09	1.19	1.18	1.21	1.31	1.41	1.45	1.53	1.68	1.78	1.81	1.89	2.01	2.07	2.08	2.05	2.05
Pittsburgh	2.08	2.16	2.15	1.95	2.09	2.06	1.99	1.99	2.09	1.97	1.98	1.95	1.99	2.00	2.00	1.99	1.96
St. Louis	1.57	1.51	1.61	1.74	1.72	1.70	1.61	1.64	1.72	1.73	1.77	1.78	1.81	2.02	1.75	1.74	1.77
San Francisco	3.46	3.74	3.44	3.83	3.53	3.57	3.62	3.61	3.69	3.77	3.76	3.89	3.70	3.78	3.67	3.81	4.02
Seattle-Tacoma	1.64	1.69	1.35	1.45	1.47	1.40	1.32	1.31	1.37	1.31	1.35	1.37	1.29	1.52	1.14	1.18	1.12
Washington/ Baltimore	5.18	5.22	6.13	5.55	5.33	5.23	5.08	5.03	4.96	5.07	5.05	4.82	5.09	5.32	5.39	5.38	5.31
Total major hubs	63.43	64.50	64.59	64.07	64.92	65.17	65.00	65.37	65.21	65.37	65.66	66.34	66.27	67.47	67.13	67.43	67.46

SOURCE: Lockheed California Company.

* In this table and in the two succeeding, the assignment of cities to hub categories is based on their respective standings in 1964.

445

TABLE 6.2. U.S. ORIGINATING AIR PASSENGERS, DOMESTIC FLIGHTS, 1949 TO 1965

(Each metropolitan area shown as percentage of U.S. total)

Medium hubs (36)	1949	1950	1951	1952	1953	1954	1955	1956	1957	1958	1959	1960	1961	1962	1963	1964	1965
Albany, N.Y.	0.36	0.37	0.39	0.39	0.41	0.39	0.39	0.37	0.38	0.36	0.37	0.35	0.39	0.36	0.33	0.32	0.32
Albuquerque	0.32	0.32	0.35	0.38	0.35	0.34	0.30	0.34	0.36	0.37	0.35	0.34	0.33	0.32	0.35	0.34	0.35
Birmingham	0.48	0.52	0.56	0.57	0.56	0.56	0.54	0.52	0.47	0.44	0.42	0.39	0.36	0.35	0.33	0.32	0.32
Buffalo	1.28	1.14	1.19	1.09	1.16	1.10	1.12	1.13	1.09	1.03	1.02	0.98	0.87	0.88	0.84	0.84	0.84
Charlotte	0.59	0.74	0.85	0.79	0.72	0.74	0.75	0.78	0.60	0.52	0.54	0.52	0.56	0.48	0.47	0.47	0.46
Columbus, Ohio	0.56	0.54	0.50	0.53	0.58	0.60	0.64	0.66	0.68	0.66	0.69	0.68	0.64	0.63	0.63	0.62	0.61
Dayton, Ohio	0.44	0.46	0.52	0.56	0.57	0.58	0.59	0.59	0.59	0.61	0.63	0.59	0.60	0.61	0.56	0.54	0.52
Des Moines	0.35	0.35	0.28	0.29	0.30	0.31	0.31	0.31	0.32	0.34	0.32	0.32	0.32	0.31	0.30	0.29	0.30
El Paso	0.38	0.35	0.30	0.48	0.46	0.44	0.43	0.44	0.43	0.42	0.40	0.39	0.35	0.30	0.31	0.32	0.31
Hartford, Conn. } Springfield, Mass. }	0.44	0.40	0.41	0.39	0.41	0.42	0.43	0.42	0.47	0.50	0.50	0.50	0.54	0.54	0.55	0.55	0.56
Indianapolis	0.74	0.73	0.79	0.80	0.90	0.85	0.83	0.81	0.86	0.86	0.84	0.80	0.77	0.73	0.73	0.72	0.70
Jacksonville, Fla.	0.76	0.76	0.77	0.78	0.77	0.78	0.76	0.75	0.68	0.62	0.62	0.59	0.60	0.57	0.55	0.53	0.52
Knoxville	0.45	0.43	0.40	0.38	0.39	0.37	0.35	0.33	0.31	0.28	0.26	0.27	0.28	0.32	0.30	0.28	0.24
Las Vegas	0.17	0.25	0.27	0.29	0.38	0.49	0.58	0.52	0.61	0.59	0.67	0.70	0.72	0.89	0.97	0.99	1.01
Louisville	0.72	0.74	0.85	0.90	0.97	0.93	0.92	0.87	0.84	0.77	0.79	0.75	0.70	0.66	0.68	0.69	0.65
Memphis	0.88	0.85	0.85	0.86	0.82	0.80	0.79	0.77	0.74	0.76	0.71	0.72	0.75	0.78	0.79	0.82	0.81
Milwaukee	0.70	0.69	0.64	0.66	0.69	0.72	0.70	0.71	0.75	0.75	0.74	0.73	0.62	0.64	0.61	0.58	0.56
Nashville	0.77	0.65	0.67	0.63	0.59	0.56	0.59	0.59	0.49	0.49	0.47	0.48	0.49	0.46	0.47	0.46	0.45
Norfolk	0.72	0.59	0.73	0.67	0.60	0.56	0.46	0.43	0.45	0.41	0.38	0.31	0.30	0.34	0.37	0.38	0.38
Oklahoma City	0.60	0.58	0.56	0.56	0.47	0.44	0.40	0.41	0.41	0.42	0.41	0.41	0.43	0.43	0.43	0.42	0.42
Omaha	0.64	0.66	0.56	0.49	0.55	0.53	0.48	0.50	0.47	0.53	0.55	0.58	0.57	0.54	0.53	0.52	0.50
Orlando	0.15	0.15	0.15	0.16	0.16	0.18	0.19	0.21	0.25	0.28	0.31	0.31	0.33	0.35	0.35	0.33	0.32
Phoenix	0.49	0.51	0.58	0.62	0.59	0.58	0.60	0.61	0.63	0.71	0.76	0.82	0.87	0.96	0.97	0.97	0.94
Portland, Ore.	1.26	1.17	0.86	0.95	0.90	0.86	0.84	0.79	0.78	0.80	0.81	0.82	0.81	0.79	0.75	0.83	0.79
Providence	0.42	0.36	0.34	0.30	0.29	0.27	0.29	0.23	0.30	0.29	0.27	0.29	0.28	0.28	0.28	0.28	0.28
Raleigh-Durham	0.26	0.27	0.29	0.27	0.26	0.27	0.27	0.28	0.27	0.27	0.27	0.26	0.27	0.25	0.26	0.28	0.28
Reno, Nevada	0.24	0.22	0.21	0.21	0.21	0.22	0.24	0.25	0.27	0.26	0.25	0.26	0.25	0.27	0.31	0.31	0.28
Richmond, Va.	0.38	0.41	0.43	0.39	0.43	0.42	0.38	0.33	0.33	0.31	0.31	0.27	0.27	0.26	0.28	0.28	0.28
Rochester, N.Y.	0.39	0.40	0.42	0.39	0.44	0.42	0.40	0.42	0.47	0.46	0.45	0.45	0.45	0.48	0.46	0.47	0.48
Sacramento	0.26	0.23	0.30	0.21	0.22	0.23	0.26	0.27	0.29	0.31	0.33	0.34	0.33	0.33	0.34	0.35	0.34
Salt Lake City	0.54	0.52	0.47	0.51	0.51	0.53	0.53	0.50	0.47	0.55	0.60	0.61	0.63	0.63	0.63	0.60	0.59
San Antonio	0.53	0.51	0.46	0.53	0.47	0.47	0.48	0.47	0.49	0.47	0.46	0.45	0.43	0.48	0.45	0.45	0.48
San Diego	0.45	0.47	0.58	0.65	0.53	0.50	0.53	0.57	0.61	0.61	0.62	0.62	0.61	0.57	0.62	0.62	0.63
Syracuse	0.54	0.54	0.58	0.50	0.53	0.47	0.45	0.47	0.48	0.50	0.51	0.52	0.55	0.53	0.49	0.48	0.48
Tampa/St. Petersburg	0.53	0.55	0.58	0.61	0.62	0.71	0.72	0.77	0.89	0.95	1.04	0.97	0.96	0.95	0.91	0.88	0.91
Tulsa	0.71	0.65	0.66	0.66	0.61	0.54	0.51	0.49	0.44	0.43	0.42	0.40	0.39	0.38	0.37	0.37	0.37
Total medium hubs	19.50	18.08	19.34	19.45	19.42	19.18	19.05	18.96	18.97	18.93	19.10	18.79	18.62	18.65	18.57	18.51	18.26

TABLE 6.3. U.S. ORIGINATING AIR PASSENGERS, DOMESTIC FLIGHTS, 1949 TO 1965

(Each metropolitan area shown as percentage of U.S. total)

Small hubs (23)	1949	1950	1951	1952	1953	1954	1955	1956	1957	1958	1959	1960	1961	1962	1963	1964	1965
Amarillo	0.28	0.24	0.22	0.23	0.18	0.18	0.19	0.16	0.17	0.16	0.16	0.16	0.15	0.15	0.15	0.15	0.14
Austin	0.25	0.22	0.20	0.19	0.17	0.17	0.17	0.17	0.17	0.17	0.17	0.16	0.16	0.16	0.16	0.16	0.17
Boise	0.20	0.18	0.15	0.16	0.14	0.16	0.15	0.15	0.16	0.17	0.17	0.16	0.17	0.16	0.14	0.14	0.14
Charleston, S.C.	0.14	0.12	0.11	0.13	0.12	0.12	0.11	0.12	0.14	0.13	0.13	0.13	0.12	0.12	0.15	0.16	0.17
Charleston, W. Va.	0.45	0.41	0.41	0.39	0.37	0.33	0.34	0.32	0.29	0.26	0.26	0.24	0.22	0.24	0.22	0.20	0.19
Chattanooga	0.19	0.19	0.19	0.18	0.19	0.20	0.20	0.20	0.20	0.19	0.18	0.17	0.17	0.16	0.15	0.15	0.15
Columbia, S.C.	0.12	0.11	0.16	0.17	0.15	0.15	0.15	0.14	0.14	0.14	0.14	0.13	0.15	0.14	0.14	0.16	0.17
Grand Rapids	0.25	0.26	0.25	0.23	0.25	0.24	0.23	0.22	0.21	0.20	0.20	0.20	0.17	0.18	0.18	0.16	0.15
Greensboro/Winston, N.C.	0.17	0.17	0.18	0.18	0.18	0.18	0.18	0.17	0.18	0.18	0.19	0.19	0.20	0.24	0.26	0.26	0.25
Harrisburg	0.14	0.13	0.14	0.13	0.15	0.14	0.15	0.14	0.15	0.17	0.18	0.15	0.15	0.14	0.14	0.14	0.14
Huntsville	—	0.01	0.02	0.02	0.02	0.03	0.04	0.05	0.06	0.09	0.10	0.10	0.11	0.15	0.18	0.20	0.20
Jackson, Miss.	0.16	0.15	0.18	0.20	0.19	0.19	0.18	0.18	0.17	0.18	0.18	0.17	0.18	0.16	0.16	0.16	0.16
Little Rock	0.23	0.19	0.19	0.21	0.20	0.20	0.21	0.21	0.20	0.20	0.19	0.19	0.19	0.22	0.22	0.21	0.22
Mobile	0.16	0.16	0.18	0.20	0.19	0.21	0.22	0.20	0.19	0.17	0.19	0.17	0.18	0.17	0.15	0.16	0.16
Moline	0.07	0.10	0.11	0.12	0.14	0.15	0.14	0.14	0.16	0.15	0.15	0.15	0.15	0.16	0.15	0.15	0.14
Newport News	—	0.04	0.07	0.09	0.08	0.08	0.10	0.11	0.10	0.10	0.10	0.11	0.13	0.13	0.13	0.14	0.14
San Bernardino	—	—	—	0.01	0.01	0.01	0.03	0.03	0.03	0.03	0.03	0.04	0.06	0.14	0.19	0.20	0.21
Shreveport	0.36	0.31	0.31	0.30	0.27	0.27	0.25	0.26	0.26	0.26	0.20	0.21	0.20	0.19	0.18	0.19	0.17
Spokane	0.51	0.49	0.30	0.33	0.30	0.28	0.28	0.27	0.25	0.25	0.26	0.26	0.23	0.23	0.21	0.22	0.20
Toledo	0.25	0.23	0.21	0.18	0.19	0.20	0.25	0.23	0.25	0.25	0.24	0.24	0.22	0.20	0.18	0.17	0.17
Tucson	0.21	0.20	0.22	0.24	0.21	0.21	0.22	0.22	0.23	0.24	0.25	0.25	0.25	0.26	0.25	0.24	0.25
West Palm Beach	0.14	0.14	0.15	0.14	0.15	0.17	0.18	0.20	0.22	0.21	0.19	0.18	0.18	0.19	0.19	0.19	0.19
Wichita	0.33	0.31	0.33	0.32	0.29	0.31	0.29	0.28	0.26	0.26	0.25	0.24	0.24	0.23	0.22	0.21	0.21
Total small hubs	4.61	4.36	4.28	4.35	4.14	4.18	4.26	4.17	4.19	4.21	4.11	3.99	3.98	4.12	4.12	4.12	4.12
Grand total all hubs—81	87.54	86.94	88.21	87.87	88.48	88.53	88.31	88.50	88.37	88.51	88.87	89.12	88.74	90.24	89.82	90.06	89.84

SOURCE: Lockheed California Company.

447

gated into four classes according to the percentage of total originating passengers of the domestic air carriers in fixed-wing scheduled service in the contiguous 48 states. These classes include large hubs (1.00 percent or more), medium (0.25 to 0.99 percent), small (0.05 to 0.24 percent), and nonhubs (less than 0.05 percent).

The 21 major metropolitan areas (treating the New York–Newark area as one) account for about one-third of the nation's population. Their share of the nation's originating air passengers will increase from 66 percent (1965) to 70 percent by 1980. (See also Table 2.8.)

The city analysis method[5] of forecasting may be used as a weather vane to identify those hubs with the highest probability of entering a "critical" stage in the 1975–1980 period. The major hubs form the basic network of the air transportation system and must be given immediate priority in relation to the access problem.

Each of the major hubs has either recently finished a major terminal or airport expansion program or is in the process of such an expansion. Because of the tremendous capital investment, schedules of depreciation, public funding problems, and general lack of room for expansion, there will be only a minimal increase in terminal capacity in the foreseeable future. One logical solution to the problem of handling the 440 percent[6] increase in passengers from 1965 to 1980 is to increase the flow rate through the terminals of these major hubs. The increase in flow rate dictates integrated collection and distribution systems. Such an approach must offer many modes of travel, using air, ground, and water vehicles and allowing the traveler a selection depending upon his destination, trip time, time of day, and social and economic requirements.

AIRPORT ACCESS AND URBAN DISTRIBUTION

All major hubs currently have an airport access problem. Some of the basic reasons for these problems are as follows:

- Inadequate airport access, as a result of insufficient approaches, bottlenecks, and lack of parking
- An excess of nonpassengers in the airport system
- The urban environment

[5] One of three methods used to forecast demand, described in *Air Traffic Demand, 1967-1990* (Lockheed California Company OEA/SST/222 1966).

[6] *Aviation Demand and Airport Facility Requirement Forecast for Large Air Transportation Hubs Through 1980.* FAA Advisory Circular No. 150-5040, August 1967.

Inadequate Airport Access

The traveling public and the air transportation industry still depend on the automobile as the major means of transport to and from the airport. From 1959 to 1964 daily surface vehicular operations to and from J. F. Kennedy Airport increased from 84,000 to 134,000. The bulk of this growth is the result of passenger demand. A significant upsurge of cargo traffic can also be anticipated when the stretch and jumbo subsonic jets go into operation. Planned road construction is insufficient to accommodate the 400,000 daily surface vehicular movements forecast for Kennedy by 1975.

Review of the critical factors affecting air transportation in southern California and metropolitan Los Angeles reveals that the problems that now confront this region are similar to those that must soon be faced by all the larger metropolitan areas.

The potential of the present facilities indicates that the airway capacity and runway acceptance rate of Los Angeles International Airport are such that 80 million passengers in and out per year can be accommodated provided there is a maximum development of runway facilities. Assuming an average 65 percent load factor, the proposed loading gate system can be expanded to handle the 80 million passengers.

The first indication of a problem occurs when the capacity of the internal roadway system is considered. Analysis indicates that the ultimate system can handle a maximum of only 56 million passengers. The capacity of the parking system associated with the internal roadways further reduces the number to 53 million passengers.

The external roadway net is the present crux of the problem. With maximum development of the freeway system, construction of new access routes, and maximum improvement of the surface street system, ground level transportation can move only 40 million passengers per year into and out of the central terminal complex.

Many of the major hub airports have aviation-related industries located at the airport. The shift-change traffic from these industries unfortunately coincides with the peak aircraft arrivals and departures, and saturation of the roadway system leading to and from the airport usually results. Recreational facilities such as major league ball parks and race tracks located near airports aggravate the problem. The only alternative for the time-restricted business traveler is to leave for the airport in sufficient time to allow for all unpredictable variables. The consequent loss of productive manhours alone represents a substantial financial loss. There is an urgent need for better integration of the airport access roadway system with the metropolitan roads and freeway systems feeding the airport.

Airport Population

When one considers that air travelers constitute only about one-half the airport population, the scope of the problem becomes overwhelming. Several studies have been conducted to gather data on the airport user.[7] One study of terminal populations at Chicago's O'Hare and Midway, Dallas/Fort Worth, Nashville, and the New York airports established the following user breakdown:

Air passengers	33–56 percent
Employees	11–16 percent
Visitors, sightseers, shoppers	31–42 percent
Service suppliers	3–7 percent

The Urban Environment

The air traveler's trips to and from the airport represent only a small percentage of the total trips made in an urban region. Accordingly, urban planners tend to dismiss air travelers as statistically insignificant. However, the economic impact of the air traveler on the urban environment must be taken into consideration. Comprehensive transportation planning for urban regions must include airport access. The air passenger, although completely controlled during the air portion of his trip, is entirely on his own in an uncontrolled environment while moving to and from airports. Many factors affect passenger flow as well as that of air freight (Figure 6.2). The most critical from the standpoint of the collection and distribution system are

- Weather
- Labor-relations disturbances
- Equipment failures
- Traffic not related to the airport
- Number of modes available

The interrelationship of these factors will vary greatly, depending on the mode, the time of day, the day of the week, and holiday-related peaks. Weather, for instance, has a variable impact on collection and distribution. Although weather will slightly impede the time constants for a high-speed ground transit system, such constraints are

[7] For example, an in-house FAA study on airport usage, 1966.

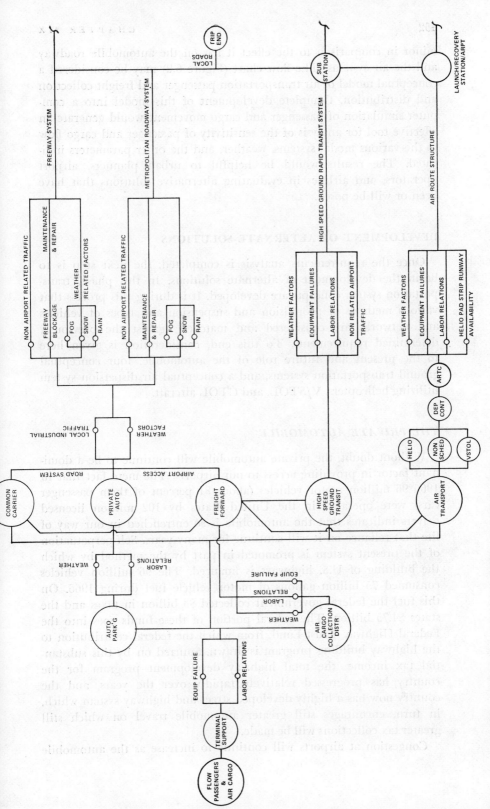

Figure 62. Collection and distribution model for air passengers and air cargo.

minor in comparison to the effect it has on the automobile roadway and the air systems. The flow chart (Figure 6.2) may be considered a conceptual model of air transportation passenger and freight collection and distribution. Complete development of this model into a computer simulation of passenger and cargo movement would generate an effective tool for analysis of the sensitivity of passenger and cargo flow to the various modal systems, weather, and the other parameters indicated. The results would be helpful to urban planners, airport operators, and airlines in evaluating alternative solutions that have been or will be posed.

DEVELOPMENT OF ALTERNATE SOLUTIONS

Once the requirements analysis is completed, the next step is to begin the development of alternate solutions. In this phase, transportation system concepts are developed. It is during this process that various methods of propulsion and suspension and types of vehicles and networks are considered and matched against the previously determined requirements. To this end, consideration is given here to the present and future role of the automobile, four conceptual ground transportation systems, and a conceptual air dispersion system utilizing helicopters, V/STOL, and CTOL aircraft.

THE PRIVATE AUTOMOBILE

Without doubt, the private automobile will continue to be a dominant factor in providing access to our airports. The mere fact that in 1966 96 million motor vehicles (about 81 percent of them passenger cars) were operated in the United States by 102 million licensed drivers indicates that the automobile is so entrenched in our way of life that reliance on it will continue for many years. Self-perpetuation of the present system is promoted in part by the method by which the building of U.S. highways is financed. The 96 million vehicles consumed 75 billion gallons of motor vehicle fuel during 1966. On this fuel the federal government collected $3 billion in taxes and the states $4.75 billion. The federal portion of these funds goes into the Federal Highway Trust Fund, from which the federal contribution to the highway building program is drawn. Spurred on by this substantial tax income, the total highway development program for the country has progressed relatively rapidly over the years, and the country now has a highly developed street and highway system which, in turn, encourages still greater automobile travel on which still greater tax collections will be made.

Congestion at airports will continue to increase as the automobile population grows. Forecasts such as the one predicting 400,000 daily vehicular operations by 1975 for New York's Kennedy Airport point up the demand for immediate stopgap measures to relieve the congestion problem. The extent of the access problem is readily apparent when peak-hour demand is taken into consideration. Assuming that peak-hour operations represent 8 percent of the daily total, there would be at Kennedy Airport in 1975 32,000 vehicular operations during the peak hour. On the basis of an extremely liberal flow capacity of 2000 vehicles per freeway lane per hour, 16 freeway lanes would be required to handle the peak-hour demand. All major metropolitan hub airports will eventually face this serious capacity-constraint problem.

New York is presently considering a spur line from the Long Island Railroad to serve Kennedy Airport. Planners for Chicago's O'Hare Airport are considering remote parking garages. Development of an efficient, possibly automatic, system of intra-airport transportation, together with the simultaneous control of the access of private automobiles and possibly taxis to the terminal areas, will be necessary if the full advantage of these concepts is to be realized.

As a stopgap service for intra-airport movement, including that to and from remote parking areas, the immediate application of minibuses looks promising. On a longer range basis, these buses might be operated under a system of flexible routing, somewhat in the fashion of a taxi system. A communication network would be required so that passengers could call a bus to a specific location to pick them up, with a control center from which a dispatcher could direct buses to specific locations using a radio communications link. Such a system might be quite effective at medium airport hubs, but at the large hubs it should be considered an emergency measure only. The major hubs require more than an upgrading of present modes.

CONCEPTUAL GROUND COLLECTION AND DISTRIBUTION SYSTEMS

If future urban transport systems are to function well, certain gaps in transport technology must be eliminated. Several classes of new transport systems can be envisaged to accomplish this end. In general, these systems are visualized as meshing with new or modernized versions of rapid transit, of which the Bay Area Rapid Transit District is the most prominent example. This does not imply that we should abandon the search for improvements in the systems built on the basis of existing technology; there is great need for improvement in these basic transport systems as well.[8]

8 See "New Transport Technology for the Big City." *New Scientist*, Jan. 26, 1967.

It appears fairly clear that in the remaining decades of the twentieth century we will see the development of an urban transportation network based on low-, medium- and high-speed systems, with a range of capacities and offering a choice between private and public service. Better coordination and interfacing of these systems into an integrated whole will be highly desirable, and the technology of the subsystems should be on a comparable level.[9]

Considerably more study is required to identify precisely the transport requirements for urban areas. A discussion of the data requirements for passenger and freight movements and a forecast of future requirements were presented in Chapter 2. These data and analyses will form the basis for generic classes of required systems. (Present projections represent only educated guesses, although there is considerable historical basis for making such guesses.)[10] For illustrative purposes we will assume the availability of operational requirements, considering that there is already an analytic basis for assuming that ground systems of the types to be described are actually needed.

Analysis of hard data for specific sites against a background of existent urban constraints will no doubt produce additional refinements in the critical operating parameters for future systems. Speeds and capacities lower or higher than those postulated here may ultimately result.

It is unrealistic to assume that overall improvements in the urban transport system and airport access can be made in one fell swoop. It is important to consider feasible individual improvements, recognizing that the overall system will be less than optimum.

The four proposed systems for ground collection and distribution of passengers as presented here were spelled out in a Stanford Research Institute report[11] but reflect the thinking of a number of other groups.

System I: Collection and Distribution

This system would employ a low-speed, high-volume transport device,[12] operating at 10–20 mph and usually with total trip lengths of less than a mile. Stops might be about 500 feet apart, with overall speed thus averaging about 7 mph. Capacities might be on the order

9 Probably the outstanding example of disparity between systems is that of modern jets served by primitive buses for collection and distribution.

10 See "The Transport Gaps" *Science Journal*, April 1967, in which the need for a low-speed transport device is identified.

11 From a 1967 Stanford Research Institute study on new systems concepts for airport access.

12 *Project* METRAN, M.I.T. Report No. 8. The M.I.T. Press, Cambridge, Mass., 1966, especially Chap. 9, the PERC system.

of 12,000 to 15,000 passengers per hour. The device envisioned would be a horizontal counterpart to the elevator. One version of this system would be used as a fine-grain distributor for the business district, providing a connection between building elevators and transit terminals (bus or rail). The vehicles should move continuously, carrying small batches of passengers — perhaps six seated passengers and six standees. The device would provide a convenient way for all passengers either already in the central business district or delivered there by other means to get to a downtown airport terminal.

A device similar to that for the central business district would be used for intraterminal movement of passengers in large airports, for example, to connect terminal buildings to loading piers. With low speed, high volume, and continuous flow, such a device would fill a serious gap in airport transport planning. In the business district and airport version of System I, most passengers might be content to stand, since trip durations would typically be only a minute or two. A second version of the system, with similar speed and capacity, could be used as a collection device for transit terminals in suburban areas, thus broadening the area served by transit systems. This version would be operating over slightly longer distances, and seats would be desirable.

System II: Intraterminal Movement

A system of intraterminal and parking-lot-to-terminal connections will be required for large complexes such as Kennedy and Los Angeles. This system would have to have a medium-volume capacity on the order of 12,000 passengers per hour one way. Speeds would be in the 40 to 50-mph range, and the distance between stops typically a few thousand feet. Vehicles might carry 20–30 seated passengers and could be coupled in short trains as required. Average speeds might be on the order of 25 mph, depending on specific stop patterns. System II would serve not only as transportation within the airport complex, including parking-lot-to-terminal, but also as a connection between the airport and off-site parking lots within a radius of 4–5 miles or less. It might also be used as basic transportation to and from close-in airports. Its principal characteristic must be a low cost commensurate with the low volumes typically envisioned for such service.

System III: Connecting Systems

This would be a high-speed system, operating at 120 to 200-mph. Stops would be on the order of 8 to 24 miles apart. The system could be exploited for several types of links in the airport access system. It could be used to connect the business district to the airport, e.g., Washington, D.C., to Dulles and Friendship. In cities of low density it could be used to connect several remote parking lots or terminals ringing the downtown area. (Los Angeles is an example.) Such a system could also connect two or three airports in an urban area.

At least two versions of system II are contemplated. The first would employ a single-mode vehicle with a conventional passenger compartment and special provisions for baggage handling. This version would be similar to modern rapid transit, although some application of unconventional technology would probably be required. On runs of 25 miles such a system could average 3 miles per minute. A second, more advanced version would employ a dual-mode vehicle capable of running on a guideway at high speed, stopping for capsule transfer of passengers at the terminal, and then switching to lower speed for moving onto the airport runway and discharging passengers directly into the planes. Passengers would be ticketed in the downtown terminal or onboard, and the airport terminal stop would be necessary only in order to pick up passengers who had driven to the terminal. A third, even more advanced version, would entirely eliminate the need for an airport passenger terminal. This version would use very large vehicles, carrying perhaps 200–300 passengers in 50-passenger "modules" or containers. The modules would contain standard aircraft seats and facilities and would be transferred intact to the plane.

System III in a lower-speed version might form the basis for a greatly improved transit option. The technology described, as one plausible way of meeting these requirements, is equally applicable to systems with a maximum speed of 80–90 mph.

System IV: High-Speed Ground Transportation System

In a class by itself is a system of high-speed ground transport for intercity travel in major U.S. corridors. Such systems, which may operate in the 200 to 500-mph range, are important to our discussion for two principal reasons:

1. These systems can be employed as coarse-grain feeders for major regional airports serving entire urban corridors, where such airports may be located up to 100 miles from the major urban centers.

2. Such systems may ultimately handle most of the short-haul (less than 300-mile) trips in the Chicago, Great Lakes, Northeast, and California corridors.

The Office of High-Speed Ground Transportation is currently studying these systems and has an extensive research and development program to advance the requisite technology.[13, 14]

HSGT systems could be operational between larger cities in the major corridors in the 1980's. If successful, systems of this type could be carrying the majority of intercity passengers in these corridors by 1990. The possible emergence of such a new mode of ground transport needs to be carefully monitored by long-range planners for airlines, aircraft manufacturers, and airports. Major inroads into the short-haul freight markets may also be expected. To some extent the advent of HSGT systems would tend to ease the problems of airports, inasmuch as it would decrease the demand for short-haul air transportation.

Planners considering sites for major new regional airports in the urban corridors should also be aware of the prospects for HSGT systems. Distance of airports from urban centers is, after all, significant mainly as a time factor. If such systems can average 250 mph, there is no reason why a major new airport should not be located 100 to 150 miles from the cities it is to serve. Conversely, it is important that airport access be taken into consideration in the development of HSGT systems. Such systems could, for example, be designed to serve as the collection and distribution network for the supersonic transport airports in the region.

Interfaces

Major delays and inconveniences in today's transportation systems occur at the interfaces — nodes where transfers take place between one link and another. Ideally we should seek to eliminate such transfers, since the evidence suggests that they are a major source of dissatisfaction to travelers. Failing this, the transfer should be made as convenient as possible, holding to a minimum the long waits, walking, and uncertainty about the next move. Much of the walking can be eliminated by careful design of the interface or by the use of moving belts; waiting time can be minimized by coordination of schedules, use of continuous flow devices (system I), and by more efficient ticketing and luggage processing. There is some opportunity for the application of new technology in designing these interfaces, but it is not

13 *Survey of Technology for High Speed Ground Transport*, PB 168648, 1965; and *Summary of Research at M.I.T. on High Speed Ground Transport*, PB 173658, Dec. 31, 1966. Both prepared for the U. S. Dept. of Commerce by M.I.T.

14 Herbert, G. R., "High Speed Ground Transportation—A Research Challenge," *Proceedings of the IEEE*, April 1968; and Hansen, Robert J., "Planning for High Speed Ground Transportation" in the same issue.

clear at this time just what direction it might take. Major studies of interface delays appear to be in order.

Networks

The use of these new systems under ideal circumstances can be visualized by an examination of networks for an urban area. In Figure 6.3 a typical transit system network is sketched, showing the strong focus on the central business district. Overlying this system would be the freeways and major streets and highways of the city. The four systems are shown for illustrative purposes; only two or three of them would generally be required, and in any case they could not be intro-

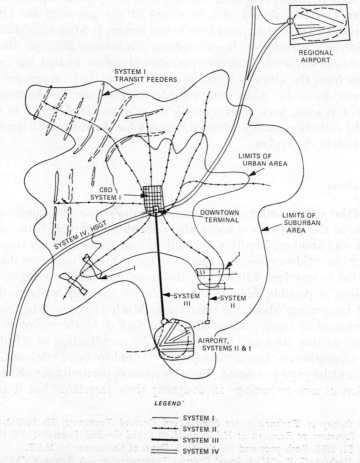

Figure 6.3. Transit network making use of the four systems discussed in the text.

duced all at once. The air traveler in the business district would simply board a horizontal counterpart to the elevator, which would discharge him at the downtown terminal. Alternatively, he might walk or take a taxi to the terminal. There he would be relieved of his baggage and ticketed through. On system III he would ride nonstop to the airport at two or three miles per minute. On arriving at the airport he would transfer to a lower-speed system (either I or II), which would take him to the loading pier. All transfers would consist of a few seconds' walk across a platform. There would be a minimum of baggage handling.

For the traveler originating in the suburbs, ticketing and baggage routing for the entire trip would take place at the transit terminal. Another example of such a network for the Los Angeles area is shown in Figure 6.4.

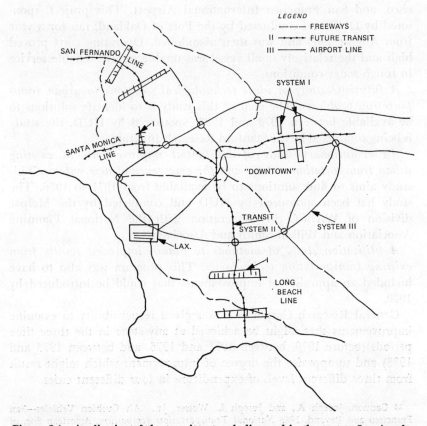

Figure 6.4. Application of the transit network discussed in the text to Los Angeles.

CURRENT GOVERNMENT-FUNDED STUDIES IN
GROUND TRANSPORTATION

Extensive transportation studies are being conducted by HUD and DOT. Many of the findings may be applicable to the airport collection and distribution problem. The following studies are particularly relevant.

The high-speed ground transit system, with special emphasis on the corridor between Boston and Washington, D.C. This study is being conducted by a number of contractors under the sponsorship of DOT.

A rapid-transit system connecting the Cleveland business district to the airport terminal. This demonstration project, sponsored by HUD, was developed by the Cleveland Transit System.

Jet skimmer air cushion vehicle demonstration project,[15] between Metropolitan Oakland International Airport, downtown San Francisco, and San Francisco International Airport. This project, sponsored by HUD and conducted by the Port of Oakland, ran for a year from August 1965 and was then abandoned. Operating costs proved high and the relatively small vessel was unable to give reliable service in rough-water conditions.

A futuristic study of ideal technological solutions to urban transportation problems. The goal of this study is to identify solutions to be available between 1973 and 1983. Sponsored by HUD, the study is being conducted by the Stanford Research Institute.

An evolutionary study of substantial improvements in existing urban transportation systems and the emergence of new systems. This study aims to find solutions to be available from 1971 to 1976. The study has been sponsored by HUD and conducted by the Melpar division of WABCO in cooperation with the National Planning Association and Wilbur Smith and Associates.

A utilization study of methods to obtain improved results from existing transportation technologies. This program was also to have included an appraisal of improvements that could be introduced by 1970.

General Research Corporation was given responsibility to examine improvements that might be achieved at any stage in the three time periods (before 1970, between 1971 and 1976, and between 1973 and 1983) and to appraise the degree of improvement which might result from three different levels of expenditure in four different cities.

---

[15] Cannon, Joseph A., and Joseph L. Wosser, Jr., "Air Cushion Vehicles—San Francisco and Beyond. *1966 National Transportation Symposium,* American Soc. of Mechanical Engineers.

SOME PROMISING TECHNOLOGIES

In addition to these and other studies and demonstration projects, the need for technological innovation in four subsystems of ground transportation has also been recognized. These are receiving attention from industry as well as government:

- Suspension
- Propulsion
- Command and control
- Tunneling

Suspension

The most promising innovation here is to use a cushion of air instead of wheels (Figure 6.5). With this cushion, a form of propulsion could be used that does not depend upon adhesion between wheels and the guideway (e.g., linear induction motors), and the vehicles could be operated under complete automatic control. Most proposals such as the four systems previously discussed incorporate two or more of these concepts in a single system. Vehicles that operate automatically on a restricted guideway but that could be driven manually

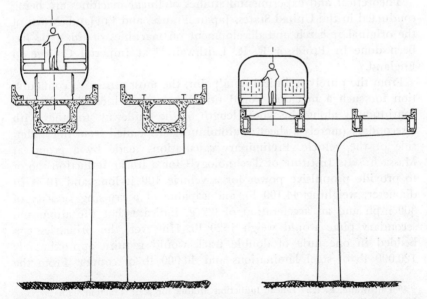

Figure 6.5. Cross sections of conventional rail vehicle (left) and air-supported vehicle on guide track (right). Air support will permit lightweight vehicles, distributed loads, and less massive elevated structures.

on a conventional road represent another proposed set of systems using some of these schemes.

Air cushion vehicles show a great deal of promise. Low vehicle weight and height are possible, and the load may be distributed over larger surfaces, with resultant simplified support structure requirements, as shown in Figure 6.5. The ride is excellent, and the vehicles are simple and reliable. Maintenance of both vehicle and guideway is reduced since there is no physical contact between the two.

Propulsion

The propulsion subsystem is being considered from several viewpoints.

Linear induction motors

The linear induction motor may be thought of as a conventional rotary induction machine, the stator of which has been cut open and unrolled to form a linear array of electromagnet coils. The inherent advantages of this type of machine are apparent: It is not necessary to mount the entire prime mover on the vehicle; there are no moving parts and no air contamination; and the system is simple, reliable, and well suited to both wheeled and air-cushion vehicles.

Theoretical and experimental studies of linear machines are being conducted in the United States, Japan, France, and England. Much of the original research and development on machines of this type has been done by Professor E. R. Laithwaite[16] at Imperial College in England.

From the purely technical standpoint, the most attractive configuration for such a machine would utilize primary windings embedded continuously along the whole length of the guideway, together with a secondary (merely a sheet of aluminum), suspended from the underside of the vehicle. Preliminary calculations made by a group at Massachusetts Institute of Technology[17] for a linear induction motor to provide propulsive power for a vehicle 100 ft long and 10 ft in diameter, weighing 44,100 lb, and capable of a cruising velocity of 300 mph and an acceleration of 0.2 g, indicate that the aluminum secondary plate would weigh 1320 lb. However, the primaries embedded in one mile of double track would require approximately 120,000 lb of steel laminations and 40,000 lb of copper. From the

16 Laithwaite, E. R., "Linear Induction Motors for Rail Traction," *Engineering*, June 14, 1963: and *Induction Machines for Special Purposes*, London, George Nerones, Ltd., May, 1966.

17 White, D. C., et al., "Some Problems Related to Electric Propulsion," PB 173639, Nov. 1, 1966.

standpoint of the vehicle, placement of the primary in the guideway is attractive, but the cost of installing the primary in a number of miles of guideway can be justified only if the traffic density over the line is high. Nonetheless, installation of a linear-induction motor with this configuration to provide supplementary power in the vicinity of stations where vehicles would normally be accelerating is an attractive possibility.

The inverse configuration, in which the primary is carried on the car and only an aluminum plate or beam need be installed in the guideway, would substantially reduce the cost of the system but introduces the problem of supplying power to the moving primary. Wayside power could be employed at speeds up to 80 mph, but no adequate means has been proposed to obtain sufficient power for speeds on the order of 300 mph. Of course, chemical fuel could be burned on board to drive a turbine and in turn a generator, but this would create air-pollution problems. The use of individual prime movers would also increase the difficulties associated with maintaining proper speeds and headway on a busy line.

Either configuration of the conventional linear induction motor requires that the air gap not exceed a fraction of an inch (3/8 in. appears to be about the maximum) if a reasonable power factor and efficiency are to be achieved. Maintenance of clearances of this magnitude with a large vehicle poses a difficult problem, particularly at high speeds, but the scheme appears basically feasible from a technical point of view. Other types of linear machines may prove even more attractive.

A group at Hovercraft Development, Limited, in Southampton, England, has demonstrated the combination of air-cushion support and linear induction motor propulsion in a six-foot model. The primary for the linear motor is on the vehicle, and the secondary is an aluminum rail in the middle of the guideway. Power is supplied to the primary of the motor through sliding contacts. Such a combination seems to offer one of the best means for achieving high-speed operation.

Pneumatic propulsion.

An alternate propulsion scheme is similar to the pneumatic tube system formerly used in department stores for transporting bills and change between the sales counters and a cashier's station. In the scheme proposed by L. K. Edwards[18] and designated the Gravity-Vacuum Transit System, trains move on rails through tubes buried

[18] Edwards, L. K., "High-Speed Tube Transportation," *Scientific American*, August 1965.

in tunnels. Pumps mounted at the surface reduce the pressure in the tubes to approximately 1 psia. When a train is ready to leave the station, a valve is opened behind it, and the atmospheric pressure applied to the rear of the train, combined with the gravity assist which results from the fact that the tunnels slope away from the stations, accelerates the train. As it approaches the next station, a valve at that station is closed, and the air ahead of the train is compressed. This action, along with the upward grade built into the guideway, decelerates the train to its stop at the station. Calculations indicate that the trip from New York to Washington, with seven intermediate stops, would take only 58 minutes, and that the system can be adapted for use where the stage lengths are as short as three miles.

Although no prototype has been built, this system does appear generally feasible. However, the entire system would be located in tunnels that would be relatively expensive to construct. On the other hand, the problem of securing right-of-way for the tunnels should be much less severe than that involved with surface or elevated systems. The tunnels would not create an eyesore, and the guideway and vehicles would be protected from vandals and from the elements.

The vehicles would be supported by steel wheels running on steel rails. Even with top speeds in excess of 400 mph, no tractive force is to be transmitted through the wheels, and the speed limit imposed by wheel lippage would thus be avoided. The achievement of good ride qualities in this system would require construction of a track that would maintain alignment to such a high degree that essentially no isolation would be required between the track and the passenger compartment.

Command and Control

The requirements for fast, safe, comfortable, and frequent ground transportation make automatic control mandatory. Automation has already been applied to certain transportation systems. Automatic elevators are commonplace; a section of the Tokyo subway system is currently running under full automatic control; the special transit system and Minirail at Expo 67 in Montreal were fully automated. The Westinghouse Electric Transit Expressway[19] (commonly called the Skybus), a rubber-tired, electrically propelled vehicle that picks up control signals electromagnetically from the guideway, has been operating on a test track near Pittsburgh since the summer of 1965 under completely automatic control. There is no window at the head end, so there is, in fact, no provision for a driver.

[19] *Transit Expressway Report, MPC Corporation,* Feb. 20, 1967.

Although there is some gap between theory and practice regarding automatic command and control subsystems, a basic "state-of-the-art" nonetheless exists.

Tunneling

New, more rapid and more economical methods of tunneling are being studied. The research and development effort is broad in scope, covering possibilities ranging from improved mechanical devices to the application of hydrostatics and lasers.[20] A point has almost been reached where tunneling is as economically feasible as cut and fill techniques. As technology progresses and innovations grow in this field, major changes in the acceptability of many proposed urban transportation systems will occur.

The United States has the technological capability to create an essentially fully automated, safe, fast transportation system that would effectively meet passenger transportation needs, including access to airports, in the densely populated areas of the nation. Although further research and development are required before a complete design for any really innovative system can be put forward, the technical aspects of a specific system design are relatively straightforward and can be carried out with a high probability of success. On the other hand, the basic decision to build any new transportation system, and, if one is to be built, the questions of specific location, source of funding for initial construction, and choice of the organization under which the system would be operated represent extremely complex and difficult questions that have not received sufficient attention.

CONCEPTUAL AIR DISTRIBUTION SYSTEM

Like the ground distribution system, the air distribution system must consider various modes in relation to the spectrum or requirements for speed, capacity, and cost of operation. All air vehicles must be evaluated with regard to economics, technical feasibility, and social acceptance.

There has been much discussion in the aviation community concerning the use of a satellite airport system as an integral part of hub air distribution. The Los Angeles Department of Airports is proposing a satellite system of airports for Southern California. The Department estimates that capacity to handle air passengers can be increased by five million passengers per year if ground transportation facilities are augmented with V/STOL and CTOL shuttle service. In this

---

[20] Moavenzadeh, F., R. B. Williamson, and F. J. McGarry, "Laser-Assisted Rock Fracture," R67-3, Dept. of Civil Engineering, M.I.T., Jan. 30, 1967.

connection, the Los Angeles Airways Helicopter System began construction of the first of a series of satellite heliports on October 12, 1967 (see Figures 6.6 and 6.7). Such concepts are reviewed in the following discussion of an advanced air dispersion system.

Air Dispersion System

An alternative for alleviation of the overcrowded or choked conditions in passenger collection and distribution around major airports is a dispersion system that breaks the large passenger groups of a single aircraft into a number of smaller groups, transporting them as closed groups to dispersed secondary traffic centers, where the public transportation systems or private automobiles would provide transportation to final destination. Traffic volume would be much smaller at the secondary traffic centers than at the major airports, and the danger of overloading or choking the ground traffic arteries would thus be greatly reduced.

The dispersion systems between the major airport and secondary traffic centers, as envisioned here, would be operated so as to serve exclusively the passengers of the large jets. Other passengers would be accepted on a space available basis only. Careful attention should be exercised to ensure that passenger routing, travel time, and convenience are not compromised. Such a dispersion system would be an integral part of the long-range trip of traveler groups, over the route: secondary traffic center to major airport to long-range aircraft to major airport to secondary traffic center.

The dispersion routes could serve suburban areas around large cities, megalopolitan areas in general, and areas remote from large cities. In the last case the primary airport would function as a regional airport instead of a large-city airport. The socioeconomic impact of this possibility must not be underestimated.

The growth of such dispersion systems depends upon the balance between supply and demand and the strong interaction between them. Flexibility and adaptability to rapidly changing conditions, routes, and numbers of passengers will be major attributes of a successful air passenger dispersion system.

Group passenger movement

To alleviate the congestion around major airports, the majority of passengers and freight will be processed not on an individual basis but in groups; combined transportation will be employed for persons and freight with a common destination. This concept has already been applied to freight processing through containerization; the equivalent

Figure 6.6. Mixed-mode transportation center, Pomona, California.

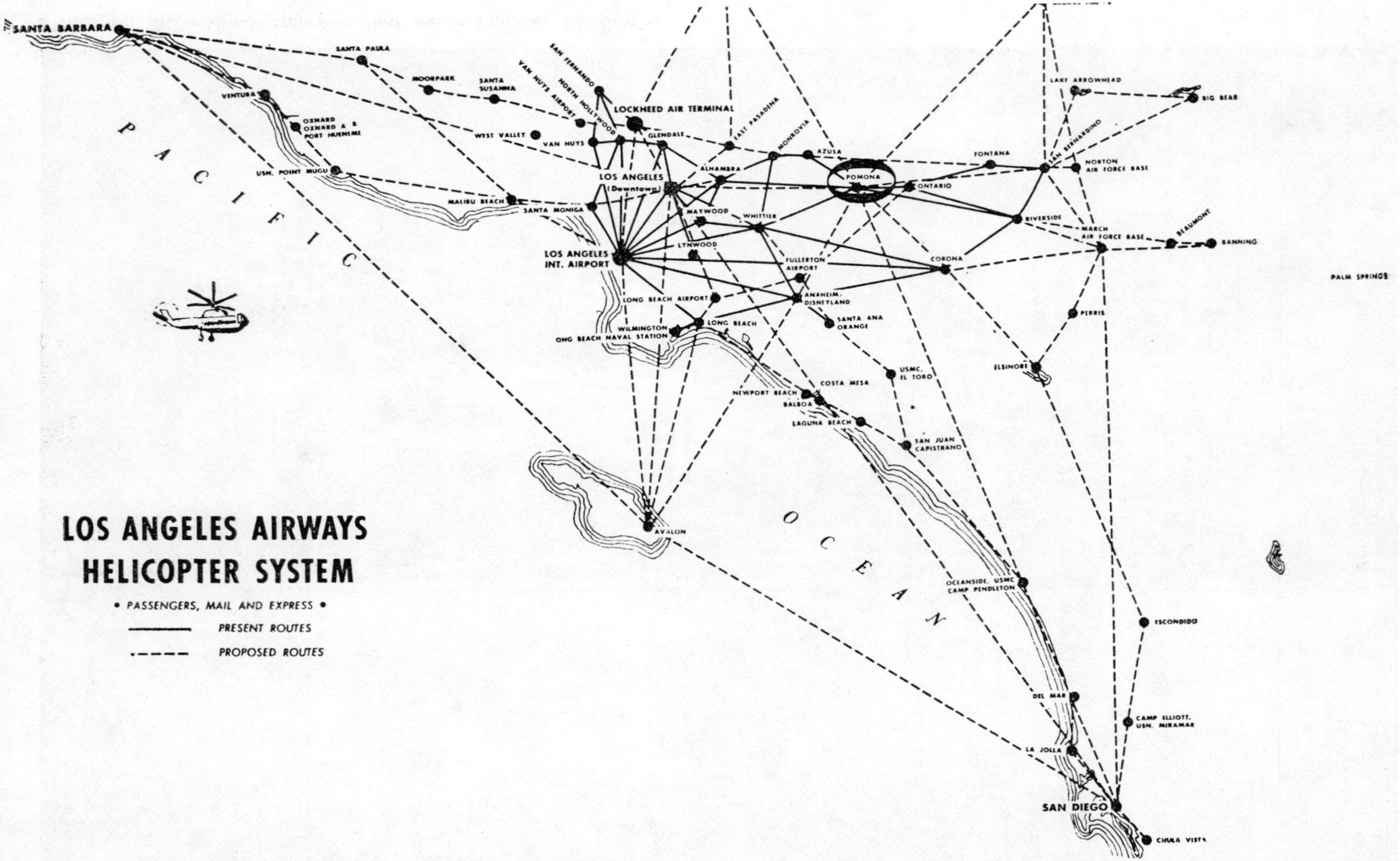

LOS ANGELES AIRWAYS HELICOPTER SYSTEM

- PASSENGERS, MAIL AND EXPRESS •
  PRESENT ROUTES
  PROPOSED ROUTES

Figure 67. The Los Angeles system of satellite heliports. Time from downtown Pomona to downtown Los Angeles is 10 minutes, from Pomona to Los

system for passengers will involve scheduled group travel to and from the primary airport, facilitated by the establishment of conveniently located subterminals. The transition from individual to group transportation will occur at these subterminals.

Dispersion by V/STOL aircraft and helicopters

Forecasts of tomorrow's air transportation system must be based on forecasts of tomorrow's technology. Advances in V/STOL aircraft and heavy-lift helicopters offer flexibility of operational routes and location of terminals, speed, safety of operation, and economy, thus assuring this mode of transportation a role in traffic dispersion to and from primary airports of the future.[21] In effect, this system shifts the interface between air and ground transportation away from the primary airports to the subterminals, or even farther. The overall system of long-range air travel, as shown in Figure 6.8 will have the following essential elements:

- High-altitude air umbrella, for long-distance travel from primary airport to primary airport.
- Low-altitude air umbrella, for group transportation from primary airport to subterminals, and from one subterminal to another subterminal.
- Ground transportation, for individuals, groups, and freight, from the subterminal by private automobile, rented automobile, subway, bus, boat or ferry.

In some cases, an extra low-altitude air umbrella will become advantageous for suburban airbus service using V/STOL aircraft.

Short-range travel (up to 500 miles) may not touch the primary airports at all. By using aircraft such as the advanced VTOL, short-range traffic could proceed from the subterminal of an air terminal cluster to other subterminals along suitable air trunk routes. Since such traffic represents a major part of total air transportation, traffic dispersion around the airport cluster would be significantly improved.

Importance of Subterminals

The primary airports that are points of departure and termination for the long-distance jets will remain passenger hubs. They will be located preferably at considerable distances from residential areas, so that noise will be less objectionable. Industries, particularly those that

---

[21] *A Systems Analysis of Short Haul Air Transportation*, **PB** 169521. Prepared for U.S. Dept. of Commerce by M.I.T., August 1965.

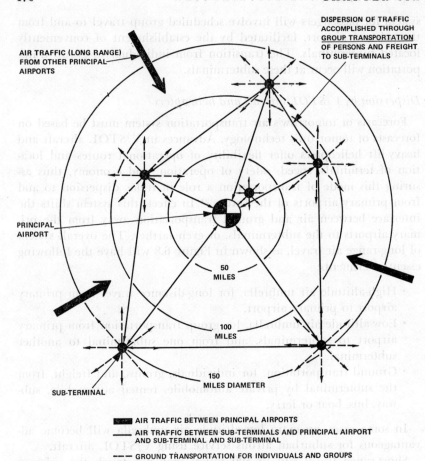

AIR TRAFFIC (LONG RANGE) FROM OTHER PRINCIPAL AIRPORTS

DISPERSION OF TRAFFIC ACCOMPLISHED THROUGH GROUP TRANSPORTATION OF PERSONS AND FREIGHT TO SUB-TERMINALS

PRINCIPAL AIRPORT

50 MILES

100 MILES

150 MILES DIAMETER

SUB-TERMINAL

▬▬▬ AIR TRAFFIC BETWEEN PRINCIPAL AIRPORTS

───── AIR TRAFFIC BETWEEN SUB-TERMINALS AND PRINCIPAL AIRPORT AND SUB-TERMINAL AND SUB-TERMINAL

─ ─ ─ GROUND TRANSPORTATION FOR INDIVIDUALS AND GROUPS

Figure 6.8. Subterminals will play an important part as interface between air and ground travel.

give service to the airport, the aircraft, and the equipment, would tend to cluster around the primary airports.

The primary airport will be mainly an exchange area for transfer from long-distance jets to short-distance aircraft. Neither passengers nor goods should normally pass in large quantities through buildings or gates at the primary airport. Transfer will be from large jets to other aircraft, either directly at the ramp or by means of transfer buses. It is estimated, for instance, that each large jet will require approximately five V/STOL aircraft, each having a load capacity of 80 passengers. Ticketing facilities and gates would be limited, and comfortable waiting rooms would be available for passengers transferring from one long-range flight to another long-range flight within a short time. Transfer passengers with a long wait would be transferred to a nearby subterminal with special stopover facilities. Subterminals would be located along the outer boundaries of business and residential areas, and would be tied in with other modes of transportation, including public ground transportation, private automobiles, and rented cars. Extensive parking facilities would be required, probably in the form of a large multistory garage with a V/STOL airport located on the roof. Aircraft noise must be kept to as low a level as technology can economically provide.

The subterminals would be the main processing centers for long-range air travel, including ticketing and baggage checking for the entire trip. Subterminals should emphasize passenger comfort and should provide waiting lounges, restaurants, small travel shops, and similar facilities. The aircraft departing from the subterminal would bring the traveler directly to the loading ramp for the large jets at the primary airport, without further processing through gates. Subterminals could also handle freight processing.

Regardless of the collection and distribution system used by a major airport, there are certain basic requirements. The system must provide

- Rapid, convenient, and economical transportation of closed groups of air travelers from large jets to a number of secondary traffic centers.
- Rapid processing of passengers and luggage at secondary traffic centers and transfer points.
- Growth potential to handle up to 10,000 passengers per hour at peak times.
- Transportation of groups of passengers to dispersed secondary terminals in such a manner that insertion into public or private ground transportation systems is achieved without local overloading or choking of the ground traffic.
- Flexibility to adapt to changing demands, routes, and stops.

The Future Outlook

The helicopter has proved its worth over the last 20 years as a reliable, flexible vehicle, but its operating costs have been high. With the expected advances in technology in the near future, VTOL-V/STOL aircraft promise a like flexibility, safe operation in a high-density traffic environment, and acceptable cost factors. They also have the potential for alleviating the congestion of airport access roads. Moreover, VTOL-V/STOL aircraft, in addition to making city center to airport service available, will offer attractive competition to high-speed ground transportation in city center to city center traffic.

In the past decade about half a billion dollars has been appropriated

by Congress for research and development of VTOL-V/STOL aircraft, mainly for military applications. Additional review of costs,
reliability, and safety will be required before these aircraft can be
certified for commercial operations.

Nonetheless, this flight regime offers such promise that the federal
government should fully support a live demonstration project in the
interests of the national transportation system. The United States is
in the fore in this area and is in a position to move ahead in refining
and improving techniques that will make VTOL–V/STOL–helicopters more attractive economically. Improvements must be made to
achieve simplicity of maintenance, longer periods between overhaul,
larger seating capacities, less noise and vibration, and suitable all-
weather navigation systems.

GENERAL AVIATION'S ROLE IN PASSENGER DISTRIBUTION

It was estimated that in 1966 general aviation carried more passengers (half of them intercity) than the scheduled air carriers. In the same
year there were more than 3000 air taxi operators, over 500 of them
operating scheduled services. Together they carried more than three
million passengers. In 1967 there were more than 300 daily scheduled
air taxi flights in and out of the New York City area. The FAA calculates that the air taxi fleet of 6000 will increase to 13,000 by 1975, during which year it will be flying more than four and one-half million
hours (see Figures 2.13 and 2.14). The statistics indicate that the air
taxi business is growing rapidly and will play a substantial role in
tomorrow's integrated air transportation system.

There are over 9000 airports available to air taxi operators which
do not have scheduled airline service. One major domestic airline
estimates that over 30,000 passengers per month connect to and from
scheduled air carrier flights by air taxi. One air taxi freight operator
deposits 40,000 pounds of freight per week at his air freight terminal.
It is this great flexibility and capability of operating in and out of a
multitude of community airports that gives general aviation a role in
the air distribution system. The air taxi business is now a hundred
million dollar industry, and this figure is expected to double by 1972.
The general aviation aircraft manufacturers have recently recognized
the impact of this segment of air transportation and are now providing
several all-purpose aircraft designed specifically for the air taxi
business.

General aviation is generally split into two major subdivisions:
scheduled and unscheduled. These actually represent four classes of
service: scheduled, nonscheduled, contract, and charter. Unfunded

and practically unregulated, the industry has grown by satisfying a need for these four types of service. If properly developed, air taxis will be able to handle 5 to 10 percent of the future collection and distribution load at major hub airports.

CURRENT GOVERNMENT-FUNDED STUDIES IN AIR TRANSPORTATION

The following are examples of government air transportation studies that relate to the airport access problem:

- *Helicopter skylounge project.* This study is designed to explore the feasibility of a 40-passenger pod and a flying crane-type helicopter combination capable of transporting passengers, baggage, and air cargo from a central terminal in the city to the airport. The project is sponsored by HUD and is being managed by the city of Los Angeles, using a consortium of aerospace corporations.
- *Role of low-altitude aircraft in urban transportation.* This study is evaluating the use of airspace up to an altitude of about 1500 feet, with the objective of increasing the capacity and improving the performance of the transportation complex in the New Jersey–New York metropolitan area. The project, sponsored by HUD, is being managed by the Eagleton Institute of Politics at Rutgers University, together with the Port of New York Authority, the city of New Brunswick, N.J., the Regional Planning Association of the New York Metropolitan Region, and Princeton University.

AIR FREIGHT TRAFFIC

In 1966 the U.S. scheduled airline industry flew two billion freight revenue ton-miles and earned slightly over 411 million dollars.[22] Median forecasts indicate that this ton-mile figure will increase by a factor of 10–14 by 1980. These data underscore the obvious importance of the air freight business in the development of the air transportation system.

Air freight is the fastest growing segment of the commercial air transportation system. Shippers are rapidly becoming aware of the total distribution cost concept, that is, the trade-off between higher ton-mile transportation costs and lower nontransportation costs such as warehousing, inventories, and obsolescence, all of which are important factors in the overall economic system of the shippers.

[22] *1967 Air Transport Facts and Figures,* American Transit Association.

In addition to all-cargo aircraft, there are the jumbo jets, which will allow large freight in the hold while carrying a full complement of passengers, and quick-change aircraft, which can be operated under passenger configurations during high-demand hours and as all-freight carriers during the night.

Increases in air freight shipments will impinge directly and adversely on the anticipated surface movement crisis. At present, 75 percent of all air freight shipments go through the major hubs. Increased volume will add appreciably to road congestion and terminal access problems and may prove to be the proverbial last straw.

Federal, regional, state, and municipal authorities, in conjunction with the air transportation industry, will have to examine in depth not only the adequacy of centralized air freight–cargo terminals in airport complexes but also concepts for pure air freight terminals located away from passenger airports yet within easy surface transportation reach of shipping centers or industrial park complexes. Any such study will also have to give full consideration to the role of future VTOL-V/STOL aircraft in freight haulage.

In point of fact, an important opportunity to make significant improvements in the handling of freight in urbanized complexes is at hand. Since we are now considering wholly new ground transport systems for inter- and intracity passenger travel, the possibility of handling freight in such a way as to increase the economic viability of such systems should be carefully considered. The following salient factors should be borne in mind:

- New systems will tend increasingly toward fully automatic operation, a large plus factor for any freight system since labor costs can be reduced.
- Passenger transport systems are subject to severe peaking characteristics; the system is used only lightly for part of the day and is almost unused during certain night hours. Freight movements might be dovetailed into the passenger movements to increase economic viability of the system and to decrease costs for each.
- The designing of terminals and other facilities for combined passenger and freight handling will be more difficult than designing for either one alone.
- The Post Office Department contracts for carrying mail by contract air carrier.

SYSTEM EVALUATION

The last phase of the system analysis process is evaluation. The alternative systems, having been specified, must be considered in the context of the total air transportation environment. The goal of the systems approach is the improvement of total system performance, as opposed to improvements in one subsystem which could degrade the total system. Conflicting requirements between passengers and freight, as well as socioeconomic factors, must be considered. The interrelationships of the airport, air traffic control, and technology are viewed in relation to proposed collection and distribution systems.

The evaluation phase is not only the most important but also the most difficult and complex of the three phases. For example, consider two concepts, the first reducing only traveler costs and the second only freight movement costs. Which system is to be preferred? Suppose further that the second system reduces air pollution while the first does not. The method of evaluation must be such that the critical trade-offs are emphasized and all factors properly weighed.

No proposed system or combination of systems will completely fulfill all the competing requirements. The systems approach, by screening out unacceptable systems and presenting alternatives based upon a quantitative, objective analysis, represents an aid in more effective decision-making. The impact of conflicting requirements and political factors may more readily be understood through the use of systems analysis.

It has not been the objective here to present firm alternative solutions to the collection and distribution problem. Instead, we have endeavored to conduct a first-rough-approximation systems analysis of the problem, to give insight into its seriousness, and to indicate the directions that a full systems analysis might take.

CONCLUSIONS AND RECOMMENDATIONS

As a result of its dynamic understanding and application of technology, the aerospace industry has developed a variety of aircraft to meet demands for the movement of passengers and cargo. At the same time this array of aircraft types, especially the airbus, jumbo jet, and SST, has brought into perspective the problems of collection and movement to airports and distribution at the end of the trip. The technological capacity of the United States must now be directed toward offering a variety of other air and ground transportation systems to ensure that the improvements in range, velocity, and capacity of aircraft will be exploited.

The private automobile was formerly an effective means for collecting and distributing the traveler during the ground legs of his trip. However, the automobile's demands for space, its vulnerability to weather, and its exemption from control by the system have made it inadequate to do the job alone. New means are required to improve the total range, velocity, capacity, and control of passenger and cargo movement.

The airport is only one factor in the urban environment. The access problem must therefore be considered in relation to the urban transportation system as a whole. Airport access problems will not be solved until the urban transportation crisis itself is greatly alleviated.

The following recommendations are framed against the technological and urban environments which have been discussed.

ANALYTICAL METHODS

The vastness of the national air transportation system, together with the uniqueness of the collection and distribution problems at each hub, indicates the need for analytical methods to study the collection and distribution problems systematically. It is recommended that a comprehensive computer model of the total air transportation system be designed and developed. This model could comprise a set of general submodels, so that data describing a specific hub airport region could be collected and the model used to diagnose the collection and distribution problem and to measure the sensitivity to change of the various parameters of the system. This model would include the following factors but would not be limited to them:

- Projections of future air traffic demands — passenger, freight, and vehicular
- Origin and destination matrices for airport users and others
- Social, economic, and political variables
- Capacity to evaluate all possible modes of airport access individually and in combination

THE AIRPORT ACCESS PROBLEM VIS À VIS URBAN PLANNING

In most regional urban planning the airport is considered as a terminal point rather than as an integral part of the urban environment. There is a specific need to integrate the airport access problem into urban planning at the regional level.

1. Liaison should be established between airlines and airport operators.
2. Urban planning groups should be instituted, and urban and airport planning seminars should be sponsored.
3. An education program should be developed to indicate the impact the air traveler of the future will have on the urban environment and its transportation system.

INADEQUATE AIRPORT ACCESS ROUTES

The major airport hubs are entering a critical stage. In almost every instance ground transportation of passengers and cargo can be identified as the weak link in improving door-to-door travel time. As a first step in defining the collection and distribution problem of the major hubs, these steps are recommended:

1. Obtain coordinated data indicating the airport access routes and identifying specific bottlenecks.
2. Analyze the capacity at the major airport hubs of the internal highway network and the parking facilities, with explicit reference to the influence of industrial complexes and organized sports on the flow of traffic.

TRANSFERRING

Transfer from one mode of transportation to another has always been considered a major deterrent to the smooth, comfortable flow of passengers. The human factors involved in transferring from one mode to another should be studied and specific ways recommended by which delays can be lessened (e.g., improved scheduling) and comfort increased (e.g., design changes that reduce walking). This research could have a major impact on all modes of urban transportation.

LIVE EXPERIMENTS

As indicated previously, many of the ground transportation systems proposed in the past decade for urban transportation are adaptable to airport access. Four such systems were discussed in this chapter:

1. Slow, continuous-flow devices for small groups, for moving within the business district or for intraterminal movement of passengers in large airports.
2. 40–50 mph vehicles for intra-airport movement and for connection to off-site parking lots.
3. 120–200 mph vehicles connecting airport to airport or business district to airport, with few stops.
4. 200–500 mph vehicles to serve urban corridors and regional airports.

Concepts involving the use of V/STOL aircraft with downtown airports and advanced helicopter satellite systems, including the sky-lounge, were also covered. The final proof of any new transportation system will come only after it has been installed and the public has had an opportunity to use and evaluate the system. It is apparent that carefully planned live experiments should immediately be implemented to facilitate the evaluation of various transportation modes being proposed.

Minibus Taxi System

As an immediate alleviant to the intra-airport movement problems of such airports as Kennedy and Los Angeles International, it is recommended that a system of dynamic routing similar to that used for taxis be inaugurated. Call boxes communicating directly with a central dispatching and control center should be available at various locations at the airport. The center would in turn be in communication with minibuses moving within the system. Passengers to be picked up at a specific location would have a minibus directed to them by means of the radio communication network. It may be possible that such a transportation system could become completely automatic. This may be an excellent testing ground for some of the automated-highway concepts being proposed. Although this would be only a stop-gap measure for the large hub airports, the concept, once tested and proved, could be effective for medium-size hubs in the future.

Low-Speed, High-Volume Transportation Devices

A definite need exists for devices operating in the 10–20 mph speed regime for total trip lengths of 1–2 miles. It is recommended that specific research be conducted to evaluate such systems as the minirail, carveyor, and advanced passenger belts for adaptation to central business districts and for intraterminal movement of passengers at large airports.

Air Dispersion System

A live demonstration of this system is recommended. Two specific hub regions should be selected, and advanced helicopters and VTOL or V/STOL aircraft should be employed to move passengers from large airports to decentralized smaller airports scattered through the hub region. As indicated previously, passengers should start from a secondary traffic center and move first to a major airport, then by long-range aircraft to another major airport, and finally to a secondary traffic center at the destination.

Cargo

The possibility of designing ground and air transportation systems that would have the flexibility to move containers of either passengers or cargo/mail simultaneously should be seriously considered. A detailed study of the feasibility and economic viability of this concept is required, to indicate the following points:

1. The technological specifications of the container and whether or not it should be certified.
2. The operational specifications of how the system would function.
3. The cost specifications to indicate the cost effectiveness of the system.
4. The implementation specifications which would supply detailed procedures for experimental operation of such a system.

7. GOVERNMENT POLICIES AND TRENDS

INTRODUCTION

The orderly planning and coordinated implementation of an over-all transportation system and attendant facilities is complicated by the diverse relationships between the federal government and the governing bodies of the states, regions, and municipalities. Basically, only those functions enumerated in the Constitution and subsequent implementing legislation are reserved for action at the federal level; all other functions become the responsibility of the state or local political jurisdiction (the "home rule" philosophy is still a very potent force in our national political life). Although the present discussion is primarily concerned with 1975 and beyond, current problems, insofar as they affect the design and funding of airports, terminals, air traffic control, and rapid transit systems, will also be considered.

GOVERNMENT POWERS, POLICIES, AND PRACTICES

The structure of government in the United States has been stable. Changes have been few, evolutionary, and slow to develop. There is no reason to expect any deviation from this pattern in the future. It is assumed, therefore, that the benefits and strictures which flow from our present system of federal, state, county, city, and regional governmental units will continue to apply to the air transportation industry. Proposals which do not recognize the statutory, constitutional, and sovereign rights of each governmental jurisdiction are impractical. At the same time, changes in emphasis can and must take place within the basic governmental structure so that it can accommodate itself, to some extent, to the changing demands placed upon it by a rapidly expanding industry. In this section, the relationship between the air

481

transportation industry and government at its various levels will be considered.

AT THE INTERNATIONAL LEVEL

In 1963, the U.S. policy on international air transportation was re-examined and the following statement was issued:[1]

. . . the primary objective of U.S. international air transport policy [is]: to develop and maintain an expanding, economically and technologically efficient international air transport system best adapted to the growing needs of the Free World, and to assure air carriers of the United States a fair and equal opportunity to compete in world aviation markets so as to maintain and further develop an economically viable service network wherever a substantial need for air transportation develops. . . ."

The basic principles of this policy include the following:

1. *Basic Framework.* The U.S. will maintain the present framework of bilateral agreements by which air routes are exchanged among nations and the rights to carry traffic on them are determined according to certain broad principles . . .
2. *Air Routes and Services.* Our policy is to provide air service where a substantial need therefor develops. . . . The demand for swift, safe passage, not forced flag flying, should determine the services offered . . .
3. *Capacity Principles.* The United States supports the "Bermuda" capacity principles[2] which flexibly govern the amount of service individual carriers may offer to the world travelling and shipping public . . . Our policy will be to oppose both arbitrary capacity restrictions and the stretching of those principles to the point of abuse . . .
4. *Air Carrier Pooling.* Our dealings with foreign carrier pools must be on a case-by-case basis. We must not encourage pools which substantially reduce competition to the detriment of the system we seek . . .
5. *Rates.* International air transport rates are now recommended by the carriers, acting through their organization, known as the International Air Transport Association (IATA), and approved by the governments concerned. This multilateral mechanism . . . should be maintained . . .
6. *Competition among U.S. Carriers.* [The policy] that U.S. flag international service shall continue to be provided by more than one carrier is sound, and deserves to be reaffirmed . . .
7. *Development of Air Cargo.* The U.S. will press for lower cargo rates of a kind best calculated to stimulate the growth of the air freight industry and benefit the shipping public . . .

[1] White House release dated April 24, 1963, indicating the President's approval of a policy statement submitted to him by an interagency steering committee.

[2] Air Services Agreement and Final Act of the Civil Aviation Conference held between the United States and the United Kingdom in Bermuda, February 11, 1946. Official Citation 60 Stat. 1499.

8. *Supporting Facilities.* The U.S. will cooperate in the development of international air traffic control and navigation systems, telecommunications, meteorological and other technical services . . .

These general principles have provided sound guidelines for industry and government. As the international operations of U.S. general aviation expand, the federal government should ensure that the ICAO mechanism provides maximum freedom of action for this type of operation without in any way derogating basic safety principles.

With respect to airports, the extension of international air traffic into interior U.S. cities which have had little or no such service will impose new requirements. Airports which were previously concerned solely with U.S. (FAA) rules and recommendations will now have to take cognizance of ICAO's standards and recommendations. Likewise, the need will arise for quarantine and federal-inspection areas, as well as for additional space allotments for handling an increased number of passengers. Financial requirements relating to international airports and ports of entry will have to be taken into consideration; it is not unreasonable to expect Congress to provide funds to pay for federal inspection areas.

Navigation and Communication Facilities

ICAO has performed a valuable service in the preparation of regional plans which delineate the basic requirements for navigation and communication facilities. An aggressive implementation program is important in order to improve the safety of international operations and warrants the full support of our government. Evidence of this is the fact that 60 percent of turbojet accidents have occurred in those areas where only 17 percent of the operations take place. Obviously, there is a critical need for an improved ground environment.

Charges for the use of navigation and communication facilities vary from nation to nation. ICAO has now been requested to conduct a study in this area,[3] with the aim of resolving inequities among nations and among the parties using the facilities, a desirable move which deserves U.S. support. It is hoped that a uniform approach to such charges will be achieved as soon as possible.

ICAO Technical Standards

ICAO has served a useful role in achieving international standardization of operation facilities. Efforts are now being made to set an

[3] ICAO Conference on Charges for Airports and Route Air Navigation Facilities, 1967. Doc. 8675, Recommendation No. 3.

international standard for noise. It should be noted, however, that this matter is still under debate within the United States.

AT THE FEDERAL LEVEL

The federal government should play an important role in the orderly development of the national transportation system by exercising leadership in the identification of important problem areas and by financing key demonstration projects. Carefully structured programs should be directed toward the development of various means of transport, some incorporating advanced technology, so that the public will be able to select those systems which best meet their requirements. However, attempts to use the federal jurisdiction over interstate commerce to arbitrarily allocate types of traffic to specific means of transportation would be both undesirable and impractical.

Airways

The development, installation, and operation of the airways system has been and should remain a federal responsibility. The ability to efficiently handle the traffic, both en route and in terminal areas, is decreasing rapidly, owing in large measure to the fact that the funding for all phases of the airway system has fallen behind the technology. An aggressive and energetic research and development program is needed, followed by adequate procurement of both the personnel to man the facilities and the required hardware.

In addition to producing a need for more efficient handling, the rapid growth in air traffic also increases the risk of mid-air collisions. In this regard the development of a practical collision-avoidance device for cockpit installation is in process. In order to ensure an effective system, however, the device must ultimately be acceptable for installation in general aircraft as well as in carrier aircraft.

In the meantime, better utilization of the existing system of navigational aids and air traffic control, together with additional equipment and personnel, would improve the situation significantly.

The U.S. air carriers have, through standardization of operations, equipment, and routes, been reasonably successful in fitting into the air traffic control system and in depending upon the system to minimize collision hazards. There are obviously basic differences between air carriers and general aviation with respect to equipment, personnel, financial resources, and regularity of operation. Nonetheless, a lessening of the general collision hazard is possible through efforts of the federal government and the general aviation segment to expand positive traffic control, establish additional radar coverage, increase the use of transponders, and require regular proficiency checks for all pilots with IFR ratings.

Additional appropriations are urgently needed for the necessary research, development, procurement, and manning of airway navigation and communications equipment. Equitable charges should be imposed on all users to offset the extensive appropriations required.

Airports

The federal government participates in planning and in certain regulatory functions with respect to the nation's airports through the Federal Aviation Administration; limited federal funds have been disbursed to public airports under the Federal Aid to Airports Program (FAAP), a grant-in-aid program. Although the communities receiving this federal money have been able to develop an extensive system of airports, the present situation is such that airport facilities are having difficulty absorbing the rapidly increasing flow of aircraft, passengers, and cargo, particularly in metropolitan areas.

The federal government has attempted to improve the nation's airport pattern by adopting a policy of fostering the development of a regional airport when such a facility can conveniently serve two or more communities having insufficient traffic to support full service at individual airports. As congestion increases at the principal airports serving major metropolitan areas, the federal government, through the CAB and FAA, should induce the diversion of both air carrier and general aviation traffic to peripheral airports. The success of this policy depends upon the suitability of the peripheral airport and available transportation to final destination.

Although such federal policies may result in a more efficient distribution of traffic among airports, the problem of accommodating traffic growth will require a major additional effort. Attention must be focused on movement between point of origin and airport and between airport and destination. The Department of Transportation should play a leading part in the overall effort, in cooperation with state, regional, and local agencies.

Funding

Estimates of need vary, but there appears to be general agreement that $4 billion in new funds will be required for airport development during the next six years (through FY 1973). At its present level, the FAAP would supply about one-twelfth of this amount, the remainder to be contributed by local communities. It has been suggested that the federal government assist in raising necessary airport funds by instituting certain other programs. Various plans have been suggested:

1. *Federal loans and loan guarantees.* Under this proposal, a government-owned corporation would be created within the Department of Transportation which would oversee a program of direct federal loans to both public and private entities to help cover the costs of new airport construction and improvement of existing public-use airports. Provision would be made for this corporation to guarantee payment of the principle and interest on municipal bonds and other securities issued for the specific purpose of financing approved airport projects. Repayable advances could be made to public agencies for land acquisition and planning purposes, and to expedite the start of construction on urgent airport projects. Provision would be made for the corporation itself to construct and operate airports in situations where a needed facility would not otherwise be built.

2. *Passenger service charges.* A "head tax," to be collected by the airlines from each passenger and payable either directly to the airport involved or into a federal airport development fund, has been suggested. Charges of this type are fairly common in Europe. If such a charge is to be imposed on a uniform, nationwide basis, appropriate federal legislation would be required.

3. *Taxes.* The imposition of additional special-purpose taxes by the federal government (e.g., increased passenger ticket taxes, air freight waybill taxes, and/or new fuel taxes) has also been suggested as a means of producing revenues for federal airport development assistance. Existing taxes are considered to be "user charges" for the use of the federal airways system and are thus not available for airport assistance programs.

One or more segments of the aviation community have expressed substantial objections to each of these proposals. Further study will be required before any generally acceptable plan can be formulated for additional federal financial assistance and means of obtaining the necessary revenues.

An important factor which warrants further study is the substantial number of privately owned and operated general aviation airports that are fulfilling a key role in the national airport system. Although these facilities are public-use airports, comparable to the many publicly owned facilities, they are not eligible for grants-in-aid under FAAP or state aid programs.

This economic handicap will cause the demise of these airports, conversion of the land to other, more profitable, uses, and the creation thereby of unacceptable gaps in the airport system. The federal government and the individual states must develop means to ensure the continuance of these airports.

Noise

The federal government has become increasingly involved in the aviation noise problem. Noise not only leads to the imposition of restrictions on operations at present airports but also makes far more difficult the selection of sites for future airports. Although the problem of noise in the vicinity of airports manifests itself locally, proposed or actual remedial measures frequently affect matters within the jurisdiction of the federal government. Thus, takeoff or landing procedures and patterns to reduce noise in communities adjacent to airports involve the FAA. Proposed limitations on noise-generation characteristics of aircraft and engines would become part of the FAA's certification procedures. Research efforts to reduce noise at the source concern the Department of Transportation, FAA, NASA, and other federal organizations. Programs for land use can be within the scope of HUD and DOT programs.

Basically, the technical attack on the noise problem is threefold: identification of a noise standard, reduction of noise at the source, and development of flight systems and procedures in the interest of noise attenuation. With respect to the first point, it is essential that all parties concerned identify and agree upon a noise standard, so that all elements of the aviation community operate from a common base.

The government agencies have embarked upon a constructive program to effect a considerable reduction of noise in the engine itself and in associated parts such as cowlings and ducts; this program should continue to be pursued aggressively under the direction of DOT. The fact that any development program of this kind, involving not only new technology but also extensive testing to ensure safety and reliability, will take time should in no way deter the effort. The achievements of such a program will in the future act to offset increased activity at airports. It is questionable whether such a program will affect equipment in use at the present time, owing to the high cost of a retrofit program. The possibility that the so-called "quiet engine" might be retrofitted depends upon the realization of its potential for lower specific fuel consumption as a result of its high bypass design. The engine could be both less noisy and more economical, as was the case with the turbofan.

The federal government should maintain an energetic leadership in the government/industry study of flight procedures and steep-glide slope approaches in the interest of noise attenuation. Smoke emanation from aircraft engines should also be the subject of study at the federal level.

Noise in relation to the use of land in the vicinity of airports is an additional aspect of the problem which requires federal attention.

Although basic determinations with respect to zoning are local matters, there are federal programs which can contribute to the alleviation of noise. HUD in particular should be able to make worthwhile contributions in this area by arranging for proper location of redevelopment projects.

Similarly, the Department of Transportation and other government agencies concerned can locate compatible projects (i.e., highway access roads, transit facilities, railroad spurs, etc.) in airport neighborhoods so that they underlie frequently used flight paths, in a true transportation corridor. In addition, eligibility for land acquisition for noise protection under the FAAP can be established.

In all of these efforts it is important to recognize that without local support no worthwhile gains will be made. Even a program which would make federal funds available for the acquisition of property and the conversion of such property to noise-compatible use would be of no consequence unless the local government can be persuaded of the value and acceptability of such a program and will participate wholeheartedly.

General Aviation

Before the airlines became the predominant mode of intercity common carriage in the United States, the operational conflicts between general aviation and air carrier traffic were few. Now, however, with larger and faster transport aircraft moving with greater frequency along the airways and into and out of airports, there is growing concern that there are basic incompatibilities between aircraft performance factors of this traffic and those of general aviation. If this concern is warranted, federal intervention will be necessary.

It was previously pointed out that means are now available to assure a safer and more efficient use of the airways, although at additional cost to the federal government and to aircraft operators for both personnel and equipment. Some of the representatives of general aviation may object to restrictions or regulations which inhibit the free use of airspace. Nonetheless, for the common good and in the interests of safety, there must be a further extension of control over general aviation flying, through regulation, certification of proficiency, and specification of equipment.

Regulation of airway use is wholly within the control of the federal government. Somewhat more complicated is the question of where the federal interest lies with respect to regulation or control of general aviation use of nonfederal airports. It is frequently pointed out that when a local sponsor accepts FAAP funds it agrees to "keep the airport open to all types, kinds and classes of aeronautical use without discrimination between such types, kinds and classes." Sometimes overlooked is the proviso "that the Sponsor may establish such fair, equal and not unjustly discriminatory conditions to be met by all users of the airport, as may be necessary for the safe and efficient operation of the airport, and provided further, that the Sponsor may prohibit or limit any given type, kind, or class of aeronautical use of the airport, if such action is necessary for the safe operation of the airport, or necessary to serve the civil aviation needs of the public."[4]

It would seem that this language may well involve the federal government in decisions on regulation, limitation, or restriction of use at congested metropolitan airports.

Classification itself is an area where federal effort would be worthwhile. The term "general aviation" is broad and imprecise. Commuter airlines, third level carriers, and certain air taxi operations share some of the characteristics of both air carrier and general aviation. Classification is sometimes based on aircraft size, sometimes on radio or navigation equipment. In some cases, distinctions are made according to the purpose of the flight or the qualifications of the crew. It is important that immediate attention be given to the development of a precise and practical method by which the various segments of the general aviation community can be classified.

Demonstration Projects

As part of the overall effort by the federal government to effect a better transportation system for the United States much work is being done in the use of advanced technology. The expenditure of federal funds in this connection is encouraged with respect to both air and ground vehicles. Intercity short-haul transportation may be a fertile field for the use of STOL or VTOL aircraft. Airport-to-city-center, interurban, and suburb-to-city-center travel might also benefit from the use of this equipment. It is recommended that the Department of Transportation conduct an intensified study in these areas.

Common Ownership of Transport Facilities

The U.S. policy with respect to common ownership of more than one type of transportation is a good one. Simply stated, common ownership is permitted when one mode is auxiliary and complementary to the other (for example, the ownership of distribution modes by one

---

4 Sponsor's Assurances: FAA Form 1624 (9-64), page 5.

or more air carriers, as is the case with the East and West Side Terminal operation in New York City). Common ownership has not been permitted, however, when such ownership might be destructive to competition.

AT THE STATE AND REGIONAL LEVELS

For operations wholly within state boundaries, state governments perform limited regulatory functions similar to those of the federal government. Thus, for example, some state regulatory bodies certify intrastate airlines and act on tariff proposals.

Airport Planning

In many states an aviation department or bureau inspects, licenses, and issues standards and regulations for airports. Application for FAAP funds by local communities are frequently required by state law to conform with state planning and to have the approval of the state department concerned. States in many instances provide grants-in-aid to airports, to supplement FAAP moneys.

There is a growing trend toward the establishment of state departments of transportation with the responsibility for overall transportation planning. Such departments may well fill a long-standing gap in planning; too often the plans for highways, transit facilities, and airports have originated with various uncoordinated groups. State transportation departments, together with regional planning groups established under state governments, can perform many essential functions. In all of these activities, the state governments must of necessity operate in a manner which does not conflict with federal activities.

Regional Airports

State governments have in some instances assumed direct responsibility for airport operation. More often they have established, either alone or by joint action with neighboring states, regional bodies to operate airports in defined areas which exceed the geographical limits of local jurisdictions. The establishment of such regional organizations is a healthy trend; more often than not, airports serve extensive geographical areas rather than individual communities. By broadening the boundaries of the operating body, the financial burden can be spread over the population served by the facility. Conflicts between local jurisdictions with respect to airport policies are lessened when all jurisdictions involved are represented on the governing board.

Establishing broader areas for airport planning and operation also facilitates the solution of problems arising from conflicts between general aviation and air carrier traffic. The development of "reliever" airports can be meshed with the development of a major terminal, so that general aviation flights will have acceptable facilities in the same area.

Financing, too, may be facilitated by the establishment of regional bodies. Since airport districts or airport boards from adjacent cities or counties have a broader tax base, the marketability of bonds is enhanced. Self-supporting authorities can also be established to encompass larger geographical areas; here, too, the financing base may be broader, particularly when other types of revenue-producing facilities are incorporated, specifically when several transportation modes are under the aegis of a single authority.

Noise

Noise is a serious problem at the state and regional levels of government, as well as at the federal and local level. More than one governor has had to heed the complaints of the people living in the vicinity of an airport and use the power of his office to secure agreement on noise-abatement measures. In the selection of a new airport facility, complaints from those who might be exposed to aircraft noise are probably the most significant obstacle faced by the developer. State legislators, too, have been brought into the conflict through the vigorous protests of their constituents. Although activity in this field has so far been limited to the individual efforts of certain legislators, it is always possible that statutory action may be taken, particularly with respect to airports controlled by state governments.

Where regional bodies operate airports, noise is a very direct problem; in some cases it has been dealt with directly through rules or regulations.

One of the problems faced by regional authorities in coping with the airport noise problem is their inability to control land use beyond the confines of the airport. In most cases the regional airport body has no control over adjacent land use, and even where the neighboring land is undeveloped the zoning power resides in local jurisdictions. For the most part, in the vicinity of developed major airports, zoning and existing land use is predetermined, and all too often the area is zoned for residential occupancy. In such situations, the regional authority has no power to change the situation, nor is there likely to exist the financial wherewithal to accomplish changes.

This situation is not likely to change in the near future. It must be emphasized once again that proposed solutions which ignore the pattern of governmental organization in the United States are impractical.

AT THE LOCAL LEVEL

Most of the publicly owned airports in the United States are the responsibility of local municipalities, and the impact of policies and decisions at the international, federal, and state levels is felt at the local level. It is imperative that local airport management keep itself informed concerning proposals and possible actions of government aviation bodies at higher levels (bilateral negotiations involving international service, ICAO activities when the local community has international services, route cases before the CAB, actions of the FAA with respect to airways and airports, and, of course, policies and actions of state bodies concerned with aviation matters).

Conversely, the higher levels of government should give timely advice to the local authority, so that there is opportunity for feedback.

Airports

In some cases, planning at the federal or regional level will indicate that a local airport is not appropriate for air carrier activity, and this presents difficult problems for local decision. In most cases municipally operated airports will continue to serve the traffic in the area. The forecast increase in activity, however, will necessitate capital expenditures far beyond the demands which have previously been made.

A limited number of methods are available whereby a municipality may obtain the required funds. Grants-in-aid, either from FAAP or the state government, have proved useful in the past. However, the future prospects for this form of financial assistance, at least in the full amounts required, are not encouraging.

It is likely that the use of revenue bonds for airport purposes will continue to increase. A requirement for general voter approval of this type of financing is the exception rather than the rule. It should be noted, however, that in a few cases such revenue bond issues have been rejected by the electorate. And, of course, there are needs for airport facilities which are non-revenue producing and for improvements at smaller airports where revenues will not be sufficient to cover the debt service requirements. Thus revenue bonds are at best only a partial solution to the problem.

Private financing may occasionally be available for airport improvements. Such financing cannot be relied upon as an overall solution, however, since the private lender will only come forward when repayment from revenues is assured. Although now the exception, such cases will become more common as air traffic grows.

There is grave doubt that all local communities will be able to individually raise the needed funds through grants or loans. Some federal action will be needed if funds are to be produced in time to meet the demands of forecast traffic.

Noise

The problem of jurisdiction with respect to noise control has already been discussed. Problems sometimes arise even when the airport is municipally operated, if it is physically located outside the municipal boundaries, or adjacent to a neighboring municipality. Zoning can be a useful device if both the airport and the adjacent areas are within the boundaries of the community, and provided the adjacent lands are undeveloped. Unfortunately, such a situation is rare.

In some instances undeveloped lands near the airport can be acquired for buffer-zone purposes. Tax relief has also been suggested as compensation for airport noise. As airports become larger, however, these remedies become more difficult to apply and consequently are of limited value.

Additional Airports

It is a rare community that has geographical boundaries large enough so that when an existing airport has become congested another facility can be located within the community limits.

When a new airport must be built by a municipality, it is most likely that it will have to be located within another jurisdiction. The consent of residents of the proposed area must be obtained in most instances, and the need must therefore be expressed to the public in a convincing manner. Establishment of a regional board, district, or authority may be helpful in overcoming public resistance by giving the residents of the new location a voice in the construction and operation of the facility.

CONCLUSIONS

1. There is an established structure of government in the United States which fixes relationships between federal, state, county, city, and regional governmental units. A change in emphasis, markedly improving cooperation between political entities, is increasingly

evident and reflects the urgent requirements of the air transport industry and associated forms of transportation.

2. *International.* The U.S. policy on international air transportation expressed in 1963 remains basically sound; ICAO is an effective mechanism for the standardization of navigation/communications requirements and overall technical standards.

3. *Federal level*

   (a) The capacity of the federal airways system is insufficient to handle the rapidly expanding requirements of increasing air traffic.

   (b) The federal government should play a major role in developing the national transportation system by exercising leadership in the identification of important problem areas and by financing key demonstration projects.

   (c) The urgent requirements for expansion and construction of airport facilities are beyond the reach of present financing programs.

   (d) The noise resulting from aircraft operations is an increasingly serious problem. Noise-abatement requirements may well prevent realization of the full potential of airport facilities.

   (e) General aviation operations are increasing even more rapidly than are air carrier activities.

   (f) Carefully planned and programmed demonstration projects provide an excellent means for the public to evaluate and select the most suitable forms of transportation. Such projects are particularly important in the development of mixed-mode solutions to the airport access problem.

4. *State level.* Increasingly, regional organizations are being set up to deal with various aspects of the transportation problem. Section 204 of the Demonstration Cities Act encourages the establishment of this type of authority. Such entities can prove effective in dealing with problems of airport site selection, airport planning and financing, mixed-mode transportation for access to and from airports, aircraft noise, and compatible land use.

5. *Local level.* A great many of the foregoing problems also occur at the local level (county or municipality). Local jurisdictions can make an important contribution to the solution of these problems. Of serious concern is the imminent loss of a significant number of privately owned public-use airports in developed or developing areas, because they are not eligible for grants-in-aid. This happens at a time when additional "reliever" airports for use by smaller aircraft in large metropolitan areas are a necessity.

RECOMMENDATIONS

1. The United States Policy on International Air Transportation (1963) should be generally supported.
2. ICAO should establish standards for additional international navigation and communication facilities which will provide maximum safety within the available technology. Charges for the use of such facilities should be allocated on an equitable basis.
3. Additional appropriations are urgently needed for the necessary research, development, procurement, and manning of U.S. airway navigation and communications equipment. The imposition of equitable charges on all users is needed to offset the extensive appropriations required.
4. Funding for airport expansion and construction should be shared by the federal, state, and local governments; the airport operator; the private sector; and the user (air cargo, passenger, shipper, and general aviation). A program must be established to insure the continued operation of key privately owned public-use general aviation airports as an integral part of the national airport system.
5. Aggressive government/industry research programs to alleviate aircraft noise should be continued under the direction of the Department of Transportation, with emphasis on the following:
   (a) Determination of an accepted standard of measurement for aircraft noise.
   (b) Development of an engine that will be both quieter and more economical.
   (c) Establishment of flight systems or procedures that will result in necessary noise attenuation with no derogation of safety.
6. The federal government should sponsor programs for the compatible use of land under the flight path in the vicinity of airports. Government and regional agencies must play an important part in such programs.
7. Adequate and equitable provision in the national air space system must be made for general aviation users. General aviation must in turn accept prescribed standards of aircraft equipment and pilot proficiency.
8. The federal funding of carefully planned demonstration projects in various phases of the overall transportation problem is necessary to enable the public to select those systems which best meet their requirements.

BIBLIOGRAPHY

There is no bibliography for Chapters 1 and 7, since the former is an overview and the latter a digest by the Panel of laws and ordinances that appear to establish trends. The bibliography for Chapter 3 is devoted exclusively to short-haul aircraft.

CHAPTER TWO

Air Transport Association of America, *Facts and Figures*. Washington, 1967.

Anderson, N., *Work and Leisure*. The Free Press, Glencoe, Ill., 1961.

Arizona State University, Division of Industrial Design and Technology, *A Study to Determine the Feasibility of Establishing a National Program for Training Skilled Aviation Personnel*. Tempe, Ariz., July 1967.

Arnold, W. J., *The Conference Board Record. 4*, No. 8, National Industrial Conference Board, Inc., New York, Aug. 1967.

Asher, Norman J., W. F. Beazer, W. A. Cox, R. F. Muth, and W. Y. Oi, *Demand Analysis for Air Travel by Supersonic Transport*. Report No. R. 118, AD–652310, Institute for Defense Analyses, Arlington, Va., Dec. 1966.

Besse, G., and G. Desmas, *Forecasting for Air Transport–Methods and Results*. ITA Studies 66/7–E, Institut du Transport Aerien, Paris, 1966.

Boeing Company, *Airport Activity Analysis–747 and SST, 1971 to 1976*. Renton, Wash., Feb. 1967.

Boeing Company, Commercial Airplane Division, *Boeing Traffic Forecast*. Report 5637, Renton, Wash., Jan. 30, 1967.

Brown, S. L., "Measuring the Elasticities of Air Travel." *Proceedings of the American Statistical Association*, Business and Economic Statistics Section, Washington, 1965, pp. 278–285.

Business International Corporation, "Business International United Nations Roundtable." Briefing Paper, New York, June 1967.

Colvard, H., J. McMinn, and G. Duren, *Characteristics of the Air Traveler, 1955–1962–1980*. Boeing Company, Seattle, Wash., 1965.

Committee for Economic Development, *Managing a Full Employment Economy*. New York, June 1966.

Crampon, T., *Home Recreation*. Long Range Planning Report No. 301, Stanford Research Institute, Menlo Park, Calif., 1966.

Deutsch, Gertrude, "Toward a Trillion-dollar GNP." *The Conference Board Record, 1*, No. 7, National Industrial Conference Board, Inc., July 1964, pp. 46–52.

Douglas Aircraft Company, *Measuring the 70's–An Air Travel Market Analysis*. Report C1–12/66–423, Long Beach, Calif., Nov. 1966.

First National City Bank, *The Port of New York Challenge and Opportunity*. New York, June 1967.

Haynes, E., *Conclusions of the President's and Chairmen's Roundtable on Corporate Planning Today for Tomorrow's World Market*. Business International, Inc., New York, Jan. 1967.

Institute of International Education. *Open Doors 1966*. New York, Sept. 1966.

Institute of International Education, *Undergraduate Study Abroad*. New York, 1966.

Johnson, Lyndon B., *Economic Report of the President*. Transmitted to the Congress Jan. 26, 1967, together with the Annual Report of the Council of Economic Advisers, Washington, 1967.

Lansing, J. B., and D. M. Blood, *The Changing Travel Market*. The University of Michigan Survey Research Center, Ann Arbor, Mich., 1964.

Lansing, J. B., *The Travel Market 1964–65*. The University of Michigan Survey Research Center, Ann Arbor, Mich., Oct. 1965.

Large, A., "Monday Holidays Plan Arouses New Interest Among Congressmen." *The Wall Street Journal*, July 26, 1967.

Lockheed California Company, a Division of Lockheed Aircraft Corporation, *Air Traffic Demand 1967–1990*. OEA/SST/222, Burbank, Cal., Nov. 1966.

Madow, P. (ed.), *Recreation in America*. H. W. Wilson, New York, 1965.

Mathematica, *Studies in Travel Demand*. Princeton, N. J., 1965.

Metropolitan Commuter Transportation Authority, *Jetports and General Aviation in the New York Metropolitan Area*. Report to Governor Rockefeller of New York, New York, March 1967.

Milton, R. P., and R. B. Johnson, *Projected World Patterns—1985, Contextual Research Papers Report No. 2, Volume I Summary and Conclusions*. Douglas Aircraft Company, and Johnson Research Associates, Santa Monica, Calif., Jan. 1966.

Morrissey, G. R., and P. L. Oster, *Long Range Forecast, The National Goal Program, 1967–1977*. 2, Douglas Aircraft Company, Huntington Beach, Calif., Dec. 1966.

National Industrial Conference Board, *A Graphic Guide to Consumer Markets*. New York, 1966.

Perle, Eugene D., "The Demand for Transportation." Depart of Geography Paper No. 95, University of Chicago, Chicago, 1964.

Port of New York Authority, Comprehensive Planning Office, *Metropolitan Transportation, 1980*. New York, 1963.

Port of New York Authority, Aviation Department, *New York's Domestic Air Passenger Market (April 1963 Through March 1964)*. New York, June 1965.

Port of New York Authority, Aviation Department, *New York's Overseas Air Passenger Market (April 1963 Through March 1964)*. New York, June 1965.

Schultz, T. W., *Problems of United States Economic Development*. 2, Committee for Economic Development, New York, May 1958.

Smith, Wilbur, and Associates, *Highway Travel in the Washington, New York, Boston Megalopolis*. New Haven, Conn., 1963.

Stanford Research Institute Long Range Planning Service, *High Speed Intercity Ground Transportation*. Client Report No. 314, Menlo Park, Calif., Mar. 1967.

Stanford Research Institute Long Range Planning Service, *The State and Local Government Market*. Client Report No. 276, Menlo Park, Calif., Mar. 1966.

Stanford Research Institute Long Range Planning Service, *The World of 1975*. Menlo Park, Calif., 1964.

Systems Analysis and Research Corporation, *Demand for Intercity Passenger Travel in the Washington-Boston Corridor*. Boston, 1963.

Transportation Association of America, *Transportation Facts and Trends*. 4th ed., Washington, Apr. 1967.

Travel Research International, *Vacation Travel Attitude Survey*. New York, June 1967.

Tri-State Transportation Commission, *Tri-State Transportation—1985, An Interim Plan.* New York, May 1966.

United Nations Educational, Scientific, and Cultural Organization (UNESCO), *World Survey of Education IV, Higher Education.* New York, 1966.

U.S. Civil Aeronautics Board Bureau of Accounts and Statistics, *Forecasts of Passenger Traffic of the Domestic Trunk Air Carriers, Domestic Operations, Scheduled Service, 1965–1975.* Staff Report No. 5, Washington, Sept. 1965.

U.S. Department of Commerce, "Approaches to the Modal Split: Intercity Transportation." Technical Paper No. 7, Washington, 1967.

U.S. Federal Aviation Agency. *Airport Capacity Criteria Used in Preparing the National Airport Plan.* AC 150–5060, Washington, Aug. 1966.

U.S. Federal Aviation Agency, *Aviation Demand and Airport Facility Requirement Forecasts for Large Air Transportation Hubs Through 1980.* Advisory Circular No. 150–5054, Airports, Washington, Aug. 1, 1967.

U.S. Federal Aviation Agency, Office of Policy Development, Economics Division, *Aviation Forecasts, Fiscal Years 1967–1977.* Washington, Jan. 30, 1967.

U.S. Federal Aviation Agency, Office of Policy Development, Economics Division, *General Aviation: A Study and Forecast of the Fleet and Its Use in 1975.* Washington, July 1966.

U.S. Office of Education, *Progress of Public Education in the United States of America 1966–67.* Report to 30th International Conference on Public Education, Geneva, Switzerland, July 1967.

U.S. Office of Education, *Projections of Educational Statistics to 1975–76.* OE–10030–66, Washington, 1966.

U.S. Office of Science and Technology, *Alleviation of Jet Aircraft Noise Near Airports.* Washington, Mar. 1966.

U.S. Senate, Committee on Aeronautical and Space Sciences, *Policy Planning for Aeronautical Research and Development.* Staff Report prepared by the Legislative Reference Service, Library of Congress, Document No. 90, 89th Congress, 2nd Session, May 19, 1966.

Yntema, T. O., *Fiscal and Monetary Policy for High Employment.* Committee for Economic Development, Fourth Publication, New York, Dec. 1966.

CHAPTER THREE

Boeing Company, *Study of Aircraft in Short Haul Transportation Systems.* NASA CR–986, National Aeronautics and Space Administration, Washington, Jan. 1968.

Fry, B. L., and J. M. Zabinsky, *Feasibility of V/STOL Concepts for Short Haul Transport Aircraft.* NASA CR–743, National Aeronautics and Space Administration, Washington, May 1967.

Lockheed California Company, *Study on the Feasibility of V/STOL Concepts for Short Haul Transport Aircraft.* NASA CR–902, National Aeronautics and Space Administration, Washington, Oct. 1967.

Marsh, K. R., *Study on the Feasibility of V/STOL Concepts for Short-Haul Transport Aircraft.* NASA CR–670, National Aeronautics and Space Administration, Washington, Jan. 1967.

McDonnell Aircraft Corporation, *Technical and Economic Evaluation of Aircraft for Intercity Short-Haul Transportation, Final Report.* Contract FA 65WA–1246, Apr. 1966.

M.I.T. Flight Transportation Laboratory, *Analysis of V/STOL Aircraft Configurations for Short Haul Air Transportation Systems.* Report FT–66–1, Cambridge, Mass., Nov. 1966.

M.I.T. Flight Transportation Laboratory, *Computerized Schedule Construction for an Airline Transportation System.* Report FT–66–3, Cambridge, Mass., Dec. 1966.

M.I.T. Flight Transportation Laboratory, *Maintenance Cost Studies of Present Air-craft Subsystems.* Report FT–66–2, Cambridge, Mass., Nov. 1966.

M.I.T. Flight Transportation Laboratory, *A Systems Analysis of Short Haul Air Transportation.* Aug. 1965, Department of Commerce, Federal Clearinghouse, Arlington, Va., PB 169 521.

M.I.T. Flight Transportation Laboratory, *Weather Conditions Affecting VTOL Airbus Operations in the Northeast Corridor.* Report FT–66–4, Cambridge, Mass., Nov. 1966.

CHAPTER FOUR

Bauer, E. N., *V/STOL Navigation in the Terminal Area.* Radio Technical Com-mission for Aeronautics, Sept. 1967.

Draper, C. S., J. W. Hursch, R. B. Trueblood, and J. H. Flanders, *Traffic Control.* New York Academy of Sciences, Apr. 5, 1967.

Joint Chiefs of Staff, *Tactical Communications and Control Systems Standards. 1,* JSC Pub. 10.

Radio Technical Commission for Aeronautics, *Universal Air-Ground Digital Com-munications Systems Standards.* Mar. 12, 1964.

Ryan, O., "Why Earlier Retirement for Air Traffic Controllers." *Journal of Air Traffic Control,* Mar. 1964.

U.S. Federal Aviation Agency, *Aviation Forecasts Fiscal Years 1967–1977.* Washing-ton, Jan. 1967.

U.S. Federal Aviation Agency, *Future Air-Ground-Air Communication Subsystem.* 6 Vols., Investigation by Communications Systems, Inc., Report No. RD-66-16. Contract FA–WA–4645.

Vickers, Tirey K., *V/STOL Navigation in High-Density Terminal Areas.* Institute of Navigation, June 1967.

CHAPTER FIVE

Ahlborn, G., and R. Horonjeff, "Jet Transports Characteristics Related to Airports." American Society of Civil Engineers, Aero-Space Transport Division, *Journal, 91,* A65–32384, Apr. 1965, pp. 33–46.

Air Transport Association of America, *Facts and Figures.* 28th ed., Washington, 1967.

Alexander, George, "Miami Congestion Problem Spurs Dispute." *Aviation Week & Space Technology,* Dec. 12, 1966, pp. 54–61.

Alexander, George, "Two-Part Tampa Terminal To Aid Passengers." *Aviation Week & Space Technology,* Nov. 28, 1966, pp. 49–55.

Annus, L. K., *Access to Airports, Selected References.* U.S. Federal Aviation Agency, Washington, Library Services Division, N66–36375, Aug. 1966.

Beckwith, W. B., "Supercooled Fog Dispersal for Airport Operations." American Meteorological Society, *Bulletin, 46,* A65–26374, June 1965, pp. 323–327.

Bishop, D. E., *Analysis of Community and Airport Relationships: Noise Abate-ment, Final Technical Report.* Vol. 2, *Development of Aircraft Noise Compati-bility Criteria for Varied Land Uses.* N66–28113 and N65–29167, Bolt Beranek and Newman Inc., Los Angeles, Calif., May 1964, Dec. 1964, Apr. 1965.

Bishop, D. E., "Judgments of the Relative and Absolute Acceptability of Aircraft Noise." *Journal of the Acoustical Society of America,* A66–82370, July 1966, pp. 108–122.

Bishop, D. E., P. A. Franken, and P. A. Washington, "The Propagation of Sound from Airport Ground Operations." NASA N67–25053, Bolt Beranek and New-man Inc., Van Nuys, Calif., May 1967.

Black, R. E., "Effects of the Super Sixty Series DC-8 on Airport Requirements." Paper 660281, Society of Automotive Engineers, National Aeronautic Meeting and Production Forum, New York, A66-29825, Apr. 25-28, 1966.

Blomquist, A. E., "Airport Planning—Past, Present, and Future." Paper 660284, Society of Automotive Engineers, National Aeronautic Meeting and Production Forum, New York, A66-29825, Apr. 25-28, 1966.

Boeing Company, Boeing 747 at the Airport. D6-13440, May 1967.

"Boeing View of Airport Problems." Airline Management and Marketing, Mar. 1967, pp. 47-50.

Botsford, A. C., and H. P. Schmidt, "Operational Considerations for Future Airport Design." Paper 65-746, Aircraft Design and Technology Meeting, Los Angeles, Calif., A66-13054, Nov. 15-18, 1965.

Brown, P. O., "Airfield Pavement Evaluation Procedures." American Society of Civil Engineers, Aero-Space Transport Division, Journal, 91, A65-32383, April 1965, pp. 15-31.

Bulban, E. J., "Texas Expanding To Meet Air Traffic Growth." Aviation Week & Space Technology, Dec. 19, 1966, pp. 39-43.

Burns, H. C., and M. A. Warskow, "Operational Planning for General Aviation Facilities at Airports." Paper 64-190, American Institute of Aeronautics and Astronautics, General Aviation Aircraft Design and Operations Meeting, Wichita, Kans., A65-18871, May 25-27, 1964.

Carter, J. W., "Burgeoning Traffic Clogs Airport Roads." Aviation Week & Space Technology, Oct. 31, 1966, pp. 167-174.

Carter, J. W., "Rail Extension To Speed Cleveland Traffic." Aviation Week & Space Technology, Nov. 7, 1966, pp. 54-59.

Cawthorn, J. M., W. L. Copeland, and H. H. Hubbard, "Factors Relating to the Airport-Community Noise Problem." NASA Conference on Aircraft Operating Problems, N65-31109, 1965, pp. 73-81.

Coleman, H. J., "London Focuses on Rail Links for Airports." Aviation Week & Space Technology, Jan. 2, 1967, pp. 39-41.

Doty, L. L., "Europe Acts To Combat Traffic Congestion." Aviation Week & Space Technology, Jan. 9, 1967, pp. 37-41.

Douglas Aircraft Company, Domestic Freight Movement Survey, Phase II. March 15, 1967.

Douglas Aircraft Company, The Future Market for Air Cargo and the Equipment Which Will Develop It. Nov. 3, 1966.

Douglas Aircraft Company, Post-1971 Materials Handling Study Final Report. Technical Report ASD-TR-67-5, prepared for the Aeronautical Systems Division, Wright-Patterson Air Force Base, Ohio.

Ferrair, Victor J., Jr., "Honk, Warble, Tweet." USAF, MC, Life Sciences Group, Aerospace Safety, 23, No. 11, Nov. 1967, pp. 8-11.

Flynn, R. G., "New Techniques for Reducing Bird Strikes at Airports." Paper 65-748, Aircraft Design and Technology Meeting, Los Angeles, Calif., A66-12584, Nov. 15-18 1965.

Gorham, J. E., Methodology and Criteria for National Airport Planning, Final Report. N66-12069, Stanford Research Institute, South Pasadena, Calif., Sept. 1964.

"Ground Access Grows as Airport Problem." Aviation Week & Space Technology, Oct. 25, 1965, pp. 185-187.

Helmes, N. B., "Air Cargo Terminal Growth Progression." Cl-25-5753, Douglas Aircraft Company, July 25, 1967.

Hersey, Irwin, "Decibels Demanding Attention." Equipment/Technology, July 1967, pp. 43-46.

Horonjeff, R. The Planning and Design of Airports. A63-17071, McGraw-Hill, New York, 1962.

International Air Transport Association, Airport Terminals. 4th ed., Dec. 1966.

Marx, Hans, "The 'Ideal' Jet Freighter." Airline Management and Marketing, Aug. 1967, pp. 42-45.

McDonnell Aircraft Corporation, *Technical and Economic Evaluation of Aircraft for Intercity Short-Haul Transportation (Final Report).* N67–10599 and N67–12024, St. Louis, Mo., April 1966.

McRae, J. L., G. Moraldi, and W. Posey, "Discussion: Airfield Pavement Evaluation Procedures." American Society of Civil Engineers, Aero-Space Transport Division, *Journal, 92,* A66–20700, Jan. 1966, pp. 163–171.

Mosby, L. B., and D. M. Rehder, "Ground Loads for Aircraft with Multiple Wheels and Multiple Landing Gear and with Requirements for Semi-Improved Airfield Operations." Paper 65–711, Canadian Aeronautics and Space Institute and American Institute of Aeronautics and Astronautics, Montreal, Canada, A66–10948, Oct. 18–19, 1965.

Nielsen, J. P., "Modulus of Deformation of Pavement Bases." American Society of Civil Engineers, Aero-Space Transport Division, *Journal, 92,* A66–20697, Jan. 1966, pp. 95–106.

O'Lone, Richard, "Growth of Air Cargo Spurs Automation." *Aviation Week & Space Technology,* Oct. 31, 1966, pp. 72–83.

O'Lone, R. G., "San Francisco May Need Regional Airport." *Aviation Week & Space Technology,* Nov. 21, 1966, pp. 55–64.

Oxford Corporation, *Improved Airport Guidance Signs (Final Report).* N65–29281, Buffalo, N.Y., Nov. 1964.

Peavey, C. D., "Airport Accessibility—A Growing Problem in the Jet Age." Paper 670322, Society of Automotive Engineers, National Aeronautic Meeting, New York, A67–25858, Apr. 24–27, 1967.

Quesada, E. R., *Noise Abatement Procedures.* N66–80418, U.S. Federal Aviation Agency, Washington, Nov. 1960.

Quick, L. H., "Megalopolis Airport Requirements." Paper 66–944, American Institute of Aeronautics, Boston, Mass., A67–12279, Nov. 29–Dec. 2, 1966.

Spater, G. A., "Airports of the Future." International Congress on Air Technology, Little Rock, Ark., A66–31283, Nov. 15–18, 1965.

Stanford Research Institute, *An Analysis of Intercity Passenger Traffic Movement Within the California Corridor Through 1980 (Final Report).* Apr. 1966.

Steele, W. S., "A New Concept for Airports and Airport Terminals." Tracey, Brunstrom and Dudley, Inc., 1967.

Stein, Kenneth J., "Airlines Plan Increased Functions for New Computers." *Aviation Week & Space Technology,* Oct. 31, 1966, pp. 210–220.

Tiemann, A. E., and M. A. Warskow, "Capacity of Airport Systems in Metropolitan Areas." American Society of Civil Engineers, Aero-Space Transport Division, *Journal, 92,* A66–20694, Jan. 1966, pp. 35–61.

"Tomorrow's Solution to Today's Air Traffic Jam." *Esquire,* Aug. 1967, pp. 84–91.

"Traffic Growth Swamps Airport Facilities." *Aviation Week & Space Technology,* Oct. 31, 1966, pp. 145–163.

U.S. Department of the Interior, Bureau of Sport Fisheries and Wildlife, *Biological Studies of the Problem of Bird Hazard to Aircraft (Final Report).* N66–15712, July 1, 1963; June 30, 1964.

U.S. Federal Aviation Agency, *Airport Capacity Criteria Used in Preparing the National Airport Plan.* Advisory Circular 150/5060, Aug. 1966.

U.S. Federal Aviation Administration, *Aviation Demand and Airport Facility Requirement Forecasts for Large Air Transportation Hubs Through 1980* AC 150/5040, Aug. 1, 1967.

Warskow, M. A., and J. E. Woodward, "Detection and Control of Aircraft on the Airport Surface." Airborne Instruments Laboratory, *Topics in Navigation and Air Traffic Control,* June 1961.

Watkins, H. D., "Airport Congestion is Forcing New Wave of Expansion." *Aviation Week & Space Technology,* Oct. 25, 1965, pp. 174–183.

Watkins, H. D., "Los Angeles Working To Ease Road Jams." *Aviation Week & Space Technology,* Nov. 14, 1966, pp. 55–67.

Wilkinson, W. H., Jr., and R. F. Ziegenfelder, "Super Airport Planning." Paper 660282, Society of Automotive Engineers, National Aeronautic Meeting and Production Forum, New York, A66–29826, Apr. 25–28, 1966.

CHAPTER SIX

"Airport-to-Downtown Bottleneck." *Traffic Quarterly, 10,* No. 1, 1956, pp. 154–163.
American Society of Civil Engineers, Air Transport Division, "Proceedings of the . . . Second National Jet Age Airport Conference, May 20–22, 1959, Houston, Texas." Ann Arbor, Mich., July 1959.
Dygert, Paul K., and Robert Horonjeff, "Hovercraft in Transportation Systems: A Preliminary View." *1966 National Transportation Symposium,* pp. 120–125.
The Glideway System: A High Speed Ground Transportation System for the Northeast Corridor of the United States. M.I.T. Report No. 7, M.I.T. Press, Cambridge, Mass., 1966.
Hovering Craft and Hydrofoil. Kalerghi Publications, London, W1, Recent issues.
Lang, A. S., and R. M. Soberman, *Urban Rail Transit: Its Economics and Technology.* M.I.T. Press, Cambridge, Mass., 1964.
Massachusetts Institute of Technology, *Bibliography of High Speed Ground Transport.* Oct. 15, 1965, Federal Clearinghouse, Arlington, Va., PB 170 581.
Massachusetts Institute of Technology, *Summary of Technology for High-Speed Ground Transport, 16 September 1965–15 September 1966.* Federal Clearinghouse, Arlington, Va., PB 173 658.
MPC Corporation, *Report on Testing and Evaluation of Transit Expressway.* Pittsburgh, Pa., 1967.
"New Transit Technology for the Big City." *New Scientist, 33,* 1967.
Nordlie, P. G., *Airport Transportation: A Study of Transportation Means Between Airports and the Metropolitan Areas They Serve.* Prepared by Human Sciences Research, Inc., Arlington, Va., for Bureau of Research and Development, U.S. Federal Aviation Agency, Department of Commerce, Office of Technical Services, Washington, Feb. 1961.
Norling, A. H., *Future U.S. Transportation Needs.* NASA CR–57005, prepared by United Research Incorporated, Cambridge, Mass., 1963. Available from Clearinghouse for Federal, Scientific and Technical Information, 5285 Port Royal Road, Springfield, Va.
Owen, Wilfred, *The Metropolitan Transportation Problem.* Anchor Book No. A 502, Doubleday, Garden City, N.Y., 1966.
Project Metran. M.I.T. Report No. 8, M.I.T. Press, Cambridge, Mass., 1967.
Richards, Brian, *New Movement in Cities.* Reinhold, New York, 1966.
Smith, Wilber, and Associates, *Transportation and Parking for Tomorrow's Cities.* New Haven, Conn., 1966.

GLOSSARY

Many abbreviations in the form of initials occur in this book and are listed here with their formal names. The long forms given are those that apply specifically to the material of the text.

ADF Automatic direction finder
AFLC Air Force Logistics Command
AIA Aerospace Industries Association
AIA American Institute of Aeronautics
AILS Advanced instrument landing system
AOCI Airport Operators Council International
APOE Aerial port of embarkation
ARTCC Air route traffic control center
ASCE American Society of Civil Engineers
ATA Air Transport Association
ATC Air traffic control
ATCA Air Traffic Controllers Association
ATCRBS Air traffic control radar beacon system
AWLS All-weather landing system
CAB Civil Aeronautics Board
CAS Collision-avoidance system
CAT Clear-air turbulence
CBR California bearing ratio
Comsat Communications satellite
CONUS Continental United States
CRAF Civil Reserve Air Fleet
CRT Cathode-ray tube
CTOL Conventional takeoff and landing
CUE Computer updating equipment
DME Distance-measuring equipment
DOT Department of Transportation
FAA Federal Aviation Administration
FAAP Federal Aid to Airports Program
FY Fiscal year

H-H High-high (above 43,000 ft) air route traffic control sector or airway
HSGT High-speed ground transportation
HUD Department of Housing and Urban Development
IATA International Air Transport Association
ICAO International Civil Aviation Organization
IDA Institute for Defense Analyses
IFF Identification, friend or foe
IFR Instrument Flight Rules
ILS Instrument landing system
INS Immigration and Naturalization Service or Inertial navigation system
LASH Lighters aboard ship
LAX Los Angeles International Airport
MAC Military Airlift Command
MSTS Military Sea Transport Service
MTBF Mean time between failures
NAS National air space system
NASA National Aeronautics and Space Administration
NICB National Industrial Conference Board
OHSGT Office of High-Speed Ground Transportation
OSD Office of the Secretary of Defense
PNdB Perceived noise decibels
PWI Pilot warning indicator

RAPCON Radar approach control
RATCC Radar air traffic control center
RPM Revenue passenger-miles
RTCA Radio Technical Commission for
    Aeronautics
RVR Runway visibility range
SAGE Semiautomatic ground
    environment
SIC Standard industrial classification
SST Supersonic transport
STOL Short takeoff and landing

TRACON Terminal radar approach
    control
UNESCO United Nations Educational,
    Scientific, and Cultural
    Organization
USAF United States Air Force
VFR Visual flight rules
VOR Very high frequency omnirange
V/STOL Vertical/short takeoff and
    landing
VTOL Vertical takeoff and landing

INDEX

ABC Program, 147
Access (airport), 8, 31–32, 90–96, 122, 123, 177, 183–184, 267, 355–358, 382–384, 390, 440–457, 476–477
Accidents, 98, 100, 102, 103, 268–270, 282
ADIZ, 267
Advisory Commission on International Education and Exchange, 63
Aerial ports of embarkation, 78, 175
Aerodynamics, 187–192, 229, 262, 281, 282, 326
Agency of International Development, 86
Airbus, 55, 299, 426, 469, 475
Air California, 118
Air Cargo, 72
Air conditioning, 394, 418, 420, 423, 425, 434, 435
Aircraft, all-purpose, 472
    automation of, 124–125, 200, 222, 223, 267, 273, 283, 288, 290, 295, 301, 307, 310, 316–317, 321, 322, 326, 329, 330, 338, 357
    damage to, 222, 236
    design of, 69, 127, 139, 221, 263, 327, 417–418
    ground movements of, 277, 362–366, 395, 436
    military, 106, 221, 253, 263, 267, 271, 273, 282, 389
    mix of, 50–58, 329, 401
    numbers of, 223, 334, 335, 363
    private, 125–126, 129, 389, 398
    separation of, 110, 128, 179, 357–358, 389
    size of, 64, 104, 174
    as subsystem, 8–9, 104, 106, 108, 110
    testing of, 128, 290, 435, 465; *see also* specific types
Aircraft Owners and Pilots Assoc., 222
Air-cushion vehicle, 149–150, 154, 155, 180, 460–463
Airfield, 210, 225, 261, 325, 330, 341, 355, 388, 397, 398, 399, 414, 421, 432
Airflow, 192–195
Airfoils, 187–189, 229
Air General (Boston), 259
Air Force Logistics Command, 78
Airlines, and common ownership, 491
    and competition, 110, 113, 114, 118, 120, 121, 179, 371, 483
    and costs, 3, 81, 269, 346, 374, 376, 378
    and demand, 171–172, 347

fleet of, 104, 222–223, 271, 301, 398
    kitchens of, 437
    routes of, 33, 36, 37, 56, 60, 110, 112, 114, 116, 118, 120, 129–130, 137, 145, 154, 155, 161, 169, 251, 347, 353, 355
    separation of, 111, 119, 121, 169, 362
Airline strikes, 37, 59
Airmen, 99, 101, 103, 125–126, 127, 177
Airport Operators Council International, 80
Airports, additional, 50, 180, 182, 250, 358, 494
    and costs, 167, 168, 183, 338, 346, 356, 392, 399
    design of, 327–328, 338, 372, 389–392, 399, 432
    districts of, 123, 177, 178, 492
    facilities of, 213, 340–341, 345, 358, 395, 399, 418, 424, 438, 471
    functions of, 343–346, 359, 373–374, 432–433
    municipal, 357, 428, 493
    network of, 31–33, 50–58, 173, 325, 335, 337
    planning of, 26, 31–32, 86–90, 122, 168, 171–172, 182, 183–184, 211, 220, 264, 330, 333, 337, 345, 353, 355, 358, 374, 385–396, 444, 457, 476, 485, 487, 490, 491, 495
    problem of, 9–12
    regional, 112, 113, 356, 396–415, 457, 458, 466, 484, 489–490
    regulation of, 84–91, 484, 489
    reliever, 490, 493
    and separation, 128–129, 166–167, 178, 251, 256, 329–330, 331
    size of, 4, 30, 38, 42, 47–57, 171, 179, 268, 354, 363, 388, 427, 444
    specialized, 378–380, 398–401, 410
    suburban, 299
    as system, 8–10
Air Route Traffic Control Centers (ARTCC), 295, 308–309, 315, 324, 451
Airspace, allocation of, 30, 47, 265
    capacity of, 313, 325
    control of, 91, 93, 95, 97, 123–125, 127–128, 176–177, 209, 270–275, 279–280, 288, 300, 317–318, 332
    requirements for, 91, 93, 95, 97, 387
    and separation, 13–14, 178, 181, 236–237, 295–296, 361
Air traffic control, airborne equipment for, 203, 208–209, 223, 262, 281–289
    and demand, 265

507

Air traffic control (*continued*)
  en route, 7–8, 98, 100, 102, 265, 266, 267,
    309, 315, 319, 328, 484
  expansion of, 14, 484–485
  facilities of, 95, 308–314
  ground, 4, 51, 124, 225, 256, 267, 276, 296,
    303, 309, 310, 311, 313, 316, 319–323,
    361–365, 389, 390, 413, 417–418, 420,
    426–427, 433, 435
  inadequacy of, 6, 13–14
  problems of, 268–270, 278, 280
  research in, 316–318
  and separation, 176–177, 256, 260, 272, 295–
    296, 316–317, 397–398, 400
  standards for, 124, 127, 483, 484
  as system, 267
  utilization of, 484
Air Traffic Controllers Association, 335
Air Traffic Control Radar Beacon System
  (ATCRBS), 310
Air Transport Association, 3, 80, 333, 334, 432
Airways, 8, 33, 93, 135, 164, 185, 208–209,
    261, 270, 271, 295, 316, 400, 449, 484–
    485, 488, 492, 494
Alaska, 118
Albany, 446
Albuquerque, 446
Alloys, 193–200
All-weather landing system (AWLS), 13, 201,
    203, 205, 209, 251, 261, 268, 281, 284, 287,
    296, 297, 299, 300, 301, 323, 327, 328–329,
    339, 353, 364, 393, 472
Altitude, 206, 221, 270–271, 276–278, 295–296,
    301, 307, 316, 473
Aluminum, 196–198, 462, 463
Amarillo, 447
American Institute of Aeronautics (AIA), 80,
    157, 164, 166
American Society of Civil Engineers, 431
American Telephone and Telegraph Company,
    137
Anaheim, 325
Appalachia Program, 147
Apron, 7, 215, 354, 361, 363, 364, 365, 391,
    394, 410, 411, 412, 414, 422
Arcon Corporation, The, 318
Asphalt, 421
ASST (advanced SST), 334
Atlanta, as air transportation hub, 7, 34, 348,
    349, 350, 351, 352, 371, 445
Austin, 446, 447
Auto-ferry, 139–140
Automated highway, 31–32, 478
Automatic direction finding (ADF), 223, 290–
    294, 296
Automobiles, 10, 17, 18, 26, 27, 30, 31–32, 52–
    53, 54, 66, 99, 132, 139–140, 146, 147, 148,
    149, 153, 168, 179, 248, 253, 259, 342, 356–
    357, 358, 371–373, 375, 402, 403, 426, 436,
    449, 451, 452–453, 466, 469, 471, 475–476
Autopilot, 223, 301
Aviation Development Council, 18, 166–167
Avionics, 187, 200–209, 221–223, 262, 284, 294–
    295, 331, 373, 393

B-17, 354
B-24, 354
Baggage, and aircraft design, 186, 369
  as airport/terminal function, 11, 31, 56, 342,
    357, 360, 367–369, 390, 403, 404, 412,
    418, 435, 436, 437, 444
  as air traffic control factor, 267
  and automation, 367–369, 370, 403, 425

and containers, 403, 407
and costs, 369, 390
Bahamas, 149, 180
Bakersfield, 144
Baltimore, 136, 143, 255, 258, 260, 261
Bay Area Rapid Transit District, 453
Bearing-to-a-station, 294
Behavior Science Corporation (BASICO), 68
Bell 204B, 257
Bell 205A, 257
Bell Jet Ranger, 257
Bell Telephone Laboratories, Inc., 24
Bendix Radio, 312
Bermuda, 149
Beuthe, M., 45
Billing, 418, 424
Birds, 393
Birmingham, 446
Blade, 194, 195, 228
Boarding area, 369, 402, 404, 407, 426
Body length, 214–215, 216, 262
Boeing Company, The, 18, 41, 50, 68, 366
Boeing 707, 1, 185, 188, 198, 210, 211, 212,
    214, 215, 216, 217, 218, 219, 263, 270, 374,
    421
Boeing 727, 218
Boeing 737, 218, 235
Boeing 747 (jumbo), 3, 50, 51, 190, 210, 211,
    212, 214, 215, 216, 217, 219, 366, 372;
    (B747-F) 374, 379, 380, 405, 425, 434, 435,
    444
Boeing-Vertol, 245, 246, 258
Boeing-Vertol 107II, 231, 257
Boeing-Vertol 107IIA, 233, 257
Boeing-Vertol 157, 236, 257
Boeing-Vertol 177, 239
Boeing-Vertol/NASA, 245
Boise, 447
Bonding, 196–200, 380
Boron, 197–200, 228
Boston, 34, 136, 138–139, 143, 144, 145, 149,
    180, 259, 261, 263, 268, 445, 460
Boundary layer, 188–192
Bréguet 941, 257
Brown, S. L., 43
Buffalo, 446
Burbank, 144, 399
Bureau of the Budget, 84–85, 92–93, 98–99,
    106–107, 114–115, 323
Bureau of the Census, 17, 19, 20, 45, 88
Bureau of Customs, 87, 106
Bureau of Education and Cultural Affairs, 115
Bureau of Internal Revenue, 106–107, 114
Bureau of Labor Statistics, 20
Bureau of Public Roads, 88, 94, 102, 146
Burlington County, New Jersey, Airport, 417
Bus, 55, 94, 146, 168, 249, 256, 342, 360, 366,
    367, 453, 455, 469, 470, 478
Business travel, 3, 24, 49, 58–59, 67–68, 157,
    158–161, 162, 163, 167, 168, 170, 173, 181,
    220, 221, 222, 251, 345, 395, 431, 449

C-5, 3; (C-5A) 78, 106, 175, 444
C-141, 106
Cabotage traffic, 128
California Corridor, 141, 143–145, 179–180,
    449, 456
Canada, 124
Canadair CL 84-1, 257
Cargo, advantages of air, 18
  and airport financing, 495
  and airport size and design, 387, 430
  collection and distribution of, 69–83, 174–
    176, 183, 381–382, 441, 451, 479

costs of, 69, 71–75, 81–83, 151–153
  growth of, 14, 18, 32, 45–46, 69, 150, 346,
    351
  and passenger mix, 378–379
  processing and handling of, 341–342, 373–
    384, 416
  retrograde, 77–78
Cargo unitization, 1975, 79
Catapult, 353, 363
Categories (landing), 56, 292, 293, 297, 328,
    329, 331, 393, 437
Cathode-ray tube (CRT), 205, 310
CBR (California Bearing Ratio), 392
Ceilometer, 329
Census of Transportation, 69
Charleston, 447
Charlotte, 446
Chattanooga, 447
Check-in, 325, 326, 327, 342, 367, 369, 390,
    404, 406
Chemical (industry), 148
Chicago, 7, 8, 33–35, 51, 171, 258, 262, 348,
    349, 350, 351, 352, 362, 371, 401, 445, 450,
    453
Chicago Corridor, 141, 143–145, 179–180
Cincinnati, 34, 445
Circuitry, electronic, 206–208, 303
Civil Aeronautics Board (CAB), 25, 37, 40–45,
    59, 69, 84–85, 88, 92–93, 94, 98, 102, 105,
    110–111, 112, 114, 115, 116, 117, 118, 119–
    120, 143, 144, 157, 252, 253, 254, 255, 260,
    485, 490
Civil Reserve Air Fleet (CRAF), 77
Civil Service Commission, 323
Clear-air turbulence (CAT) detector, 201, 203,
    209, 287, 290
Cleveland, 34, 258, 309, 445, 460
Cleveland Transit System, 460
Climb-out, 294, 295, 300
Coast Guard, 88, 94, 102
Coast Survey, 88
Collins Radio Company, 312
Collisions, 30, 266, 268, 270, 272, 333
Collision-avoidance system (CAS), 201, 203,
    209, 221, 283, 287–288, 289, 296, 303, 304,
    312–313, 318, 484
Columbia, S.C., 447
Columbus, Ohio, 446
Combined Station/Towers (FAA), 302
Committee on Aeronautical & Space Sciences,
    25
Committee for Economic Development, 22
Common ownership, 489–490
Communications, 93, 97, 98, 102, 104, 201,
    202–203, 206, 209, 267, 272, 277, 289, 301–
    308, 316, 318, 321–322, 327, 331, 344, 345,
    357, 377, 394, 396, 483, 485, 494, 495
Commuter services, 398, 404
Composites, 196–200, 228, 229, 281
Computer aid, 13, 77, 78, 79, 80, 98, 100, 102,
    174, 175, 200, 201, 205–207, 221–222, 267,
    272, 279, 287, 290–294, 296, 299, 303–308,
    309–311, 332–333, 367, 370, 381–382, 417–
    418, 423–427, 442, 443, 444, 452, 476
Computer Updating Equipment (CUE), 309
Comsat, 256, 332
Concessions, 10, 87, 90, 357, 372–373, 402, 414
Concorde, 110
Conflict detection, 315, 323
Connecticut General Life Insurance Company,
    132
Connecticut Transportation Authority, 138
Connie, 212, 214, 215

Consumer price index, 21, 42–44, 169
Containers, 10, 14, 31, 73–74, 77, 79, 80, 82–
    83, 154, 175, 177, 181, 183, 343, 379, 380,
    381, 383, 404–405, 406, 409, 418–419, 422,
    423, 431, 433, 466, 479
CONUS, 77–78
Conventional takeoff and landing (CTOL),
    186, 187–209, 210–221, 223–226, 261–263,
    264, 452, 465
Corps of Engineers Method, 392, 421
Corridors, 140–145, 179–180, 249, 298, 456–457
Corrosion, 200
Council of Economic Advisers, 20
Council on Student Travel, 63
Coupling, 285, 434–435
Credit cards, 370
Crew, 124, 200–202, 205, 206, 208–209, 267,
    275, 276, 285, 286–287, 289, 294, 296, 299,
    302, 308, 344, 345, 373, 426, 489
Cryogenic fuel, 419
Customs, 55, 56, 87, 115, 302, 338, 342, 343,
    344, 380, 382, 437

Dallas/Fort Worth, as hub, 34, 354, 357, 370,
    445, 450
Dampers, 203
Dayton, 446
Deck, 217, 262
Delay, 1, 3, 4, 5, 13, 15, 57, 132, 153, 209, 262,
    268, 269, 270, 275, 276, 280, 284, 299, 300,
    311, 315, 325, 328, 331, 333, 345, 353, 357,
    358, 361, 365, 389, 397, 401, 410, 425, 443,
    457, 458, 477
Demonstration Cities Act, 494
Demonstrations, 11, 12, 94, 123, 427, 431, 432,
    434, 440, 460, 472, 484, 489, 494, 495; see
    also High-Speed Ground Systems
Demurrage, 380
Denver, 34, 445
Department of Agriculture, 86–87, 94–95, 100–
    101, 108–109, 116–117
Department of Commerce, 21, 23, 70, 88–89,
    94–95, 100–101, 108–109, 116–117, 138–139,
    158, 166, 254
Department of Defense, 25, 75–79, 86–87, 94–
    95, 100–101, 106–107, 114–115, 175
Department of Health, Education, and Wel-
    fare, 63, 88–89, 94–95, 100–101, 108–109,
    118–119
Department of Housing and Urban Develop-
    ment, 88–89, 94–95, 100–101, 108–109, 118–
    119, 123, 254, 257, 430, 431, 439–440, 460,
    473, 487, 488
Department of the Interior, 86–87, 94–95, 100–
    101, 108–109, 116–117
Department of Justice, 86–87, 94–95, 100–101,
    106–107, 114–115
Department of Labor, 22, 88–89, 94–95, 100–
    101, 108–109, 118–119
Department of State, 63, 86–87, 94–95, 100–
    101, 106–107, 110, 114–115
Department of Transportation, 88–89, 94–95,
    101–102, 108–109, 118–119, 123, 130, 136–
    138, 139–140, 254, 255, 334, 427, 430, 439,
    444, 460, 485, 487, 488, 489, 495
Des Moines, 446
Detroit, as hub, 34, 258, 445
Detroit Metropolitan, 370
DHC Buffalo, 257
DHC Twin Otter, 257, 260, 261
Display, 202, 203, 204–205, 208–209, 222, 223,
    267, 279, 281, 282, 284, 286, 287, 288, 289,
    294, 295, 296, 297, 300–301, 302, 305, 306,
    308, 309, 310, 314, 317, 321, 484

Distance measuring equipment (DME), 201, 203, 223, 291, 294, 296, 301
Distance-to-a-station, 294
DMS, 160, 161, 165, 353
Docks, 380, 423
Doppler Navigator, 292
Douglas, 40, 41, 42
Douglas DC-3, 211, 212, 214, 215, 353, 373
Douglas DC-6A, 373
Douglas DC-8, 185, 211, 212, 214, 215, 216, 217, 238, 263, 270, 391, 420
Douglas DC-9, 218, 235
Drag, 187–188, 189, 190, 191, 192, 194–195, 214, 218, 229
Drainage, 385, 393
Drift, 294
Dulles International Airport, 89, 361, 371, 404, 415, 456

Eagleton Institute of Politics, Rutgers University, 473
Eastern Air Terminal (Boston), 415
Economic Development Administration, 88
Economic Report of the President, 20
Educational travel, 3, 57–63, 168, 172–174, 476
Edwards, L. K., 463
E-glass, 197
Electra, 216
Electrical (industry), 148
Electronics, 24–25, 281, 307, 308, 322, 328, 363
El Paso, 446
Empennage, 190
Employment, 18, 25, 27, 29, 51–52, 79, 82, 92, 93, 99, 104, 169, 340, 341, 344, 353, 356–357, 360, 361, 365, 450; see also Labor
Engineering, 385, 391, 394
Equal Employment Opportunity Commission, 84–85, 92–93, 98–99, 104–105, 112–113
Equipment, of air traffic control, 200–209, 221–223, 265–336, 484–485; see also Air Traffic Control
  handling of, 80, 83, 339, 343, 366, 367, 370–373, 423, 424–426, 427
  for servicing, 298, 299, 307, 344, 347, 357, 363, 425, 429–430, 437
Esquire, 397
Eurocontrol, 97, 124
Europe, 2, 96, 149, 486
Executive Office, 84–85, 92–93, 98–99, 106–107, 114–115
Expo 67, 464
Export-Import Bank of Washington, 84–85, 92–93, 98–99, 104–105, 112–113
Express traffic, 17, 18, 33, 73, 174, 182, 414, 468

Fan, 218–219, 228, 284
Fare(s), 2, 4, 32, 33, 37–45, 46, 49, 52, 57, 58, 59, 67, 91, 137, 139, 141, 149, 150, 179, 186, 251, 256, 258, 259, 344, 364, 368, 369, 409
Fatigue, 200, 285
Federal Aid to Airports Program, 86, 361, 485, 488, 490, 492
Federal-Aid Highway Act of 1962, 183
Federal Aviation Agency (FAA), 6–7, 25, 28, 33–40, 38–45, 47–49, 80, 88–89, 94, 95, 100, 102, 103, 108, 118, 123, 156, 158–166, 167, 171, 181, 220, 221, 222, 223, 235, 268, 287, 293, 302, 303, 308–309, 312, 318, 320, 323, 328, 331, 334, 335, 341, 344, 354, 358, 385, 387, 388, 389, 392, 397, 414–415, 422, 444, 472, 485, 487, 492
Federal Communications Commission, 84–85, 92–93, 98–99, 104–105, 112–113

Federal Highway Trust Fund, 452
Federal inspection areas, 483
FH 1100, 257
Fiberglass, 199
Financing, of airports, 5–6, 84, 86–91, 314, 325, 331, 337, 354, 355, 356, 396, 421, 427–428, 432, 446, 483, 485–486, 491–496
  of demonstrations, 11, 434, 484, 489, 494, 495
  of highways, 92, 356, 452
  of land banks, 430
  of system, 8–9, 14–15, 93–97, 333, 334, 484, 495
Fire, 339, 343, 395, 419–420, 436
First National City Bank of New York, 36
Flap, 206, 224
Flatbed trailers, 380
Flexing, 285
Flight Service Stations, 302, 308
Florida, 139–140, 141, 146, 149, 180, 371
Fog, 270, 279, 329, 330, 391–392, 436, 451
Food, 341, 401, 416, 417, 434–435
Fortune, 22
Fox, Francis, 7
France, 462
Freight, and airport design, 388, 391
  costs of, 18, 33, 75, 443, 482, 486
  and demand, 70
  flow of, 353, 450–451, 466–469, 470, 471
  growth of, 14, 18, 150–154, 174, 180–181, 471; see also Cargo
Frequency, 93, 98, 203, 277, 290, 291, 292, 302, 307, 331
Fresno, 144, 145
Friendship Airport, 456
FSS, 267
Fuel, 7, 192, 194, 213, 227, 251, 294, 296, 343, 344, 362, 385, 393, 395, 396, 397, 410, 413, 416, 417, 418, 419, 423, 433–434, 452, 463, 486
Fumes, 411

Gas, 411
Gas turbines, 138–139, 283
Gate, 225, 325, 327, 341, 359, 360, 363, 364, 366, 368, 412, 413–414, 419–420, 424, 435, 441, 449, 470, 471
Gear, 353, 363–364, 420, 434
General Accounting Officer, 84, 90, 98, 104, 110
General Aviation, classes of, 12–13, 220, 472–473, 488–489
  and cooperation, 13, 105
  fleet of, 221, 270, 272, 303, 333, 432
  growth of, 4, 155–156, 158–164, 202, 281, 337, 338, 339, 341, 347, 349, 354, 363
  proficiency of, 13, 107, 109, 265, 288–289, 294, 301, 303, 313–314, 332, 363, 484–485, 495
  and routes, 31–32, 56, 156, 483
  and separation, 49, 105, 109, 111, 156–158, 164–167, 176, 179, 282–283, 328, 357, 361, 362, 363, 365, 397, 398, 399, 427, 428, 485
Generators, 307, 463
Geodetic Survey, 88
Geologists, 391
George Washington Parkway, 361
Glide, 201, 291, 292, 295, 422, 487
Governmental role, federal level, 5–6, 11, 26, 27, 28, 29, 38, 83, 84–88, 90–95, 98–103, 104–109, 110–119, 122, 130–135, 323, 440, 472, 481–495
  international level, 90–91, 96–97, 102–103, 110–111, 118–119, 120–121

municipal/local level, 90–91, 96–97, 102–103, 110–111, 118–119, 120–121
state/regional level, 15, 89–90, 102–103, 108–109, 481–495
Grand Rapids, 447
Graphite, 197, 228
Gravity-Vacuum Transit Systems, 463–464
Great Lakes Corridor, 141, 146, 456
Greensboro, 447
Greyhound Bus Terminal (St. Louis), 415
Gross National Product (GNP), 2, 20–23, 25, 45–46, 60–61, 68, 150–151, 169, 217
Ground transportation, 2, 5, 10, 69, 79–80, 81–82, 157, 180–181, 185, 255, 326, 353, 355, 358–360, 368, 395, 397, 398, 406, 429, 440–441, 453–459, 461–466, 469, 471, 474, 477, 488, 490
Guideway, 456, 461, 462, 463, 464

Hail, 279, 280
Harrisburg, 447
Hartford, 136, 143, 261, 446
Hawaiian Islands, 149, 398
Health, 302, 342, 428, 436
Heating, 393, 422
Helicopter, 39, 40, 55–57, 56, 128, 129, 163, 227, 228, 229, 230, 230–235, 231, 232, 233, 234, 235–236, 237, 238, 239, 240, 244, 249, 250, 252–253, 254, 255, 256, 258, 259–260, 261, 263, 341, 358, 371, 383–384, 390, 394–395, 406, 410, 421, 428, 451, 452, 469, 471–472, 473, 477, 478
Helipads, 230, 235, 451
Heliports, 185, 235, 260, 280, 394, 466, 468
High-High (sectors), (H-H), 295
High-Speed Ground Systems, 46, 94, 96, 123, 135–150, 179–180, 248, 254, 256, 258, 261, 341, 358, 380, 382, 384, 397, 402–403, 405, 439–440, 442, 450–451, 456–457, 458, 460
Holland, Kenneth, 62
Hollywood, 325
Honeycomb (bonding), 198–199
Houston, 34, 445
Hovercraft, 257
Hovercraft Development, Limited, 463
Hubs, 3, 4, 6–7, 11, 13, 47–57, 122, 123, 132, 157, 166, 168, 171, 177, 179, 256, 258, 260, 261, 325, 332, 337, 339, 344, 346, 353, 356, 358, 361, 364, 372, 380, 384, 395, 401, 404, 406, 409, 411, 426, 429, 440–441, 442, 444–448, 449, 453, 465, 466, 473, 478, 485, 494
Hughes 500, 257
Human factor, 322, 442, 477
Huntsville, 447
Hydrants, 418, 423, 434
Hydrogen, 186
Hydroplaning, 328
Hydrostatics, 465
Hyperbolic measuring systems, 201, 203, 290–294
Hypersonic transport (HST), 186, 334

IBM, 309, 310
Ice, 273, 275, 279, 280, 281, 328, 330, 393, 437
Identification, 292, 304, 307, 310, 311, 317, 318, 331
IFR, 222–223, 230, 235, 265, 275, 303, 316, 338, 363, 364, 387, 389, 437, 485
Immigration, 302
Immigration and Naturalization Service, 87, 107, 114
Imperial College, 462
Income, 2, 8, 20, 21, 23, 27, 38–46, 58–59, 64–65, 66–67, 151, 154, 168, 169–170, 173

Indianapolis, 446
Industrial Fund, 76
Inertial navigation system (INS), 201, 202–203, 296, 299, 300, 301
Influence Charts method, 392
Inlet geometry control, 285
Institut du Transport Aérien, 36
Institute for Defense Analyses (IDA), 42, 44
Institute of International Education, 62, 63
Instrumentation, 122, 124, 126, 177, 202, 203, 204, 206, 266, 276, 297, 310, 313, 319, 327
Instrument Landing System (ILS), 268, 292, 293, 297, 298, 300, 301, 324
International Air Transport Association (IATA), 91, 110, 270, 324, 334, 482
International Civil Aviation Organization (ICAO), 36, 37–38, 41, 69, 87, 88, 91, 95, 97, 110, 268, 270, 324, 334, 483–484, 492, 494, 495
Interstate Commerce Commission (ICC), 84–85, 88, 92–93, 94, 98–99, 102, 104–105, 112–113
Inventories, 14, 18, 417, 424, 473
Investment, 5, 11, 12, 42, 49, 80–81, 149, 166, 167, 178–179, 182, 248, 253, 254, 256, 257, 261, 264, 338, 355, 368, 370, 376, 410, 419, 434, 448

Jackson, 447
Jacksonville, 136, 139–140, 141, 446
Japan, 97, 462
Jet Aircraft Noise Panel, 28–29
Jet aircraft, and accidents, 269, 271, 288
as air taxi, 163
for cargo, 376
general aviation, 221, 222, 283
mix of, 49–51, 361, 397
and noise, 12, 217–220
routes of, 298, 466, 469–471
size of, 284–285
technology of, 190, 211–213, 264
Jet Global Airport, 417
J. F. Kennedy International Airport, 4, 18, 50–53, 167, 268–269, 274, 357, 371, 401, 449, 453, 455
Johnson, President Lyndon B., 132, 135
Joint Chiefs of Staff (JCS), 306
Joint Economic Committee, 22
JT8D, 218

Kansas City, 34, 347, 348, 349, 350, 351, 445
KC 135, 185
Kennedy, President John F., 135
Knoxville, 446

Labor, 20, 27, 79, 92–93, 111–121, 169, 442, 450–451, 474
LaGuardia Airport, 18, 51, 167
Laithwaite, E. R., 462
Laminar flow (control), 187–188, 189–190
Lambert–St. Louis Terminal, 263
Landing aids, 88, 97, 108, 203, 206, 213, 223, 230, 235, 267, 268–275, 277, 279, 284, 297–298, 301, 315, 319
Landing areas, 191, 285, 317, 324, 327, 328, 329, 331, 363–364, 392–395, 396, 486
Landing fees, 49, 109, 133, 179, 360
Landscaping, 393
Land use (airports), 4, 8, 12, 30, 83, 87, 89, 91, 122, 129, 153, 154, 172, 176, 218, 220, 256, 263, 267, 268, 284, 317, 324, 325, 330, 337, 338, 341, 355, 359, 360, 363, 365, 366, 372, 373, 377, 378, 381, 382, 385, 388, 389, 390, 393–394, 396, 412, 427, 429–430, 437, 443, 444, 448, 486, 487–488, 491, 494, 495

Lansing, John B., 24
Lasers, 465
LASH, 80
Las Vegas, 446
Launching aids, 363
Lift, 186, 187–188, 189, 190–191, 192, 194–195, 215, 218, 224, 225, 229, 284
Lighting, 97, 122, 329, 358, 360
Limousine, 10, 179, 262, 342, 358
Linear design, 299, 389–391, 413, 431
Linear Induction Motors, 461–463
Ling-Temco-Vought, 241, 242, 243
Little Rock, 447
Load Classification Number methods, 392
Localizer, 201, 291, 292, 297
Lockheed, 40, 41, 42, 258
Lockheed CL-879, 247
Lockheed CL-1026, 234, 257
Lockheed-Georgia Company, 74
Lockheed L-300 Air Freighter, 74
Logan Airport, 259
Logistics, 14, 314, 382, 424, 433
London, 295
Long Beach, 399, 459
Long Island, 261
Long Island Railroad, 453
Long Island Sound, 261
Loran C, 203, 290–294
Los Angeles, 7, 33–34, 144, 171, 230, 249, 258, 262, 311, 324–326, 346, 347, 348, 349, 350, 351, 352, 353, 354, 361, 362, 384, 396, 399, 400, 407, 410, 417, 445, 449, 455, 456, 459, 465, 468, 473
Los Angeles Airways, 249, 466, 468
Los Angeles International Airport, 7, 324–326, 355, 356, 357, 358–359, 371, 392, 399, 401, 421, 449, 459, 468
Los Angeles Union Station, 325
Louisville, 446
Lounge, 327, 366, 371, 390, 404, 407, 417, 477
LTV C-142, 257

MacArthur Airport, 54
McDonnell-Douglas Corporation, 312
Mail, 17, 18, 33, 73, 76, 86–87, 94, 100, 116–117, 182, 185, 342, 388, 391 414, 422–423, 431, 468, 474, 479
Maintenance, 7, 79, 80, 185, 214, 216, 221, 251, 257, 287, 322, 339, 343, 344, 357, 363, 373, 388, 389, 391, 397, 398, 407, 413, 419, 423–424, 425, 436, 451, 461, 472
Manhattan, 56, 149
Manufacturers, 14, 38–80, 81, 126–127, 133, 156, 158, 170–171, 176, 182, 183, 185–186, 202, 208, 218, 223, 252, 254, 256, 257, 258, 259, 261, 263, 264, 281, 338, 341, 382, 395, 434, 457
Maritime Administration, 88, 94, 102
Maritime Board, 88, 94, 102
Martha's Vineyard, 149
Massachusetts Institute of Technology, 269, 293, 415, 462
Mean-time-between-failures (MBTF), 207–208, 287
Mechanics, 99, 101, 103, 125–126, 177
Melpar, 460
Memphis, 446
Mercuric iodide, 393
Meteorology, 8, 265, 267, 276, 302, 329, 334, 392–393, 483
Methane, 194, 419
Metroline, 248–261
Metropolitan Commuter Transportation Authority, 53

Metropolitan Oakland International Airport, 460
Metroports, 248, 249, 250, 251, 253, 256, 325–326, 329, 330, 399
Miami, 7, 34, 51, 347, 348, 349, 350, 351, 352, 445
Miami International Airport, 7, 371
Midway Airport, 450
Military Airlift Command (MAC), 70, 76–79, 175, 183
Milwaukee, 208, 446
Miniaturization, 202, 206–208, 221, 293
Minirail, 464, 478
Minneapolis-St. Paul, 34, 445
Missouri River Corridor, 141
Mobile, 447
Moline, 447
Moses, L. N., 45
Moss, W. W., 269
Myopia, 312
Motel, 342
Military Sea Transport-Service (MSTS), 76, 78
Multiple Destination Port Concept, 175

Nantucket, 149, 180
Nashville, 446, 450
National Aeronautics, 164
National Aeronautics and Space Administration (NASA), 25, 84–85, 92–93, 98–99, 104–105, 112–113, 245, 487
National Aeronautics and Space Council, 86–87, 92–93, 100–101, 106–107, 114–115
National Airport Plan, 427–428, 430
National airspace system (NAS), 265, 310–312, 314, 317, 318, 319, 321
National Bureau of Standards, 183
National Company, The, 312
National Education Association, 63
National Industrial Conference Board, 22, 65
National Interstate Highway Program, 145–147, 180
National Labor Relations Board, 84–85, 92–93, 98–99, 104–105, 112–113
National Mediation Board, 84–85, 92–93, 98–99, 106–107, 112–113
National Planning Association, 22, 460
National Transportation Safety Board, 88, 94, 102, 111, 115
Navigation, 8, 91, 93, 95, 97, 99, 102, 124, 125, 126, 127–128, 177, 200, 201, 202–203, 206–209, 222, 262, 265, 266, 269, 270, 273, 275, 282, 284, 289–298, 299, 301, 303, 307, 313, 316, 317, 318, 319, 321, 323, 327, 329, 331, 387, 472, 483, 484–485, 489, 494, 495
Newark Airport, 7, 18, 33–35, 51, 167, 171, 445, 448
New Brunswick, 260, 473
New Haven, 136, 143
New Haven Railroad, 138–139
New Jersey, 260, 473
New Orleans, 34, 445
Newport News, 447
New York, 6, 7, 18, 33–36, 50–57, 58–59, 136–139, 143, 149, 150, 167, 171, 230, 249, 258, 260, 261, 274, 295, 309–310, 311, 348, 349, 350, 351, 352, 353, 362, 371, 396, 397, 401, 410, 417, 445, 446, 448, 450, 453, 464, 472, 473, 490
New York Airways, 249
Noise, 1, 4–5, 7, 8, 12, 15, 26, 28–29, 30, 32, 108, 127, 131, 132, 172, 183–184, 217–220, 228, 235, 251, 258, 263–264, 267, 274, 275, 277, 280, 285, 291, 295, 298, 300, 324–331, 334, 338, 353, 364, 372, 385, 388, 393, 396,

398, 411, 412, 422, 428–430, 443, 469, 471, 472, 484, 487–488, 491–495
Norfolk, 446
North American Rockwell, 150, 151, 155, 318
Northeast Corridor, 135–145, 146, 179–180, 253, 258, 440, 456
Northwest Corridor, 141, 146
No-show, 370, 410
Nuclear power, 155, 186, 419

Obsolescence, 14, 318, 319, 473
Occupations (of passengers), 66, 67, 168, 172–173
Office of Education, 60, 61
Office of High Speed Ground Transportation, 136, 140, 456–457
Office of Policy Development, 35, 158
Office of Science and Technology, 28, 86–87, 92–93, 100–101, 106–107, 114–115
O'Hare International Airport, 371, 391, 450, 453
Oil, 70, 146, 148, 424
Oklahoma City, 446
Omaha, 446
OMEGA, 203, 290–294
Omnirange, 223
Ontario Air Terminal, 399
Orlando, 446
Outdoor Recreation Resources Review Commission, 22
Overhaul, 339, 344, 357, 373, 436, 472
Overrun, 394
Overseas storage depots, 78, 175
Oxnard air terminal, 399

Pacific Area Travel Association, 69
Pacific Southwest Airways, 144
Pallets, 343, 380, 381, 418
Palmdale Airport, 399
Pan American Airways, 269
P&W (Pratt & Whitney, Inc.), 41
Paperwork, 380, 381, 382
Paris Nord, 215, 357
Parking, aircraft, 216, 341, 344, 345, 361, 363, 364–365, 369, 373, 413, 428, 440, 442
    automobile, 7, 47, 48–49, 51, 52–53, 56–57, 90, 123, 137, 145, 267, 325, 326, 327, 328, 339, 340, 342, 356–358, 359, 360, 367, 368, 388, 390, 391, 396, 398, 403, 411, 412, 414, 436, 448, 449, 451, 453, 456, 471, 477
Pasadena Freeway, 361
Passengers, collection and distribution of, 7, 181, 337, 425, 439–480
    entertainment of, 201, 206
    flow of, 9–10, 49–57, 302, 323, 328, 337, 371–372, 426–427, 442, 444–445, 477
    general aviation, 31, 156, 157, 168
    growth in traffic of, 17–18, 33–45, 48, 168, 171, 187, 285, 345, 346, 347, 365
    routes of, 17–18, 32, 33–34, 37, 38, 39, 40, 41, 51, 55–56, 59, 77, 142–149, 153, 156, 157, 171, 182, 259, 444
Pavement, 388, 392, 394, 421–422, 432–433
Peaks, 4, 10, 49–55, 171, 179, 303–304, 311, 314, 320, 323, 324–325, 341, 347, 350, 353, 357–358, 361, 365–366, 384, 386–387, 389, 398, 412, 444, 449, 450, 453, 471, 474
Pennsylvania Railroad, 136, 137, 139
Personnel, 99, 101, 103, 309, 314, 319–323, 332, 343, 423, 424, 436, 484, 488
Peru, 332
Philadelphia, 34, 136, 137, 143, 258, 260, 445
Philadelphia International, 371

Phoenix, 446
Piedmont Corridor, 141
Pierce, John R., 24
Pilot, proficiency of, 13, 101, 103, 124, 127–128, 179, 220, 235, 281, 282–283, 288–289, 321, 328, 485, 495
    responsibilities of, 190, 193–196, 198–199, 233, 276–277, 283–284, 286–287, 293, 297–298, 299, 301, 306, 308, 312–314, 315, 316, 317, 318, 319, 320, 322, 323, 327 329, 363, 364
Pittsburgh, 34, 348–352, 445, 464
Planning Research Corporation, 68
Pneumatic air, 435, 436, 463
Policy on International Air Transportation, 495
Pollution, 1, 4–5, 7, 15, 108, 127, 148, 396, 411, 429, 444, 463
Pomona, 467, 468
Population, age of, 3, 64
    change in, 68, 166
    of Corridors, 135, 141, 179
    education of, 3, 60–62, 173
    growth of, 1, 2, 3, 8, 17, 19–20, 38, 46, 42–45, 154, 157, 158, 168, 169, 170, 187, 345
    and leisure, 64
    suburban, 27, 153, 180
    urban, 26–27, 148, 217, 325, 359, 405, 441, 448, 465
Portland, 136, 143, 145, 446
Portland Cement Association method, 392, 421
Port of New York Authority, 35, 36, 51, 58–59, 67, 69, 89, 97, 103, 108, 258, 445, 474
Post Office Department, 86–87, 94–95, 100–101, 108–109, 116–117, 423, 474
Power, 104, 187, 215, 218, 263, 394, 411, 419, 420, 423
Precipitation, 278, 392
Pressure, 278, 301, 464
Princeton, 260
Princeton University, 473
Propulsion, 4, 107, 185, 186, 191, 192–195, 200, 225, 226, 227–228, 229, 262, 281, 284, 452, 461–464
Providence, 136, 138, 143, 145, 261, 446
PSA, 118
Puerto Rico, 149

Quarantine, 87, 88, 109, 118

Radar, 201, 203, 209, 223, 266, 271, 278–279, 296, 297, 301, 303, 308–309, 311, 312, 317, 321, 324, 326, 331, 364, 485
Radar Air Traffic Control Centers, 310, 311, 312, 313–314
Radar Approach Control, 309
Radial layout, 371, 388, 389, 431
Radiation, 8, 277–278, 280, 297
Radio, 93, 98, 202–203, 290–295, 296, 303, 308, 312, 331, 358, 453, 478, 489
Radio Technical Commission for Aeronautics, 306
Railroad, and airport location, 11, 386, 391, 488
    and cargo, 18, 27, 70, 73, 79, 83, 150–154, 343, 379–380, 381, 434
    and competition, 132
    and passengers, 46, 249, 251, 379–380
    terminal, 168, 171, 455
Rain, 276, 279, 280, 451
Raleigh–Durham, 446
Ramp, 215–216, 329, 366, 389, 404, 405, 420, 421, 435, 470, 471

Range-bearing measuring systems, 201
Records, 321, 343, 369, 370, 406, 423
Recreation, 8, 23, 89, 111, 168, 170, 173, 339, 357, 361
Regional Planning Association of the New York Metropolitan Region, 473
Reliability, 206–209, 221, 227, 228, 283, 287, 294, 297, 302, 306, 403, 443, 461, 471, 472, 487
Reno, 446
Rental, 90, 433, 436
Republic Airport, 54, 56
Resources for the Future, 23
Revenue, of airlines, 32, 37–38, 42–45, 183, 186, 210, 285, 331
    of airport, 90, 255, 332, 353, 356, 360, 372, 373, 490, 491–492
    of air transportation industry, 133–134, 178–179, 182, 220, 379–380, 473
    from automobiles, 452
    of general aviation, 164
    from land reserves, 430
    of rail demonstrations, 137, 139
Richmond, 136, 143, 446
Right-of-way, 10, 359, 368, 406–407, 429–430, 464
Riverside, 399
Roads, construction of, 325, 449
    as highway systems, 7, 27, 80, 94, 96, 123, 131, 145–147, 148, 180, 183, 248, 332, 339, 341, 361, 384, 385, 386, 388, 390, 391, 398, 409, 433, 444, 449, 452–453, 458, 459, 461, 466, 474, 475, 488, 490
    speed limits of, 429
    terminal, 327, 394; see also Access, Trucking
Rochester, 446
Rocket, 93, 353
Runway, 3, 7, 49, 50, 51, 53, 56, 192, 206, 213, 225, 235, 260, 267, 268, 274, 276, 277, 279, 292, 293, 298–299, 305, 315, 316–317, 324, 325, 326–327, 328, 330, 338, 340, 341, 344, 347, 353, 354, 361, 362–364, 367, 385, 387, 388, 389, 390, 391, 394, 398, 412, 421–422, 437, 449, 451, 456
Runway Visual Range (RVR), 268, 329

S-61L, 257
S-65 (CH-53), 257
S-65 Compound, 257
Sacramento, 144, 145, 446
SAE Subcommittee AGE-2A, 305, 418
Safety, 6, 8, 88, 94, 98–103, 124–125, 127–128, 131, 147, 201, 270–288, 297, 299–301, 305, 327, 331, 332, 340, 362, 364, 387, 388, 392, 393, 396, 398, 400, 411, 412, 419, 420–421, 437, 443, 469, 472, 495
SAGE, 301
St. Lawrence Seaway, 88, 94, 102
St. Louis, 34, 348, 349, 350, 351, 352, 415, 445
St. Paul, 164
St. Petersburg, 446
Salt Lake City, 446
San Antonio, 446
San Bernadino, 399, 447
San Diego, 144, 258, 446
San Fernando, 325, 459
San Francisco, 34, 144, 230, 249, 326, 445, 460
San Francisco International Airport, 371, 460
Santa Monica, 399, 459
SAS, 120, 178, 223, 251, 282, 285–286
Satellite, for communications, 93, 97, 98, 267, 273, 278, 295–296, 300, 307, 313
    for terminal, 123, 176, 182, 307–308, 324–

326, 329, 345, 355, 357, 359, 367, 372, 373, 393–415, 422, 442, 465
Scanning, 203
Scott Air Force Base, 78, 175
Seaboard Coast Line Railroad, 139–140
Seattle (Tacoma), as air transportation hub, 34, 83
Securities and Exchange Commission, 84–85, 92–93, 98–99, 106–107, 112–113
Security, 87, 106, 342, 344, 394
Semiconductors, 207
Sensor, 290–294, 296, 300, 302, 338, 437
Separation (standards), 289, 294–296, 311, 313, 316–317, 319, 331, 387, 389
Sequencing, 311–312, 315, 319
Service, 6, 10, 302, 344, 353, 363, 414, 417, 418, 419, 424, 425, 426, 431, 434–436
SESL method, 392
Shaw AFB, 291
Ship, 9, 80, 83, 97, 131, 149–150, 154–155, 180, 343, 383, 418, 429, 448
Shops, 342, 372, 450, 471
Short Skyvan, 257
Shreveport, 447
Shuttle, 330, 360, 381, 401, 465
Sightseers, 357, 358, 359, 360, 450
Signs, 358, 360
Signaling, 203–204, 206, 290, 291, 327
Skin friction, 189–190, 285
Skybus, 53, 372, 384, 407, 417, 464
Smoke, 4, 487
Snow, 276, 279, 328, 330, 344, 437, 451
Socialization, 126–127, 177–178
Society of Automotive Engineers, The, 83
Soil, 386, 391–392, 432
Solar flares, 277–278, 290
Sonic boom, 218, 263, 277, 280, 285, 294, 295, 300, 330, 419
Southampton, 150
Southwest, 146
Soviet Union, 393
Spacing, 311–312, 313, 315, 316, 319, 328, 330
Specific fuel consumption (SFC), 193, 487
Speed, 13, 44–45, 187, 192, 195, 222, 223–224, 226, 227, 272, 302, 304, 312, 327 328, 331, 353, 357, 363, 397, 402, 407, 429, 437, 454–457
Sperry Rand, Sperry Division, 312
Spokane, 447
Springfield, 446
Squall Lines, 273, 279
SRI, 415
Standardization, 11, 14, 97, 334, 367, 368, 370, 387, 404, 406, 409, 418–419, 434, 483, 484, 494, 495
Standard Metropolitan Statistical Areas, 444
Stanford Research Institute, 22, 65, 120, 415, 453, 459
Star-angle sensing, 296
Station-keeping, 313–314, 316
Steel (industry), 148, 462
Steering angle, 422
STOL, 55–57, 56, 123, 186, 192, 223–225, 226–227, 253, 257, 258, 260–261, 265, 298–299, 325–326, 410–415, 422, 435, 485
Storage, 343, 380, 396, 417
Storms, 273–274, 392
Stratocruiser, 211, 212, 214, 215
Strip printing, 318, 319, 345
Structures, 104, 187, 195–200, 227, 229, 262, 281, 286, 295
Subsonic aircraft, 3, 80, 187–188, 193, 200, 206, 210, 216, 218–220, 262, 263, 278, 291, 386, 439

Subterminals, 469-471
Suburbs, 27, 32, 137, 152–153, 157, 171, 180, 182, 217, 299, 402–403, 412, 455, 458–459, 466, 469
Subway, 11, 469
Supersonic transport, 3, 50–55, 80, 106, 108, 187, 188, 190, 193, 200, 201, 205, 211, 212, 214, 215, 216, 217, 218–220, 262, 263, 265, 271, 272, 277, 278, 280, 285, 286, 288, 290, 292, 294, 295, 296, 298, 300, 302, 332, 334, 386, 419, 421, 422, 427, 434, 435, 439, 457, 475
Suspension, 138, 452, 453
Sweep (wing), 185, 187–189, 191, 224
Syracuse, 446

Tail, 216, 262
Takeoff, 108, 185, 187, 191, 194, 213, 219, 230, 235, 275, 277, 279, 284, 285, 294, 295, 298, 316, 317, 319, 321, 324, 326–327, 329, 353, 363–364, 389, 398, 414, 487
Tampa, 372, 446
Tax, 89, 90, 122, 131, 133–134, 164, 177, 325, 332, 345, 343, 428, 452, 486, 490, 492
Taxi, air, 55, 104, 110, 116, 128, 157, 159–162, 163–164, 167, 168, 181, 220, 221, 259–261, 361, 393, 472–473, 490
    automobile, 179, 259, 342, 356, 358, 411, 426, 436, 453, 478
Taxiway, 51, 53, 56, 213, 214–215, 267, 325, 326, 327, 328, 329, 340, 341, 361, 362–364, 388, 389, 394, 398, 413, 422
Technicians, 322
Telemetry system, 302, 308, 423, 426
Television, 273, 409
Temperature, 276–277, 278, 280, 285, 294, 295, 316
Terminal, additional, 268, 394, 448
    buildings of, 47, 54, 56, 364–365, 366–367, 410, 435
    and cargo, 10, 377–378, 379, 405, 474
    congestion of, 123, 268, 270, 272, 304, 311, 315, 347, 353, 356
    design of, 261, 326–327, 337, 353, 355, 367, 388–389, 390
    facilities of, 11, 302, 310–311, 339–340, 371, 398
    flow at, 262, 365–375
    functions of, 177, 342–345
    international, 343
    location of, 177, 248, 341, 369, 372, 444, 455, 456, 458, 469
    problems of, 80
    as subsystem, 7–8, 185; see also Satellite
Teterboro Airport, 18, 54
Texas Corridor, 141
Thickness (wing), 187–189
Thrust, 186, 191–192, 193–195, 206, 219, 227, 353
Thunderstorms, 273, 279, 290
Ticketing, 56, 123, 137, 177, 255, 267, 325, 342, 367, 369–371, 403, 406, 407–409, 456, 457, 459, 470, 471
Tie-down, 345, 354
Tires (aircraft), 328, 421
Titanium, 196–197
Tokyo, 464
Toledo, 447
Total distribution, 14, 72, 73, 75, 78, 79, 81–82, 168, 174–176, 183, 431, 473
Tourists, 395, 431
Towers (control), 97, 267, 268, 302, 308–309, 320, 324
Towing, 327, 419–420, 422

Tracking (radar), 311, 312, 317, 324
TRACON, 80
Training (of personnel), 99, 101, 103, 108, 110–121, 125–126, 137, 298, 314, 320, 322, 332, 335, 357, 361, 373
Transistor, 207, 221
Transmitter, 290, 292, 312
Transonic aircraft, 187, 188
Transponder, 122, 176–177, 201, 203, 223, 292, 311, 313, 485
Transportation Association of America, 17
Travel Research Institute, 69
Treasury Department, 86–87, 94–95, 100–101, 106–107, 114–115
Trenton, 136, 143, 260
Trucking, 18, 27, 70, 72, 73, 75, 79–80, 82, 94, 180–181, 343, 358, 361, 381, 383, 384, 418
Tucson, 447
Tulsa, 446
Tunnel, 409, 421, 464, 465
Turbine (engines), twin-, 193–195, 212, 230, 393, 463
Turbofan, 193, 212, 218–219, 487
Turbojet, 193, 272, 284, 354, 483
Turboprop, 224, 226, 227, 241, 272, 354
Turbulence, 273–274, 275, 276, 277, 278, 279, 280, 281, 282, 286, 392
Turbulent flow, 189–190
Turnoffs, 327
Twentieth Century Fund, 22

Undersecretary of Commerce for Transportation, 88, 94, 102
Unemployment, 20, 169
UNESCO, 61–62
United Aircraft Corporate Systems Center, 138
United Aircraft–Sikorsky, 244, 258
United Aircraft–Sikorsky S-611, 232
United Aircraft–Sikorsky S65, 2-engine, 237
    3-engine, 240
United Aircraft–Sikorsky S-64B, 238
United Airlines, 269, 270, 293
United Nations, 90–91, 96–97, 102–103, 110–111, 120–121
UNIVAC File II, 309
University of Michigan Survey (Research Center), 23, 24, 69
Urban Transportation Administration, 431
USAF, 70, 76–79, 309, 392
Usage charges, 85, 87, 89, 91, 93, 95, 97, 99, 124, 133, 171, 332, 483, 485, 486, 495
USASI MH5 Committee, 418
Utilities, 411, 423
Utility Airplane Council of the AIA, 157, 164, 166

Vacation time, 3, 64, 345
Van Nuys Airport, 399
Vietnam, 77, 422
VHF omnirange, (VOR), 201, 203, 208, 290, 291, 294, 296, 301
Visibility, 268, 276, 278, 279, 280, 281, 283, 297, 298, 329, 331, 334, 361, 392
Visitors, 11, 356, 358, 359, 360, 391, 395, 450
V/STOL, 32, 122, 123, 124, 177, 180, 230, 235, 241, 242, 243, 244, 248–261, 263, 264, 271, 280, 283–284, 288, 289, 298–299, 300, 301, 314, 315–316, 317, 327, 330, 342, 359, 395–396, 398, 399, 407, 409, 422, 429, 442, 451, 452, 465, 469, 471–472, 474, 477, 478
VTOL, 185, 186, 192, 200, 224–225, 226–230, 230–248, 253, 257, 260, 265, 272, 284, 289, 299, 325, 326, 329, 334, 408, 410–415, 422, 435, 471–472, 474, 478, 489

Visual Flight Rules (VFR), 54, 235, 275, 280, 303, 312, 313, 315, 319, 320, 321, 387

WABCO, 460
Wages, 13, 20, 110, 395
Waiting rooms, 10, 470, 471
Warehousing, 18, 343, 381, 436, 473
Washing, 436
Washington, D.C., 34, 89, 129, 136–138, 139–140, 143, 255, 258, 348, 349, 350, 351, 352, 361, 396, 444, 445, 456, 460, 464
Washington National Airport, 89
Waste disposal, 344, 394, 411, 418, 420, 434, 435
Water, 394, 411, 417, 420, 434
Wave, 187–188, 189, 190, 191, 279, 290, 291
Weather, 53, 56, 97, 98, 100, 102, 124, 203, 222, 261, 262, 272, 273–274, 275–281, 282, 284, 286, 289, 292, 296, 297, 298, 299, 302, 311, 320, 323, 331, 339, 345, 347, 364, 372, 392, 397, 398, 410, 437, 441, 442, 450–451, 475
Weather Bureau, 25, 88, 102, 392
Weight, 206–208, 212, 213, 215, 219, 221, 227,

229, 231, 232, 233, 234, 235, 236–247, 262, 283, 306, 354, 380, 405, 419, 421, 422, 433, 461
Westchester, 54, 56
Westergaard analysis, 392
Westinghouse Electric Transit Expressway, 464
West Palm Beach, 447
Wheels, 420, 421, 434, 461, 464
Wichita, 447
Wilbur Smith and Associates, 460
Wilmington, 143
Wind, 275, 276–277, 278, 279, 280, 295, 297, 326, 330, 363, 392
Windings, 462
Wing, 187, 188, 189, 190, 191–192, 215–216, 223–224, 235, 242, 243, 245, 262, 281, 422
Winston, 447
Wires, 206–209
World Bank, 90
World War II, 339, 354

Zoning, 87, 89, 91, 122, 176, 263, 338–339, 341, 393, 394, 396, 411, 429–430, 488, 491, 493